Instructor's Resource Manual
to accompany

Introductory
Electronic Devices and Circuits

Seventh Edition

Robert T. Paynter

PEARSON

Prentice
Hall

Upper Saddle River, New Jersey
Columbus, Ohio

Copyright © 2006 by Pearson Education, Inc., Upper Saddle River, New Jersey 07458.
Pearson Prentice Hall. All rights reserved. Printed in the United States of America. This publication is protected by Copyright and permission should be obtained from the publisher prior to any prohibited reproduction, storage in a retrieval system, or transmission in any form or by any means, electronic, mechanical, photocopying, recording, or likewise. For information regarding permission(s), write to: Rights and Permissions Department.

Pearson Prentice Hall™ is a trademark of Pearson Education, Inc.
Pearson® is a registered trademark of Pearson plc
Prentice Hall® is a registered trademark of Pearson Education, Inc.

Instructors of classes using Paynter, *Introductory Electronic Devices and Circuits, Seventh Edition,* may reproduce material from the instructor's resource manual for classroom use.

10 9 8 7 6 5 4 3 2 1

ISBN 0-13-171715-4

CONTENTS

Practice Problem Solutions   1

Lab Manual Solutions   75

Test Item File   189

PRACTICE PROBLEM SOLUTIONS

CHAPTER 2

EXAMPLE PRACTICE PROBLEMS (CH 2)

2-1. The applied voltage is dropped across the reverse-biased diode. Therefore, $V_{R1} = V_{R2} = 0$ V

2-2. Using the ideal model, $I_T = \dfrac{V_S}{R_T} = \dfrac{12\,\text{V}}{800\,\Omega} = 15\,\text{mA}$

2-3. $V_R = V_S - 0.7\,\text{V} = 15\,\text{V} - 0.7\,\text{V} = 14.3\,\text{V}$

2-4. Using the practical model,
$$I_T = \frac{V_S - V_F}{R_T} = \frac{5\,\text{V} - 0.7\,\text{V}}{510\,\Omega} = 8.43\,\text{mA}$$

2-5. $I_T = \dfrac{V_S - 0.7\,\text{V}}{R_T} = \dfrac{2\,\text{V} - 0.7\,\text{V}}{550\,\Omega} = 2.36\,\text{mA}$

2-6. There are two forward-biased diodes. Therefore,
$$I_T = \frac{V_S - 1.4\,\text{V}}{R_T} = \frac{6\,\text{V} - 1.4\,\text{V}}{800\,\Omega} = 5.75\,\text{mA}$$

2-7. Using the ideal model, $I_T = \dfrac{V_S}{R_T} = \dfrac{6\,\text{V}}{800\,\Omega} = 7.5\,\text{mA}$

Error (%) $= \dfrac{|5.75\,\text{mA} - 7.5\,\text{mA}|}{5.75\,\text{mA}} \times 100 = 30.4\,\%$

2-8. $V_{\text{pk}} = 175$ V. Adding a safety margin: $V_{RRM} = 175\,\text{V} \times 1.2 = 210$ V. Thus, diodes 1N4004 through 1N4007 could be used in this circuit.

2-9. $I_F = \dfrac{100\,\text{V} - 0.7\,\text{V}}{51\,\Omega} = 1.95\,\text{A}$. Adding a safety margin: $I_0 = 1.95\,\text{A} \times 1.2 = 2.34$ A (minimum)

2-10. $I_F = \dfrac{20\,\text{V} - 0.7\,\text{V}}{68\,\Omega} = 284\,\text{mA}$

$P_F = 284\,\text{mA} \times 0.7\,\text{V} = 199\,\text{mW}$. Adding a safety margin: 199 mW $\times$ 1.2 = 239 mW (min)

2-11. $P_F = 750\,\text{mA} \times 0.7\,\text{V} = 525$ mW. This exceeds the 500 mW rating.

2-12. $V_F = 0.7\,\text{V} + (12\,\text{mA} \times 8\,\Omega) = 0.796$ V

2-13. $I_{ZM} = \dfrac{P_{D(\text{max})}}{V_Z} = \dfrac{1\,\text{W}}{27\,\text{V}} = 37\,\text{mA}$

2-14. The derating value is found as (4.0 mW) (125°C–75°C) = 200 mW. Now, $P_{D(\text{max})}$ at 125°C is found as 500 mW – 200 mW = 300 mW.

2-15. The V_Z rating for the replacement component must be 75 V. The $P_{D(\text{max})}$ rating can be any value that is greater than or equal to 4 W. Only one diode in the figure fulfills both requirements: the 1N5374A.

2-16. $P_D = I_Z V_Z = (175\,\text{mA})(6.8\,\text{V}) = 1.19$ W. The diode would need parameters of $V_Z = 6.8$ V and $P_D \geq 1.19$ W. We could use the 1N5921A or 1N5342A.

2-17. The *minimum* value of V_F is used.
$$R_S = \frac{V_{\text{out(pk)}} - V_F}{I_F} = \frac{14\,\text{V} - 1.4\,\text{V}}{20\,\text{mA}} = 630\,\Omega.$$
The lowest standard value above 630 Ω is 680 Ω.

PRACTICE PROBLEMS (CH 2)

1. The three components are in series, with the diode pointing toward the negative (–) side of the source.
2. EFV: The arrow should point in the direction of electron flow (*against* the diode arrow). CFV: The arrow should point in the direction of conventional current (*in the direction indicated by the arrow.*)
3. The three components are in series, with the diode pointing toward the positive (+) side of the source.
4. In figures (a) and (c), the diodes are reverse biased; $I = 0$. In figure (b), the diode is forward biased. Electron flow is *against the arrow*. Conventional flow is *with the arrow*.
5. In Figure 2.45a, D_1 is reverse biased and D_2 is forward biased. Both diodes in the other two figures are forward biased. For each conducting diode, electron flow is *against the arrow* and conventional flow is *with the arrow*.
6. (a) D_1 is reverse biased, so $V_{D1} = V_S = 6$ V.
   (b) D_1 is forward biased, so $V_{D1} = 0$ V (ideal).
   (c) D_1 is reverse biased, so $V_{D1} = V_S = 3$ V (ignoring the source polarity).
7. D_1 is reverse biased; therefore, $V_{D1} = V_S = 10$ V and $V_{R1} = 0$ V. D_2 is forward biased; therefore, $V_{D2} = 0$ V and $V_{R2} = 10$ V.
8. $V_{D1} = V_S = 6$ V, $V_{R1} = 0$ V, $I_T = 0$ A
9. $V_{D1} = 0.7$ V, $V_{R1} = V_S - V_F = 1\,\text{V} - 0.7\,\text{V} = 0.3$ V,
   $$I_T = \frac{V_S - V_F}{R_1} = \frac{0.3\,\text{V}}{100\,\Omega} = 3\,\text{mA}$$
10. $V_{D1} = V_S = 3$ V, $V_{R1} = V_{R2} = 0$ V, $I_T = 0$ A
11. $V_{D1} = V_S = 10$ V, $V_{R1} = 0$ V, $I_1 = 0$ A, $V_{D2} = 0.7$ V, $V_{R2} = V_S - V_F = 9.3$ V,
    $$I_2 = \frac{V_S - V_F}{R_2} = \frac{9.3\,\text{V}}{1.8\,\text{k}\Omega} = 5.17\,\text{mA}$$
12. There are *two* forward biased diodes, so
    $V_{R1} = V_S - (V_{D1} + V_{D2}) = 5\,\text{V} - 1.4\,\text{V} = 3.6$ V and
    $$I_T = \frac{V_S - 1.4\,\text{V}}{R_1} = \frac{3.6\,\text{V}}{200\,\Omega} = 18\,\text{mA}$$
13. There are two forward-biased diodes, $V_{D1} = V_{D2} = 0.7$ V, $I_T = \dfrac{V_S - 1.4\,\text{V}}{R_T} = \dfrac{9\,\text{V} - 1.4\,\text{V}}{300\,\Omega} = \dfrac{7.6\,\text{V}}{300\,\Omega} =$ 25.3 mA, $V_{R1} = I_T R_1 = (25.3\,\text{mA})(100\,\Omega) = 2.53$ V, $V_{R2} = I_T R_2 = (25.3\,\text{mA})(200\,\Omega) = 5.06$ V
14. % of error $= \dfrac{|13.2\,\text{V} - 12.8\,\text{V}|}{13.2\,\text{V}} \times 100 = 3.03\,\%$

15. Error (%) = $\dfrac{|880\,\mu A - 750\,\mu A|}{880\,\mu A} \times 100 = 14.8\,\%$

    This error is not acceptable.

16. Error (%) = $\dfrac{|160\,mV - 144\,mV|}{160\,mV} \times 100 = 10\%$ This error is acceptable.

17. $I_T = \dfrac{V_S - 1.4\,V}{R_1 + R_2} = \dfrac{5\,V - 1.4\,V}{300\,\Omega} = 12\,mA$ and
    $V_{R2} = I_T R_2 = (12\,mA)(200\,\Omega) = 2.4\,V$ The meter is measuring 2.54 V, and
    Error (%) = $\dfrac{|2.54\,V - 2.4\,V|}{2.54\,V} \times 100 = 5.51\%$

18. $I_T = \dfrac{V_S - 2.1\,V}{R_1 + R_2 + R_3} = \dfrac{5\,V - 2.1\,V}{340\,\Omega} = 8.53\,mA$ and
    $V_{R2} = I_T R_2 = (8.53\,mA)(120\,\Omega) = 1.02\,V$. The meter is measuring 970 mV, and
    Error (%) = $\dfrac{|970\,mV - 1.02\,V|}{970\,mV} \times 100 = 5.15\%$

19. To provide a safety margin, the minimum value of V_{RRM} is found as $V_{RRM} = 1.2 V_{S(pk)} = (1.2)(100\,V) = 120\,V$.

20. The maximum reverse voltage across D_1 equals the peak value of V_{R2}, found as
    $V_{R2} = V_S \dfrac{R_2}{R_T} = (100\,V_{pk}) \dfrac{5\,k\Omega}{10\,k\Omega} = 50\,V$.

    Providing a safety margin, the minimum value of V_{RRM} is found as $V_{RRM} = 1.2 V_{R2(pk)} = (1.2)(50\,V) = 60\,V$.

21. The maximum reverse voltage across D_1 equals the negative peak value of V_{R2}, found as
    $V_{R2} = V_S \dfrac{R_2}{R_T} = (-200\,V_{pk}) \dfrac{8.2\,k\Omega}{9.2\,k\Omega} = -178\,V$.

    Providing a safety margin, the minimum value of V_{RRM} is found as $1.2 V_{R2(pk)} = (1.2)(-178\,V) = 214$ V. The minimum practical value of V_{RRM} greater than 214 V is 250 V.

22. $I_F = \dfrac{V_S - V_F}{R_1} = \dfrac{50\,V - 0.7\,V}{5.1\,k\Omega} = 9.67\,mA$, and
    $I_0 = 9.67\,mA \times 1.2 = 11.6\,mA$ (minimum)

23. From problem 22, $I_F = 9.67\,mA$. $P_F = I_T V_F = (9.67\,mA)(0.7\,V) = 6.77\,mW$. Providing a safety margin, $P_{D(max)} = 1.2\,P_F = (1.2)(6.77\,mW) = 8.12\,mW$ (minimum).

24. $I_0 = \dfrac{P_{D(max)}}{V_F} = \dfrac{1.2\,W}{0.7\,V} = 1.71\,A$. Providing a safety

    margin, $I_F = 0.8 I_0 = (0.8)(1.71\,A) = 1.37\,A$ (maximum).

25. $I_0 = \dfrac{P_{D(max)}}{V_F} = \dfrac{750\,mW}{0.7\,V} = 1.07\,A$. Providing a

    safety margin $I_F = 0.8 I_0 = (0.8)(1.07\,A) = 856\,mA$ (maximum).

26. $V_F = 0.7\,V + I_F R_B = 0.7\,V + (10\,mA)(5\,\Omega) = 0.75\,V$

27. $V_F = 0.7\,V + I_F R_B = 0.7\,V + (8.2\,mA)(12\,\Omega) = 0.798\,V$

28. Equation (2.5) is transposed to obtain
    $I_F = \dfrac{V_F - 0.7\,V}{R_B}$ For $V_F = 0.8$ V:
    $I_F = \dfrac{0.8\,V - 0.7\,V}{20\,\Omega} = 5\,mA$

29. $V_R = I_R R_1 = (10\,\mu A)(10\,k\Omega) = 100\,mV$

30. The peak reverse value of V_S is 100 V. Providing a safety margin, $V_{RRM} \geq (1.2)(100\,V) = 120\,V$. Thus, any diode from 1N5402 through 1N5408 could be used.

31. Under *electrical characteristics*, the maximum reverse current is shown to be 100 µA (rated at $T = 150°C$).

32. The surge current rating is the same for all diodes in the series: 200 A for 1 cycle.

33. The minimum V_{RRM} rating is found as 225 V × 1.2 = 270 V. The minimum I_0 rating is found as 24.5 A × 1.2 = 29.4 A. From Figure 2.27, the 1N3495 has these minimum acceptable ratings.

34. The minimum V_{RRM} rating is found as 170 V × 1.2 = 204 V. The minimum I_0 rating is found as 3.6 A × 1.2 = 4.32 A. From Figure 2.27, the MR754 has these minimum acceptable ratings.

35. The minimum V_{RRM} is 470 V × 1.2 = 564 V. The minimum I_0 rating is found as $\dfrac{2.8\,W}{0.7\,V} \times 1.2 = 4.8\,A$.

    From Figure 2.27, the MR756 has these minimum acceptable ratings.

36. $Z_Z = \dfrac{\Delta V_Z}{\Delta I_Z} = \dfrac{25\,mV}{1\,mA} = 25\,\Omega$

37. Figures (a), (c), (d), and (e) are biased for normal zener operation. In each case, the device points to the (+) terminal of the source.

38. For each conducting diode, electron flow *is with the arrow* and conventional flow is *against the arrow*.

39. $I_{ZM} = \dfrac{P_{D(max)}}{V_Z} = \dfrac{1\,W}{6.8\,V} = 147\,mA$

40. $I_{ZM} = \dfrac{P_{D(max)}}{V_Z} = \dfrac{10\,W}{24\,V} = 417\,mA$

41. Derating value = (8 mW/°C)(120°C − 50°C) = 560 mW, P_D at 120°C = 5 W − 560 mW = 4.44 W (maximum)

42. Derating value = (1.67 mW/°C)(150°C − 50°C) = 167 mW, P_D at 150°C = 250 mW − 167 mW = 83 mW (maximum)

43. The lowest P_D rating ≥ 1.8 W is 5 W. The only diode with ratings of 28V/5W is the 1N5362A.

44. The P_D ratings ≥ 1.2 W are 1.5 W and 5 W. The diodes with these ratings and V_Z = 6.8 V are the 1N5921A and the 1N5342A. Either of these can be used.

45. $P_D = I_{ZM}V_Z = (150 \text{ mA})(12 \text{ V}) = 1.8 \text{ W}$ Providing a safety margin, $P_{D(\max)} = 1.2P_D = (1.2)(1.8 \text{ W}) = 2.16 \text{ W}$. From Figure 2.34, only the 1N5349A can be used in this application.

46. $R_{S(\min)} = \dfrac{V_{\text{out(pk)}} - V_F}{I_F} = \dfrac{20 \text{ V} - 1.5 \text{ V}}{18 \text{ mA}} = 1028 \ \Omega$

(Use 1.1 kΩ standard)

47. $R_{S(\min)} = \dfrac{V_{\text{out(pk)}} - V_F}{I_F} = \dfrac{32 \text{ V} - 1.6 \text{ V}}{20 \text{ mA}} = 1520 \ \Omega$

(Use 1.6 kΩ standard)

48. (a) Both readings are high. The diode is *open*.
(b) Good. (c) Good. (d) Both readings are low. The diode is *shorted*.

49. The diode is *good*.

50. V_R is always equal to V_S, so V_F is 0 V. This is the symptom of a *shorted* diode.

51. V_R is always 0 V, so V_F is always equal to V_S. Since this is true even when the diode is forward biased, the device is *open*.

52. The voltage across the resistor equals the difference between the source voltage (V_S) and the zener voltage (V_Z). Therefore,

$I_T = \dfrac{V_S - V_Z}{R} = \dfrac{16 \text{ V} - 5.1 \text{ V}}{120 \ \Omega} = 90.8 \text{ mA}$

53. $I_T = \dfrac{V_{R1}}{R_1} = \dfrac{9 \text{ V}}{820 \ \Omega} = 11 \text{ mA}$, and

$P_Z = V_Z I_T = (12 \text{ V})(11 \text{ mA}) = 132 \text{ mW}$

54. Connect the ohmmeter so that it reverse-biases the diode. This effectively removes the diode from the circuit.

55. Derating value = (6.67 mW/°C)(150°C − 50°C) = 667 mW. At 150°C, P_D = 1 W − 667 mW = 333 mW. The maximum current at that temp is found as $I_{ZM} = \dfrac{P_D}{V_Z} = \dfrac{333 \text{ mW}}{7.5 \text{ V}} = 44.4 \text{ mA}$

56. The 1N4738A has the following ratings: V_Z = 8.2 V and P_D = 1 W. The derating factor for the device is 6.67 mW/°C for temperatures above 50°C. For the circuit in Figure 2.56,

$I_T = \dfrac{V_S - V_Z}{R_1} = \dfrac{60 \text{ V} - 8.2 \text{ V}}{910 \ \Omega} = 56.9 \text{ mA}$ and

$P_D = V_Z I_T = (8.2 \text{ V})(56.9 \text{ mA}) \cong 467 \text{ mW}$. At $T = 150°C$, the 1N4738A is limited to

$P_{D(\max)} = 1 \text{ W} - (6.67 \text{ mW/°C})(150°C - 50°C)$

$= 1 \text{ W} - 667 \text{ mW} = 333 \text{ mW}$. Since this value is lower than the circuit requirement (467 mW), the component cannot be used.

57. According to the component spec sheet, the 1N5341 has a rating of V_Z = 6.2 V @ I_{ZT} = 200 mA.

58. The power dissipation of the diode when operated at V_Z equals the product of V_Z and I_{ZT}, and varies from diode to diode. For the 1N5364 (a 33 V, 5 W zener), $V_Z I_{ZT} = (33 \text{ V})(40 \text{ mA}) = 1.32 \text{ W}$. (Student results will likely vary from this value.)

59. Yellow light has a range of approximately 565 to 590 nanometers (nm). Yellow LEDs are rated somewhere in this range.

CHAPTER 3

EXAMPLE PRACTICE PROBLEMS (CH 3)

3-1. $I_S = \dfrac{N_P}{N_S} I_P = \left(\dfrac{1}{12}\right)(250 \text{ mA}) = 20.8 \text{ mA}$

3-2. $V_{S(\text{pk})} = \dfrac{N_S}{N_P} V_{P(\text{pk})} = \left(\dfrac{1}{10}\right)(180 \text{ V}) = 18 \text{ V}$,

$V_{L(\text{pk})} = V_{S(\text{pk})} - 0.7 \text{ V} = 18 \text{ V} - 0.7 \text{ V} = 17.3 \text{ V}$

3-3. $V_{S(\text{pk})} = \dfrac{V_{S(\text{rms})}}{0.707} = \dfrac{12 \text{ V}}{0.707} = 17 \text{ V}$, $V_{L(\text{pk})} = V_{S(\text{pk})} - V_F = 17 \text{ V} - 0.7 \text{ V} = 16.3 \text{ V}$

3-4. $V_{P(\text{pk})} = \dfrac{120 \text{ V}}{0.707} = 170 \text{ V}$

$V_{S(\text{pk})} = \dfrac{N_S}{N_P} V_{P(\text{pk})} = \left(\dfrac{1}{12}\right)(170 \text{ V}) = 14.2 \text{ V}$

$V_{L(\text{pk})} = V_{S(\text{pk})} - 0.7 \text{ V} = 13.5 \text{ V}$

$I_{L(\text{pk})} = \dfrac{V_{L(\text{pk})}}{R_L} = \dfrac{13.5 \text{ V}}{8.2 \text{ k}\Omega} = 1.65 \text{ mA}$

3-5. $V_{P(\text{pk})} = \dfrac{120 \text{ V}}{0.707} = 170 \text{ V}$

$V_{S(\text{pk})} = \dfrac{N_S}{N_P} V_{P(\text{pk})} = \left(\dfrac{1}{14}\right)(170 \text{ V}) = 12.1 \text{ V}$

$V_{L(\text{pk})} = V_{S(\text{pk})} - 0.7 \text{ V} = 11.4 \text{ V}$

$V_{\text{ave}} = \dfrac{V_{L(\text{pk})}}{\pi} = \dfrac{11.4 \text{ V}}{\pi} = 3.63 \text{ V}$

3-6. $I_{\text{ave}} = \dfrac{V_{\text{ave}}}{R_L} = \dfrac{24 \text{ V}}{2.2 \text{ k}\Omega} = 10.9 \text{ mA}$

3-7. $V_{S(\text{pk})} = \dfrac{48 \text{ V}}{0.707} = 67.9 \text{ V}$, $V_{L(\text{pk})} = V_{S(\text{pk})} - 0.7 \text{ V} = 67.9 \text{ V} - 0.7 \text{ V} = 67.2 \text{ V}$

3-8. $I_{L(pk)} = \dfrac{V_{L(pk)}}{R_L} = \dfrac{67.2\,\text{V}}{12\,\text{k}\Omega} = 5.6\,\text{mA}$

$I_{ave} = \dfrac{I_{L(pk)}}{\pi} = \dfrac{5.6\,\text{mA}}{\pi} = 1.78\,\text{mA}$

3-9. Using the approach demonstrated in the example:

$V_{S(pk)} = \dfrac{36\,\text{V}}{0.707} = 50.9\,\text{V}$, $V_{L(pk)} = V_{S(pk)} - 0.7\,\text{V} =$

$50.9\,\text{V} - 0.7\,\text{V} = 50.2\,\text{V}$,

$V_{ave} = \dfrac{V_{L(pk)}}{\pi} = \dfrac{50.2\,\text{V}}{\pi} = 16\,\text{V}$. Reversing the

voltage polarities: $V_{S(pk)} = -50.9\,\text{V}$,
$V_{L(pk)} = -50.2\,\text{V}$, $V_{ave} = -16\,\text{V}$.

3-10. $V_{S(pk)} = \dfrac{24\,\text{V}}{0.707} = 33.9\,\text{V}$, $V_{L(pk)} = \dfrac{V_{S(pk)}}{2} - 0.7$

$\text{V} = 16.95\,\text{V} - 0.7\,\text{V} = 16.3\,\text{V}$,

$V_{ave} = \dfrac{2V_{L(pk)}}{\pi} = \dfrac{32.6\,\text{V}}{\pi} = 10.4\,\text{V}$.

3-11. $I_{L(pk)} = \dfrac{V_{L(pk)}}{R_L} = \dfrac{16.3\,\text{V}}{2.2\,\text{k}\Omega} = 7.41\,\text{mA}$,

$I_{ave} = \dfrac{V_{ave}}{R_L} = \dfrac{10.4\,\text{V}}{2.2\,\text{k}\Omega} = 4.73\,\text{mA}$

3-12. $V_{S(pk)} = \dfrac{18\,\text{V}}{0.707} = 25.5\,\text{V}$

$V_{L(pk)} = V_{S(pk)} - 1.4\,\text{V} = 24.1\,\text{V}$

$V_{ave} = \dfrac{2V_{L(pk)}}{\pi} = \dfrac{48.2\,\text{V}}{\pi} = 15.3\,\text{V}$

$I_{ave} = \dfrac{V_{ave}}{R_L} = \dfrac{15.3\,\text{V}}{1.2\,\text{k}\Omega} = 12.8\,\text{mA}$

3-13. [This example has no practice problem.]

3-14. $V_{S(pk)} = \dfrac{12\,\text{V}}{0.707} = 17\,\text{V}$, $V_{L(pk)} = V_{S(pk)} - 2\,V_F =$

$17\,\text{V} - (2)(0.95\,\text{V}) = 15.1\,\text{V}$,

$V_{ave} = \dfrac{2V_{L(pk)}}{\pi} = \dfrac{30.2\,\text{V}}{\pi} = 9.61\,\text{V}$

3-15. $V_{S(pk)} = \dfrac{N_S}{N_P} V_{P(pk)} = \left(\dfrac{1}{2}\right)(170\,\text{V}) = 85\,\text{V}$,

$I_{surge} = \dfrac{V_{S(pk)}}{R_W + R_B} = \dfrac{85\,\text{V}}{8.5\,\Omega} = 10\,\text{A}$

3-16. [This example has no practice problem.]

3-17. $V_{S(pk)} = \dfrac{24\,\text{V}}{0.707} = 33.9\,\text{V}$

$V_{L(pk)} = \dfrac{V_{S(pk)}}{2} - 0.7\,\text{V} = 16.3\,\text{V}$

Assuming that $V_{dc} \cong V_{L(pk)} = 16.3\,\text{V}$:

$I_L = \dfrac{V_L}{R_L} = \dfrac{16.3\,\text{V}}{1.5\,\text{k}\Omega} = 10.9\,\text{mA}$

$V_r = \dfrac{I_L t}{C} = \dfrac{(10.9\,\text{mA})(8.33\,\text{ms})}{330\,\mu\text{F}} = 275\,\text{mV}_{PP}$

$V_{dc} = V_{L(pk)} - \dfrac{V_r}{2} = 16.3\,\text{V} - \dfrac{275\,\text{mV}}{2} = 16.2\,\text{V}$

3-18. $I_T = \dfrac{V_{in} - V_Z}{R_S} = \dfrac{15\,\text{V} - 12\,\text{V}}{1.5\,\text{k}\Omega} = 2\,\text{mA}$

3-19. $I_L = \dfrac{V_Z}{R_L} = \dfrac{12\,\text{V}}{12\,\text{k}\Omega} = 1\,\text{mA}$

3-20. $I_Z = I_T - I_L = 2\,\text{mA} - 1\,\text{mA} = 1\,\text{mA}$

3-21. $I_T = \dfrac{V_{in} - V_Z}{R_S} = \dfrac{20\,\text{V} - 5.1\,\text{V}}{1\,\text{k}\Omega} = 14.9\,\text{mA}$,

$I_{L(max)} = I_T - I_{ZK} = 14.9\,\text{mA} - 5\,\text{mA} = 9.9\,\text{mA}$,

$R_{L(min)} = \dfrac{V_Z}{I_{L(max)}} = \dfrac{5.1\,\text{V}}{9.9\,\text{mA}} = 515\,\Omega$

3-22. $V_{r(out)} = V_r \dfrac{Z_Z \| R_L}{(Z_Z \| R_L) + R_S} =$

$(1.2\,\text{V}_{pp})\dfrac{22.2\,\Omega}{22.2\,\Omega + 91\,\Omega} = 235\,\text{mV}_{pp}$

3-23. $V_{S(pk)} = \dfrac{24\,\text{V}}{0.707} = 33.9\,\text{V}$,

$V_{pk} = V_{S(pk)} - 1.4\,\text{V} = 32.5\,\text{V}$

$I_R = \dfrac{V_{pk} - V_Z}{R_S} = \dfrac{32.5\,\text{V} - 10\,\text{V}}{500\,\Omega} = 45\,\text{mA}$

$V_r = \dfrac{I_R t}{C} = \dfrac{(45\,\text{mA})(8.33\,\text{ms})}{470\,\mu\text{F}} = 798\,\text{mV}_{pp}$

$V_{r(out)} = V_r \dfrac{Z_Z \| R_L}{(Z_Z \| R_L) + R_S} =$

$(798\,\text{mV}_{pp})\left(\dfrac{19.9\,\Omega}{519.9\,\Omega}\right) = 30.5\,\text{mV}_{pp}$,

$V_{dc} = V_Z = 10\,\text{V}$, $I_L = \dfrac{V_Z}{R_L} = \dfrac{10\,\text{V}}{5.1\,\text{k}\Omega} = 1.96\,\text{mA}$

PRACTICE PROBLEMS (CH 3)

1. $V_S = \dfrac{N_S}{N_P} V_P = \left(\dfrac{1}{2}\right)(65\,\text{V}) = 32.5\,\text{V}$

2. $V_S = \dfrac{N_S}{N_P} V_P = \left(\dfrac{1}{10}\right)(150\,\text{V}) = 15\,\text{V}$

3. From Problem 1: $V_S = 32.5$ V

$$V_{S(pk)} = \frac{V_{S(rms)}}{0.707} = \frac{32.5 \text{ V}}{0.707} = 46 \text{ V}$$

4. From Problem 2: $V_S = 15$ V

$$V_{S(pk)} = \frac{V_{S(rms)}}{0.707} = \frac{15 \text{ V}}{0.707} = 21.2 \text{ V}$$

5. $\dfrac{N_P}{N_S} = \dfrac{V_P}{V_S} = \dfrac{40 \text{ V}}{320 \text{ V}} = \dfrac{1}{8}$ (1 : 8)

6. $I_S = \dfrac{N_P}{N_S} I_P = \left(\dfrac{12}{1}\right)(250 \text{ mA}) = 3$ A

7. From Problem 3: $V_{S(pk)} = 46$ V
$V_{L(pk)} = V_{S(pk)} - 0.7 \text{ V} = 46 \text{ V} - 0.7 \text{ V} = 45.3$ V

8. From Problem 4: $V_{S(pk)} = 21.2$ V
$V_{L(pk)} = V_{S(pk)} - 0.7 \text{ V} = 21.2 \text{ V} - 0.7 \text{ V} = 20.5$ V

9. $V_{S(pk)} = \dfrac{12 \text{ V}}{0.707} = 17$ V,
$V_{L(pk)} = V_{S(pk)} - 0.7 \text{ V} = 17 \text{ V} - 0.7 \text{ V} = 16.3$ V

10. From Problem 9: $V_{L(pk)} = 16.3$ V

$$I_{L(pk)} = \frac{V_{L(pk)}}{R_L} = \frac{16.3 \text{ V}}{10 \text{ k}\Omega} = 1.63 \text{ mA}$$

11. From Problem 7: $V_{L(pk)} = 45.3$ V

$$V_{ave} = \frac{V_{L(pk)}}{\pi} = \frac{45.3 \text{ V}}{\pi} = 14.4 \text{ V}$$

12. From Problem 8: $V_{L(pk)} = 20.5$ V

$$V_{ave} = \frac{V_{L(pk)}}{\pi} = \frac{20.52 \text{ V}}{\pi} = 6.53 \text{ V}$$

13. From Problem 9: $V_{L(pk)} = 16.3$ V

$$V_{ave} = \frac{V_{L(pk)}}{\pi} = \frac{16.3 \text{ V}}{\pi} = 5.19 \text{ V}$$

14. From Problem 11: $V_{L(pk)} = 45.3$ V and

$$V_{ave} = 14.4 \text{ V}. \quad I_{ave} = \frac{V_{ave}}{R_L} = \frac{14.4 \text{ V}}{3.3 \text{ k}\Omega} = 4.36 \text{ mA}$$

Reversing the voltage polarities: $V_{L(pk)} = -45.3$ V
$V_{ave} = -14.4$ V.

15. From Problem 12: $V_{L(pk)} = 20.5$ V and

$$V_{ave} = 6.53 \text{ V}. \quad I_{ave} = \frac{V_{ave}}{R_L} = \frac{6.53 \text{ V}}{5.1 \text{ k}\Omega} = 1.28 \text{ mA}$$

Reversing the voltage polarities: $V_{L(pk)} = -20.5$ V
and $V_{ave} = -6.53$ V.

16. From Problem 13: $V_{L(pk)} = 16.3$ V and

$$V_{ave} = 5.19 \text{ V}. \quad I_{ave} = \frac{V_{ave}}{R_L} = \frac{5.19 \text{ V}}{10 \text{ k}\Omega} = 519 \text{ μA}$$

Reversing the voltage polarities: $V_{L(pk)} = -16.3$ V
and $V_{ave} = -5.19$ V.

17. Diode PIV equals the peak secondary voltage. In Problem 4, we calculated the value of $V_{S(pk)} = 21.2$ V. Thus, PIV = 21.2 V.

18.

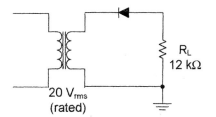

$$V_{S(pk)} = \frac{20 \text{ V}}{0.707} = 28.3 \text{ V}, \quad V_{L(pk)} = V_{S(pk)} - 0.7 \text{ V}$$

$$= 27.6 \text{ V}, \quad V_{ave} = \frac{V_{L(pk)}}{\pi} = \frac{27.6 \text{ V}}{\pi} = 8.79 \text{ V}$$

Reversing the polarities: $V_{S(pk)} = -28.29$ V, $V_{L(pk)} = -27.59$ V, and $V_{ave} = -8.78$ V. PIV $= V_{S(pk)} = 28.3$ V

19. $V_{S(pk)} = \dfrac{18 \text{ V}}{0.707} = 25.5 \text{ V}, \quad V_{L(pk)} = \dfrac{V_{S(pk)}}{2} - 0.7 \text{ V}$

$$= 12.75 \text{ V} - 0.7 \text{ V} = 12.05 \text{ V}, \quad V_{ave} = \frac{2V_{L(pk)}}{\pi} =$$

$$\frac{24.1 \text{ V}}{\pi} = 7.67 \text{ V}, \quad I_{ave} = \frac{V_{ave}}{R_L} = \frac{7.67 \text{ V}}{10 \text{ k}\Omega} = 767 \text{ μA}$$

20. $V_{S(pk)} = \dfrac{24 \text{ V}}{0.707} = 33.9 \text{ V}, \quad V_{L(pk)} = \dfrac{V_{S(pk)}}{2} - 0.7 \text{ V}$

$$= 16.95 \text{ V} - 0.7 \text{ V} = 16.25 \text{ V}, \quad V_{ave} = \frac{2V_{L(pk)}}{\pi} =$$

$$\frac{32.5 \text{ V}}{\pi} = 10.35 \text{ V}, \quad I_{ave} = \frac{V_{ave}}{R_L} = \frac{10.35 \text{ V}}{8 \text{ k}\Omega} = 1.29 \text{ mA}$$

21. $V_{S(pk)} = \dfrac{30 \text{ V}}{0.707} = 42.4 \text{ V}, \quad V_{L(pk)} = \dfrac{V_{S(pk)}}{2} - 0.7 \text{ V}$

$$= 21.2 \text{ V} - 0.7 \text{ V} = 20.5 \text{ V}, \quad V_{ave} = \frac{2V_{L(pk)}}{\pi} =$$

$$\frac{41 \text{ V}}{\pi} = 13.1 \text{ V}, I_{ave} = \frac{V_{ave}}{R_L} = \frac{13.1 \text{ V}}{6.2 \text{ k}\Omega} = 2.11 \text{ mA}$$

22. Diode PIV equals the peak secondary voltage. In Problem 19, we calculated the value of $V_{S(pk)} = 25.5$ V. Thus, PIV = 25.46 V.

23. Diode PIV equals the peak secondary voltage. In Problem 20, we calculated the value of $V_{S(pk)} = 33.9$ V. Thus, PIV = 33.9 V.

24. Diode PIV equals the peak secondary voltage. In Problem 21, we calculated the value of $V_{S(pk)} = 42.4$ V. Thus, PIV = 42.4 V.

25. Simply reverse the polarities of the output voltages that were calculated in Problem 19, as follows: $V_{L(pk)} = -12.05$ V and $V_{ave} = -7.67$ V. The current remains the same: 767 μA.

26.

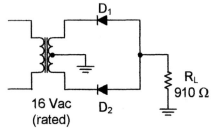

16 Vac
(rated)

$V_{S(\text{pk})} = \dfrac{16\,\text{V}}{0.707} = 22.6\,\text{V}, \; V_{L(pk)} = \dfrac{V_{S(pk)}}{2} - 0.7V =$

$11.3\,\text{V} - 0.7\,\text{V} = 10.6\,\text{V}, \; V_{\text{ave}} = \dfrac{2V_{L(\text{pk})}}{\pi} =$

$\dfrac{21.2\,\text{V}}{\pi} = 6.75\,\text{V}, \; I_{\text{ave}} = \dfrac{V_{\text{ave}}}{R_L} = \dfrac{6.75\,\text{V}}{910\,\Omega} = 7.42\,\text{mA}$

Reversing the voltage polarities: $V_{L(\text{pk})} = -10.6\,\text{V}$ and $V_{\text{ave}} = -6.75\,\text{V}$. PIV $= V_{S(\text{pk})} = 22.6\,\text{V}$.

27. $V_{S(\text{pk})} = \dfrac{36\,\text{V}}{0.707} = 50.9\,\text{V}, \; V_{L(\text{pk})} = V_{S(\text{pk})} - 1.4\,\text{V} =$

$49.5\,\text{V}, \; V_{\text{ave}} = \dfrac{2V_{L(\text{pk})}}{\pi} = \dfrac{99\,\text{V}}{\pi} = 31.5\,\text{V},$

$I_{\text{pk}} = \dfrac{V_{L(\text{pk})}}{R_L} = \dfrac{49.5\,\text{V}}{10\,\text{k}\Omega} = 4.95\,\text{mA}, \;$ and

$I_{\text{ave}} = \dfrac{V_{\text{ave}}}{R_L} = \dfrac{31.5\,\text{V}}{10\,\text{k}\Omega} = 3.15\,\text{mA}$

28. $V_{S(\text{pk})} = \dfrac{16\,\text{V}}{0.707} = 22.6\,\text{V}, \; V_{L(\text{pk})} = V_{S(\text{pk})} - 1.4\,\text{V} =$

$21.2\,\text{V}, \quad V_{\text{ave}} = \dfrac{2V_{L(\text{pk})}}{\pi} = \dfrac{42.4\,\text{V}}{\pi} = 13.5\,\text{V},$

$I_{\text{pk}} = \dfrac{V_{L(\text{pk})}}{R_L} = \dfrac{21.2\,\text{V}}{10\,\text{k}\Omega} = 2.12\,\text{mA}, \;$ and

$I_{\text{ave}} = \dfrac{V_{\text{ave}}}{R_L} = \dfrac{13.5\,\text{V}}{10\,\text{k}\Omega} = 1.35\,\text{mA}$

29. From Problem 28, $V_{S(\text{pk})} = 22.6\,\text{V}$. Therefore, PIV $= 22.6\,\text{V}$. Adding a safety margin, $V_{RRM} = 1.2 \times \text{PIV} = (1.2)(22.6\,\text{V}) = 27.2\,\text{V}$ (minimum).

30.

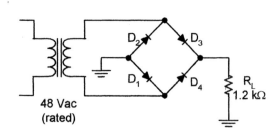

48 Vac
(rated)

$V_{S(\text{pk})} = \dfrac{48\,\text{V}}{0.707} = 67.9\,\text{V}, \; V_{L(\text{pk})} = V_{S(\text{pk})} - 1.4\,\text{V} =$

$66.5\,\text{V}, \; V_{\text{ave}} = \dfrac{2V_{L(\text{pk})}}{\pi} = \dfrac{133\,\text{V}}{\pi} = 42.3\,\text{V},$

$I_{\text{ave}} = \dfrac{V_{\text{ave}}}{R_L} = \dfrac{42.3\,\text{V}}{1.2\,\text{k}\Omega} = 35.3\,\text{mA} \;$, and

PIV $= V_{S(\text{pk})} = 67.9\,\text{V}$

31. $V_{S(\text{pk})} = \dfrac{12.5\,\text{V}}{0.707} = 17.7\,\text{V}, \; V_{L(\text{pk})} = V_{S(\text{pk})} - 0.7\,\text{V}$

$= 17\,\text{V}, \; I_{\text{surge}} = \dfrac{V_{S(\text{pk})}}{R_W + R_B} = \dfrac{17\,\text{V}}{7\,\Omega} = 2.43\,\text{A}$

32. $V_{S(\text{pk})} = \dfrac{36\,\text{V}}{0.707} = 50.9\,\text{V}$

$I_{\text{surge}} = \dfrac{V_{S(\text{pk})}}{R_W + R_B} = \dfrac{50.9\,\text{V}}{14\,\Omega} = 3.64\,\text{A}$

33. From problem 31, $V_{L(\text{pk})} = 17\,\text{V}$. Assuming that

$V_{\text{dc}} \cong 17\,\text{V}: \; I_L = \dfrac{V_L}{R_L} = \dfrac{17\,\text{V}}{5\,\text{k}\Omega} = 3.4\,\text{mA}:$

$V_r = \dfrac{I_L t}{C} = \dfrac{(3.4\,\text{mA})(16.67\,\text{ms})}{1000\,\mu\text{F}} = 56.7\,\text{mV}_{\text{pp}}$, and

$V_{\text{dc}} = V_{L(\text{pk})} - \dfrac{V_r}{2} = 17\,\text{V} - \dfrac{56.7\,\text{mV}_{\text{pp}}}{2} = 16.97\,\text{V}$

34. $V_{S(\text{pk})} = \dfrac{56\,\text{V}}{0.707} = 79.2\,\text{V}, \; V_{L(\text{pk})} = \dfrac{V_{S(\text{pk})}}{2} - 0.7\,\text{V} =$

$39.6\,\text{V} - 0.7\,\text{V} = 38.9\,\text{V}$. Assuming that

$V_{\text{dc}} \cong \quad 38.9 \;\text{V}: \; I_L = \dfrac{V_L}{R_L} = \dfrac{38.9\,\text{V}}{500\,\Omega} = 77.8\,\text{mA}:$

$V_r = \dfrac{I_L t}{C} = \dfrac{(77.8\,\text{mA})(8.33\,\text{ms})}{1000\,\mu\text{F}} = 648\,\text{mV}_{\text{pp}}$, and

$V_{\text{dc}} = V_{L(\text{pk})} - \dfrac{V_r}{2} = 38.9\,\text{V} - \dfrac{648\,\text{mV}_{\text{pp}}}{2} = 38.6\,\text{V}$

35. $V_{S(\text{pk})} = \dfrac{18\,\text{V}}{0.707} = 25.5\,\text{V}, \; V_{L(\text{pk})} = V_{S(\text{pk})} - 1.4\,\text{V} =$

$24.1\,\text{V}$. Assuming that $V_{\text{dc}} \cong 24.1\,\text{V}: \; I_L = \dfrac{V_L}{R_L} =$

$\dfrac{24.1\,\text{V}}{820\,\Omega} = 29.4\,\text{mA}, \; V_r = \dfrac{I_L t}{C} = \dfrac{(29.4\,\text{mA})(8.33\,\text{ms})}{470\,\mu\text{F}}$

$= 521\,\text{mV}_{\text{pp}}$, and $V_{\text{dc}} = V_{L(\text{pk})} - \dfrac{V_r}{2} = 24.1\,\text{V} -$

$\dfrac{521\,\text{mV}_{\text{pp}}}{2} = 23.8\,\text{V}$

36. $V_{S(\text{pk})} = \dfrac{24\,\text{V}}{0.707} = 33.9\,\text{V}, \; V_{L(\text{pk})} = V_{S(\text{pk})} - 1.4\,\text{V} =$

$32.5\,\text{V}$. Assuming that $V_{\text{dc}} \cong 32.5\,\text{V}: \; I_L = \dfrac{V_L}{R_L} =$

$\dfrac{32.5\text{ V}}{200\,\Omega} = 163\text{ mA},\ V_r = \dfrac{I_L t}{C} = \dfrac{(163\text{ mA})(8.33\text{ ms})}{1200\,\mu\text{F}}$

$= 1.13\text{ V}_{pp},\text{ and }V_{dc} = V_{L(pk)} - \dfrac{V_r}{2} = 32.5\text{ V} -$

$\dfrac{1.13\text{V}_{pp}}{2} = 31.9\text{ V}$

37. From Problem 36, $V_{S(pk)} = 33.9$ V. Therefore, PIV $= 33.9$ V.

38. From Problem 31, $V_{S(pk)} = 17.7$ V. With the capacitive filter, PIV $\cong 2V_{S(pk)} = 35.4$ V.

39. $I_T = \dfrac{V_S - V_Z}{R_S} = \dfrac{10\text{ V} - 6\text{ V}}{300\,\Omega} = 13.3\text{ mA}$

40. $I_L = \dfrac{V_Z}{R_L} = \dfrac{6\text{ V}}{2\text{ k}\Omega} = 3\text{ mA}$

41. From Problems 39 and 40: $I_T = 13.3$ mA and $I_L = 3$ mA. $I_Z = I_T - I_L = 10.3$ mA

42. From Problem 39: $I_T = 13.3$ mA. $I_L = \dfrac{V_Z}{R_L} =$

$\dfrac{6\text{ V}}{3\text{ k}\Omega} = 2\text{ mA, and }I_Z = I_T - I_L = 11.3\text{ mA}$

43. From Problem 39: $I_T = 13.3$ mA. $I_{L(max)} = I_T - I_{ZK}$ $= 13.3\text{ mA} - 1\text{ mA} = 12.3\text{ mA, and}$

$R_{L(min)} = \dfrac{V_Z}{I_{L(max)}} = \dfrac{6\text{ V}}{12.3\text{ mA}} = 488\,\Omega$

44. $I_T = \dfrac{V_S - V_Z}{R_S} = \dfrac{100\text{ V} - 51\text{ V}}{1.1\text{ k}\Omega} = 44.5\text{ mA}$

45. From Problem 44: $I_T = 44.5$ mA. $I_L = \dfrac{V_Z}{R_L} =$

$\dfrac{51\text{ V}}{5\text{ k}\Omega} = 10.2\text{ mA, and }I_Z = I_T - I_L = 34.3\text{ mA}$

46. From Problem 44: $I_T = 44.5$ mA. $I_{L(max)} = I_T - I_{ZK}$ $= 44.5\text{ mA} - 5\text{ mA} = 39.5\text{ mA, and}$

$R_{L(min)} = \dfrac{V_Z}{I_{L(max)}} = \dfrac{51\text{ V}}{39.5\text{ mA}} = 1.29\text{ k}\Omega$

47. $I_T = \dfrac{V_S - V_Z}{R_S} = \dfrac{12\text{ V} - 10\text{ V}}{80\,\Omega} = 25\text{ mA},\ I_L = \dfrac{V_Z}{R_L} =$

$\dfrac{10\text{ V}}{500\,\Omega} = 20\text{ mA, and }I_Z = I_T - I_L = 5\text{ mA}$

48. $V_{r(out)} = V_r\dfrac{Z_Z \parallel R_L}{(Z_Z \parallel R_L) + R_S} =$

$(770\text{ mV}_{pp})\left(\dfrac{7.87\,\Omega}{87.87\,\Omega}\right) = 69\text{ mV}_{pp}$

49. Assuming that the circuit is operating normally,

$V_{dc} = V_Z = 9.1\text{ V},\ I_L = \dfrac{V_Z}{R_L} = \dfrac{9.1\text{ V}}{2\text{ k}\Omega} = 4.55\text{ mA}$

50. $V_{S(pk)} = \dfrac{12\text{ V}}{0.707} = 17\text{ V},\ V_{pk} = V_{S(pk)} - 1.4\text{ V} =$

$15.6\text{ V},\ I_R = \dfrac{V_{pk} - V_Z}{R_S} = \dfrac{15.6\text{ V} - 9.1\text{ V}}{200\,\Omega} = 32.5\text{ mA},$

$V_r = \dfrac{I_R t}{C} = \dfrac{(32.5\text{ mA})(8.33\text{ ms})}{1000\,\mu\text{F}} = 271\text{ mV}_{pp},$

$V_{r(out)} = V_r\dfrac{Z_Z \parallel R_L}{(Z_Z \parallel R_L) + R_S} =$

$(271\text{ mV}_{pp})\left(\dfrac{9.95\,\Omega}{209.95\,\Omega}\right) = 12.8\text{ mV}_{pp}$

51. $V_{S(pk)} = \dfrac{56\text{ V}}{0.707} = 79.2\text{ V},\ V_{pk} = V_{S(pk)} - 1.4\text{ V} =$

$77.8\text{ V},\ I_R = \dfrac{V_{pk} - V_Z}{R_S} = \dfrac{77.8\text{ V} - 33\text{ V}}{510\,\Omega} =$

$87.8\text{ mA},\ V_r = \dfrac{I_R t}{C} = \dfrac{(87.8\text{ mA})(8.33\text{ ms})}{470\,\mu\text{F}} =$

$1.56\text{ V}_{pp},\ V_{r(out)} = V_r\dfrac{Z_Z \parallel R_L}{(Z_Z \parallel R_L) + R_S} =$

$(1.56\text{ V}_{pp})\left(\dfrac{47.6\,\Omega}{557.6\,\Omega}\right) = 133\text{ mV}_{pp},\ V_{dc} = V_Z = 33\text{ V},$

$I_L = \dfrac{V_Z}{R_L} = \dfrac{33\text{ V}}{1\text{ k}\Omega} = 33\text{ mA}$

52. The circuit has no output voltage. Since the primary fuse is intact, the problem is not a shorted load. Therefore, the problem is most likely caused by an open transformer winding or an open rectifier diode (D_1).

53. The output is characteristic of a half-wave rectifier, indicating that one of the diodes is not conducting. Either D_1 or D_2 is open. (Note: If the display traces are in sync, the waveforms indicate that D_2 is the open diode.)

54. Since the fuse is not blown, the problem is an open component. The "open" faults that could cause V_{ave} to drop to 0 V are (a) an open bridge rectifier, (b) an open transformer, (c) an open line input to the transformer primary, or (d) an open series resistor.

55. For the circuit shown, $V_{S(pk)} = \dfrac{30\text{ V}}{0.707} = 42.4\text{ V}$

$V_{pk} = V_{S(pk)} - 1.4\text{ V} = 4\text{ V},\ I_R = \dfrac{V_{pk} - V_Z}{R_S} =$

$\dfrac{41\text{ V} - 10\text{ V}}{470\,\Omega} = 66\text{ mA}$. If the load opens, the full value of I_R is drawn through the zener diode. Since $I_{ZM} = 30$ mA, the diode will be destroyed.

56. The replacement diode must be rated at $V_Z = 10$ V and have a $P_{D(max)}$ rating that exceeds the maximum required power dissipation for the component in the circuit. Maximum zener power dissipation occurs if the load opens. The value of P_D with an open load is found as follows: $V_{S(\text{pk})} = \dfrac{30\,\text{V}}{0.707} = 42.4\,\text{V}$

$V_{\text{pk}} = V_{S(\text{pk})} - 1.4\,\text{V} = 41\,\text{V}$, $I_{Z(\text{max})} = I_R = \dfrac{V_{\text{pk}} - V_Z}{R_S} = 66\,\text{mA}$. $P_Z = V_Z I_{Z(\text{max})} = 660\,\text{mW}$

Adding a 20% safety factor, the minimum acceptable zener power rating is approximately 792 mW. Figure 2.34 shows five diodes with ratings of $V_Z = 10\,\text{V}$ and $P_{D(\text{max})} \geq 792\,\text{mW}$: the 1N4740, MLL4740, 1N3020A, 1N5925A, and 1N5347A. (As shown, the MLL4740 has a body style that differs from the other components. This diode can be used only if it matches the body style of the component being replaced.)

57. According to its spec sheet, the 1N759A has nominal ratings of $V_Z = 12\,\text{V}$ and $Z_Z = 30\,\Omega$. As indicted by the V_Z rating, the dc output voltage (V_{dc}) is correct and does not indicate a problem. The *worst-case* output ripple (V_r) is found using the maximum transformer secondary voltage and *ideal* diode values of $V_F = 0\,\text{V}$, as follows:
$V_{S(\text{max})} = 1.2 V_S = (1.2)(36\,\text{V}) = 43.2\,\text{V}$,
$V_{S(\text{pk})} = \dfrac{43.2\,\text{V}}{0.707} = 61.1\,\text{V}$, $\quad V_{\text{pk}} \cong V_{S(\text{pk})} = 61.1\,\text{V}$
$I_R = \dfrac{V_{\text{pk}} - V_Z}{R_S} = \dfrac{61\,\text{V} - 12\,\text{V}}{2.2\,\text{k}\Omega} = 22.3\,\text{mA}$
$V_r = \dfrac{I_R t}{C} = \dfrac{(22.3\,\text{mA})(8.33\,\text{ms})}{1000\,\mu\text{F}} = 186\,\text{mV}_{\text{pp}}$

Since the measured ripple exceeds the worst-case ripple (even without considering the ripple reduction of the zener regulator), a problem is indicated, most likely a leaky filter capacitor.

58. The replacement components must have V_{RRM} and I_0 ratings that are at least 20% greater than the circuit PIV and average forward current. The minimum ratings are found as follows:
$\text{PIV} \cong V_{S(\text{pk})} = \dfrac{56\,\text{V}}{0.707} = 79.2\,\text{V}$
$V_{RRM} = 1.2 \times \text{PIV} = 95\,\text{V}$ (minimum)
$V_{L(\text{pk})} = \dfrac{V_{S(\text{pk})}}{2} - 0.7\,\text{V} = 39.6\,\text{V} - 0.7\,\text{V} = 38.9\,\text{V}$,
$V_{\text{ave}} = \dfrac{2 V_{L(\text{pk})}}{\pi} = \dfrac{77.8\,\text{V}}{\pi} = 24.8\,\text{V}$
$I_{\text{ave}} = \dfrac{V_{\text{ave}}}{R_L} = \dfrac{24.8\,\text{V}}{150\,\Omega} = 165\,\text{mA}$.

Since this average forward current is produced by the diode *pair*, the current through each diode is half the value of I_{ave}, or 82.5 mA Adding a 20% safety margin, $I_0 = 99\,\text{mA}$ (minimum). So, the required replacement component ratings are $V_{RRM} \geq 95\,\text{V}$ and $I_0 \geq 99\,\text{mA}$. According to the spec sheet (Figure 2.25), any diode from 1N4002 through 1N4007 can be used.

59. The secondary current is found as follows:
$V_{S(\text{pk})} = \dfrac{36\,\text{V}}{0.707} = 50.9\,\text{V}$, $V_{\text{pk}} = V_{S(\text{pk})} - 1.4\,\text{V} = 49.5\,\text{V}$, and
$I_S = I_{RS} = \dfrac{V_{\text{pk}} - V_Z}{R_L} = \dfrac{37.5\,\text{V}}{2.2\,\text{k}\Omega} = 17\,\text{mA}$. Since
$V_P I_P = V_S I_S$ (ideally), the *peak* primary current be found using the rated transformer voltages and the peak secondary current (I_S), as follows:
$I_P = \dfrac{V_S I_S}{V_P} = \dfrac{(36\,\text{V})(17\,\text{mA})}{120\,\text{V}} = 5.1\,\text{mA}$ Converting this value to rms, $I_P = (.707)(5.1\,\text{mA}) = 3.61\,\text{mA}$. Adding a 20% safety margin, the fuse must be rated at $I_P \geq (1.2)(3.61\,\text{mA}) = 4.33\,\text{mA}$. At this low value of primary current, any of the fuses listed could be used safely in the circuit.

60. The component is *not* connected correctly as shown. Pins 2 and 3 need to be reversed for proper component operation. The NTE6240 has an average forward current rating of 16 A (maximum). Using the 80% guideline, $I_L = (0.8)(16\,\text{A}) = 12.8\,\text{A}$ (maximum).

61. The 7805 is a +5 V regulator. Therefore, $V_L = +5\,\text{V}$ and $I_L = \dfrac{5\,\text{V}}{500\,\Omega} = 10\,\text{mA}$

CHAPTER 4

EXAMPLE PRACTICE PROBLEMS (CH 4)

4-1. $V_L = \dfrac{R_L}{R_L + R_S} V_{\text{in}} = \left(\dfrac{510\,\Omega}{610\,\Omega}\right)(15\,\text{V}_{\text{pk}}) = 12.5\,\text{V}_{\text{pk}}$

4-2. The load is in parallel with a conducting diode, so $V_L = V_F = -0.7\,\text{V}$ and $V_{RS} = -V_{\text{in}} + 0.7\,\text{V} = V_{RS} = -15\,\text{V}_{\text{pk}} + 0.7\,\text{V} = -14.3\,\text{V}_{\text{pk}}$

4-3. During the positive alternation of the input, $V_L = V_F = 0.7\,\text{V}$ and $V_{RS} = V_{\text{in}} - 0.7\,\text{V} = 12\,\text{V}_{\text{pk}} - 0.7\,\text{V} = 11.3\,\text{V}_{\text{pk}}$. During the negative alternation of the input,
$V_L = \dfrac{R_L}{R_L + R_S} V_{\text{in}} = \left(\dfrac{1.1\,\text{k}\Omega}{1.2\,\text{k}\Omega}\right)(-12\,\text{V}_{\text{pk}}) = -11\,\text{V}_{\text{pk}}$

4-4. [This example has no practice problem.]

4-5. $T_C = 5 R_{D1} C = (5)(8\,\Omega)(4.7\,\mu\text{F}) = 188\,\mu\text{s}$
$T_D = 5 R_L C = (5)(1.2\,\text{k}\Omega)(4.7\,\mu\text{F}) = 28.2\,\text{ms}$

PRACTICE PROBLEMS (CH 4)

1. $V_L = \dfrac{R_L}{R_L + R_S} V_{in} = \left(\dfrac{9.1\,\text{k}\Omega}{10.1\,\text{k}\Omega}\right)(20\,\text{V}_{pk}) \cong 18\,\text{V}_{pk}$

2. The waveform is shown below. The positive peak value was calculated in Problem 1, and the negative peak value equals the cathode voltage of the conducting diode.

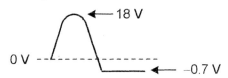

3. $V_L = \dfrac{R_L}{R_L + R_S} V_{in} = \left(\dfrac{33\,\text{k}\Omega}{35.2\,\text{k}\Omega}\right)(-12\,\text{V}_{pk}) =$
$-11.3\,\text{V}_{pk}$

4. The waveform is shown below. The negative peak value was calculated in Problem 3, and the positive peak value equals the anode voltage of the conducting diode.

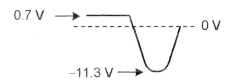

5. When the input is at its positive peak, D_1 is reverse biased and

$V_L = \dfrac{R_L}{R_L + R_S} V_{in} = \left(\dfrac{820\,\Omega}{870\,\Omega}\right)(4\,\text{V}_{pk}) = 3.77\,\text{V}_{pk}$

During the negative alternation, $V_L = V_F = -0.7\,\text{V}$. The output waveform is shown below.

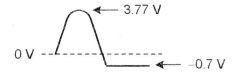

6. During the positive alternation, $V_L = V_F = 0.7\,\text{V}$. When the input is at its negative peak, D_1 is reverse biased and

$V_L = \dfrac{R_L}{R_L + R_S} V_{in} = \left(\dfrac{2.2\,\text{k}\Omega}{2.32\,\text{k}\Omega}\right)(-8\,\text{V}_{pk})$
$= -7.59\,\text{V}_{pk}$

The output waveform follows.

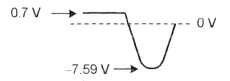

7. During the negative alternation of the input cycle, D_1 is forward biased, and the output is clipped at $-2\,\text{V} - 0.7\,\text{V} = -2.7\,\text{V}_{pk}$. During the positive half-cycle of the input, the diode is reverse biased and

$V_L = \dfrac{R_L}{R_L + R_S} V_{in} = \left(\dfrac{1.5\,\text{k}\Omega}{1.65\,\text{k}\Omega}\right)(7\,\text{V}_{pk}) = 6.36\,\text{V}_{pk}$

8. During the negative alternation of the input cycle, D_1 is forward biased, and the output is clipped at $-8\,\text{V} - 0.7\,\text{V} = -8.7\,\text{V}_{pk}$. During the positive half-cycle of the input, the diode is reverse biased and

$V_L = \dfrac{R_L}{R_L + R_S} V_{in} = \left(\dfrac{1.5\,\text{k}\Omega}{1.65\,\text{k}\Omega}\right)(12\,\text{V}_{pk}) = 10.9\,\text{V}_{pk}$

The output waveform is shown below.

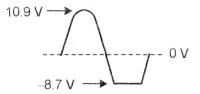

9. During the positive alternation of the input cycle, D_1 is forward biased, and the output is clipped at $4\,\text{V} + 0.7\,\text{V} = 4.7\,\text{V}_{pk}$. During the negative alternation of the input, the diode is reverse biased

and $V_L = \dfrac{R_L}{R_L + R_S} V_{in} = \left(\dfrac{2.4\,\text{k}\Omega}{3.6\,\text{k}\Omega}\right)(-11\,\text{V}_{pk}) =$
$-7.33\,\text{V}_{pk}$

The output waveform is shown below.

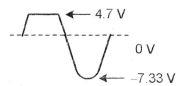

10. The cathode of D_1 is at 2 V. To forward bias the diode, the input must reach $2\,\text{V} + 0.7\,\text{V} = 2.7\,\text{V}_{pk}$. With a peak value of +2 V, the diode never turns on. As a result,

$V_L = \dfrac{R_L}{R_L + R_S} V_{in} = \dfrac{2.4\,\text{k}\Omega}{3.6\,\text{k}\Omega}(\pm 2\,\text{V}_{pk}) = \pm 1.33\,\text{V}_{pk}$

The output waveform follows.

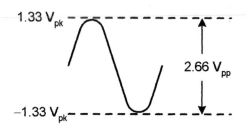

1.33 V$_{pk}$

2.66 V$_{pp}$

−1.33 V$_{pk}$

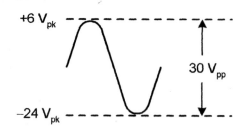

+6 V$_{pk}$

30 V$_{pp}$

−24 V$_{pk}$

11. V_{ave} falls halfway between the positive and negative peaks. Therefore, $V_{ave} = -12$ V.

12. V_{ave} falls halfway between 0 V and +14 V. Therefore, $V_{ave} = +7$ V.

13. $T_C = 5R_{D1}C = (5)(24\ \Omega)(4.7\ \mu F) = 564\ \mu s$
$T_D = 5R_LC = (5)(2.2\ k\Omega)(4.7\ \mu F) = 51.7$ ms

14. The circuit is a positive clamper, so it will shift the input signal in the positive direction. Assuming that the diode is an ideal component, the negative peak of the output signal will equal 0 V. Since the input signal is 14 V$_{pp}$, the output signal is also 14 V$_{pp}$.

15. $T_C = 5R_{D1}C = (5)(8\ \Omega)(33\ \mu F) = 1.32$ ms
$T_D = 5R_LC = (5)(1.2\ k\Omega)(33\ \mu F) = 198$ ms

16. $T_C = 5R_{D1}C = (5)(14\ \Omega)(1\ \mu F) = 70\ \mu s$
$T_D = 5R_LC = (5)(1.5\ k\Omega)(1\ \mu F) = 7.5$ ms

17. The negative clamper has a diode reference (return) of 0 V. Assuming the diode is ideal, the 12 V$_{pp}$ output signal has a positive peak value of 0 V, as shown below.

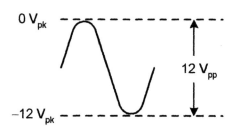

0 V$_{pk}$

12 V$_{pp}$

−12 V$_{pk}$

18. The positive clamper has a diode reference (return) of +3 V. Assuming the diode is ideal, the 9 V$_{pp}$ output signal has a negative peak value of +3 V, as shown below.

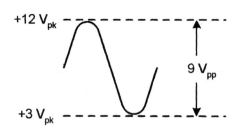

+12 V$_{pk}$

9 V$_{pp}$

+3 V$_{pk}$

19. The negative clamper has a diode reference (return) of +6 V. Assuming the diode is ideal, the 30 V$_{pp}$ output signal has a positive peak value of

20. The negative clamper has a +6 V reference. Assuming the diode is ideal, the 18 V$_{pp}$ output signal has the peak values shown below.

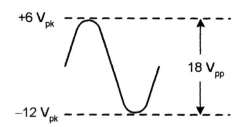

+6 V$_{pk}$

18 V$_{pp}$

−12 V$_{pk}$

21. The positive clamper has a −10 V reference. Assuming the diode is ideal, the 36 V$_{pp}$ output signal has the peak values shown below.

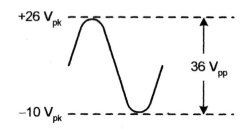

+26 V$_{pk}$

36 V$_{pp}$

−10 V$_{pk}$

22. $V_{C1} \cong V_{S(pk)} = 15$ V, $\quad V_{C2} \cong 2V_{S(pk)} = 30$ V

23. $V_{C1} \cong V_{S(pk)} = 48$ V, $\quad V_{C2} \cong 2V_{S(pk)} = 96$ V

24. $V_{C1} \cong V_{S(pk)} = 24$ V, $\quad V_{C2} \cong V_{S(pk)} = 24$ V,
$V_{C3} \cong 2V_{S(pk)} = 48$ V

25. $V_{S(pk)} = \dfrac{25\ V}{0.707} = 35.4$ V, $\quad V_{C1} \cong V_{S(pk)} = 35.4$ V,
$V_{C2} \cong V_{S(pk)} = 35.4$ V, $\quad V_{C3} \cong 2V_{S(pk)} = 70.8$ V

26. $V_{S(pk)} = \dfrac{20\ V}{0.707} = 28.3$ V
$V_{dc} = V_{C3} \cong 2V_{S(pk)} = 56.6$ V

27. $V_{S(pk)} = \dfrac{20\ V_{pp}}{2} = 10$ V, $\quad V_{dc} = V_{C3} \cong 2V_{S(pk)} = 20$ V

28. $V_{C1} \cong V_{S(pk)} = 20$ V, $\quad V_{C2} \cong 2V_{S(pk)} = 40$ V,
$V_{C3} \cong V_{S(pk)} = 20$ V, $\quad V_{C4} \cong 3V_{S(pk)} = 60$ V

29. $V_{S(pk)} = \dfrac{15\ V}{0.707} = 21.2$ V, $V_{C1} \cong V_{S(pk)} = 21.2$ V,
$V_{C2} \cong 2V_{S(pk)} = 42.4$ V, $V_{C3} \cong V_{S(pk)} = 21.2$ V,
$V_{C4} \cong 3V_{S(pk)} = 63.6$ V

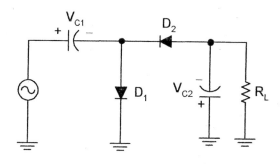

30. $V_{C1} \cong V_{S(pk)} = 18$ V, $V_{C2} \cong 2V_{S(pk)} = 36$ V,
$V_{C3} \cong V_{S(pk)} = 18$ V, $V_{C4} \cong 2V_{S(pk)} = 36$ V,
$V_{C5} \cong 4V_{S(pk)} = 72$ V

31. $V_{S(pk)} = \dfrac{36 \text{ V}}{0.707} = 50.9$ V, $V_{C1} = V_{C3} \cong V_{S(pk)} = 50.9$ V,
$V_{C2} = V_{C4} \cong 2V_{S(pk)} = 102$ V, $V_{C5} \cong 4V_{S(pk)} = 204$ V

32. $V_{S(pk)} = \dfrac{48 \text{ V}}{0.707} = 67.9$ V, $+V_{dc} = V_{S(pk)} = +67.9$ V,
$-V_{dc} = -V_{S(pk)} = -67.9$ V

33. $V_{S(pk)} = \dfrac{36 \text{ V}}{0.707} = 50.9$ V, $+V_{dc} = V_{S(pk)} = +50.9$ V,
$-V_{dc} = -V_{S(pk)} = -50.9$ V

34. The circuit is not clipping the input signal. Thus, D_1 is open. (The reason for the reduced output voltage is the voltage-divider action of R_L and R_S.)

35. The 0 V output indicates that R_S is open. With R_S open, the anode of D_1 is returned (via R_L) to ground. As a result, the +10 V potential at the cathode of D_1 reverse biases the component, and there is 0 V across the load.

36. The waveform hasn't shifted, indicating that D_1 is not providing a rapid charge path for C_1. Thus, D_1 is open.

37. The circuit is operating properly.

38. The output waveform should be referenced below 10 V (V_Z), not 0 V. The circuit is operating as if the zener diode isn't there. Thus, the zener diode is shorted.

39. The circuit is clipping the input signal, not clamping it. This indicates that C_1 is shorted, since the circuit is acting as if C_1 isn't there. Note that D_1 prevents the zener diode from conducting during the positive alternation of V_S.

40. V_{C4} is half of its normal value. You would check C_3, D_3, and D_4. There is no need to check the voltage source since V_{C2} is normal.

41. The circuit is operating properly.

42. The circuit is a clipper designed to limit the output signal to 5 V + 0.7 V = +5.7 V. For the input waveform shown, the peak output is found as follows: $V_{S(pk)} = \dfrac{12 \text{ V}}{0.707} = 17$ V, and $V_{L(pk)} =$

$\dfrac{R_L}{R_L + R_S} V_{S(pk)} = \left(\dfrac{100 \ \Omega}{400 \ \Omega}\right)(17 \text{ V}) = 4.25$ V   This

corresponds to an rms value of 3 V.

43. During the positive alternation of V_S, D_1 conducts and charges C_1 to the polarity shown below. During the negative alternation of VS, D_2 turns on. The combination of V_S and C_1 now charges C_2 to the polarity shown in the figure.

44. D_4 is the reversed component. If you compare the circuit to the one in Figure 4.43, you'll see that the anode of the component should be connected to C_4.

45. During the positive alternation of the input signal, the zener turns on and clips the output when $V_L = V_Z = 6.8$ V. During the negative alternation of the input signal, the zener turns on (forward operation) when $V_L = V_F = -0.7$ V. The resulting waveform is shown below.

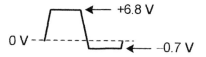

46. During the positive alternation of the input signal, the dual-zener clipper conducts when $V_L = V_{Z2} + V_{F(D1)} = 10.7$ V. During the negative alternation, the dual-zener clipper conducts when $V_L = -V_{Z1} - V_{F(D2)} = -10.7$ V. The resulting waveform is shown below.

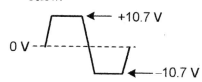

47. The output wave shape does not change. The circuit operation changes as follows: $V_L = V_{Z1} + V_{F(D2)} = 10.7$ V during the positive alternation of the input, and $V_L = -V_{Z2} - V_{F(D1)} = -10.7$ V during the negative alternation of the input.

48. According to their spec sheets, the 7815 and 7915 provide +15 V and –15 V outputs, respectively. These are the values of V_A and V_B.

49. Using the 7800 & 7900 series regulators, the circuit can be altered to provide +12 V and –8 V outputs by substituting the 7812 for the 7815 and the 7908 for the 7915. (Other regulators may be used, so your students may choose regulators that do not match those listed here.)

11

CHAPTER 5

EXAMPLE PRACTICE PROBLEMS (CH 5)

5-1. At $V_r = 4 \text{ V}_{dc}$, $C = 51$ pF and

$$f_r = \frac{1}{2\pi\sqrt{LC}} = \frac{1}{2\pi\sqrt{(3.3 \text{ mH})(51 \text{ pF})}} = 388 \text{ kHz}.$$

At $V_r = 10 \text{ V}_{dc}$, $C = \frac{51 \text{ pF}}{1.8} = 28.3$ pF, and

$$f_r = \frac{1}{2\pi\sqrt{LC}} = \frac{1}{2\pi\sqrt{(3.3 \text{ mH})(28.3 \text{ pF})}} = 521 \text{ kHz}$$

5-2. From problem 5-1: $f_r = 388$ kHz @ $V_R = 4 \text{ V}_{dc}$.

When $V_R = 10 \text{ V}_{dc}$: $C = \frac{C_t}{C_R} = \frac{51 \text{ pF}}{1.07} = 47.7$ pF and

$$f_r = \frac{1}{2\pi\sqrt{LC}} = \frac{1}{2\pi\sqrt{(3.3 \text{ mH})(47.7 \text{ pF})}} = 401 \text{ kHz}.$$

5-3. The point where the curve (Figure 5.8) intersects the $T = 150°C$ line corresponds to a derating value of approximately 18%. With a P_{PK} rating of 1.5 kW, the maximum value of P_{PK} at $T = 150°C$ is found as $P_{PK} = (0.18)(1.5 \text{ kW}) = 270$ W.

5-4. $R_d = \frac{V_V - V_P}{I_V - I_P} = \frac{200 \text{ mV} - 100 \text{ mV}}{250 \text{ } \mu A - 5 \text{ mA}} = \frac{100 \text{ mV}}{-4.75 \text{ mA}} = -21.1 \text{ } \Omega$

PRACTICE PROBLEMS (CH 5)

1. 500 ppm (parts per million) corresponds to a multiplier of 500×10^{-6}. Using this value, $\Delta C = (50 \text{ pF})(500 \times 10^{-6}/°C) = 25 \times 10^{-15}$ F/°C.

2. 800 ppm (parts per million) corresponds to a multiplier of 800×10^{-6}. Using this value, $\Delta C = (48 \text{ pF})(800 \times 10^{-6}/°C) = 38.4 \times 10^{-15}$ F/°C.

3. At $V_r = 3 \text{ V}_{dc}$: $C = 48$ pF and

$$f_r = \frac{1}{2\pi\sqrt{LC}} = \frac{1}{2\pi\sqrt{(1 \text{ mH})(48 \text{ pF})}} = 726 \text{ kHz}$$

At $V_r = 12 \text{ V}_{dc}$: $C = \frac{48 \text{ pF}}{4.8} = 10$ pF and

$$f_r = \frac{1}{2\pi\sqrt{LC}} = \frac{1}{2\pi\sqrt{(1 \text{ mH})(10 \text{ pF})}} = 1.59 \text{ MHz}$$

4. At $V_r = 4 \text{ V}_{dc}$: $C = 68$ pF and

$$f_r = \frac{1}{2\pi\sqrt{LC}} = \frac{1}{2\pi\sqrt{(100 \text{ } \mu H)(68 \text{ pF})}} = 1.93 \text{ MHz}$$

At $V_r = 10 \text{ V}_{dc}$: $C = \frac{68 \text{ pF}}{1.12} = 60.7$ pF and

$$f_r = \frac{1}{2\pi\sqrt{LC}} = \frac{1}{2\pi\sqrt{(100 \text{ } \mu H)(60.7 \text{ pF})}} = 2.04 \text{ MHz}$$

5. Since the x-axis is measured in seconds, we are interested in the point where the $T_C = 35°C$ curve intersects the $t = 0.008$ line. Going left from this point, $P_{PK} = 4$ kW.

6. For this problem, $t = 0.015$ s. Going left from the $t = 0.015$ line and the $T_C = 35°C$ curve, $P_{PK} = 3$ kW.

7. The resonant frequency of an LC circuit is found as

$f_r = \frac{1}{2\pi\sqrt{LC}}$. Transposing this equation, the

value of C required to produce a 200 kHz resonant frequency is found as

$$C = \frac{1}{(2\pi f_r)^2 L} = \frac{1}{[2\pi(200 \text{ kHz})]^2(47 \text{ mH})} \cong$$

13.5 pF. From the curve, $C = 13.5$ pF at an approximate value of $V_R = 8 \text{ V}_{dc}$.

8. The following nominal values are shown on the data sheet: $V_{BR} = 200 \text{ V}$ @ $I_T = 1 \text{ mA}$ and $V_C = 274 \text{ V}$ @ $I_{PP} = 5.5 \text{ A}$ (where V_C and I_{PP} are the clamping voltage and maximum pulse current). Using these values, a working approximation of Z_Z can be found as $Z_Z = \frac{\Delta V}{\Delta I} = \frac{74 \text{ V}}{5.499 \text{ A}} = 13.5 \text{ } \Omega$.

9. $V_{in(pk)} = \frac{120 \text{ V}}{0.707} \cong 170 \text{ V}$. An increase of 30% results in a peak value of $170 \text{ V} \times 1.3 = 221 \text{ V}$. The diode must turn on above 170 V (min) to avoid conducting under normal operation. Using min/max values, the 1N6302A and 1N6303A are suitable as they turn on between 170 V and 221 V.

10. The resonant frequency of the LC circuit is found as

$f_r = \frac{1}{2\pi\sqrt{LC}}$. Transposing this equation, the

value of C required to produce a 100 kHz resonant frequency is found as

$$C = \frac{1}{(2\pi f_r)^2 L} = \frac{1}{[2\pi(100 \text{ kHz})]^2(47 \text{ mH})} \cong 54 \text{ pF}.$$

Using the MV104 diode capacitance curve obtained online, $C = 54$ pF at an approximate value of $V_R = 1.4 \text{ V}_{dc}$.

CHAPTER 6

EXAMPLE PRACTICE PROBLEMS   (CH 6)

6-1. $I_C = \beta I_B = (350)(50\ \mu A) = 17.5$ mA

6-2. $I_C = \beta I_B = (400)(50\ \mu A) = 20$ mA,
$I_E = I_C + I_B = 20$ mA $+ 50\ \mu A = 20.05$ mA

6-3. $I_B = \dfrac{I_E}{\beta+1} = \dfrac{12\ \text{mA}}{141} = 85.1\ \mu A$,

$I_C = I_E - I_B = 12$ mA $- 85.1\ \mu A \cong 11.9$ mA

6-4. $I_B = \dfrac{I_C}{\beta} = \dfrac{80\ \text{mA}}{170} \cong 471\ \mu A$,

$I_E = I_C + I_B = 80$ mA $+ 471\ \mu A \cong 80.5$ mA

6-5. $\alpha = \dfrac{\beta}{\beta+1} = \dfrac{349}{350} = 0.997$

$I_C = \beta I_B = (349)(1\ \text{mA}) = 349$ mA
$I_C = \alpha I_E = (0.9971)(350\ \text{mA}) = 348.99$ mA
The two values of I_C are close enough to be
considered equal. The slight difference is due to
rounding off the value of α.

6-6. $I_{B(\text{max})} = \dfrac{I_{C(\text{max})}}{\beta_{(\text{max})}} = \dfrac{1\ \text{A}}{120} = 8.33$ mA

PRACTICE PROBLEMS   (CH 6)

1. $I_C = \beta I_B = (320)(12\ \mu A) = 3.84$ mA
2. $I_C = \beta I_B = (400)(30\ \mu A) = 12$ mA
3. $I_C = \beta I_B = (254)(1.01\ \text{mA}) = 257$ mA
4. $I_C = \beta I_B = (144)(82\ \mu A) = 11.8$ mA
5. $I_E = I_C + I_B = 1.1$ mA $+ 20\ \mu A = 1.12$ mA
6. $I_E = I_C + I_B = 344$ mA $+ 1.1$ mA $\cong 345$ mA
7. (a) $I_C = \beta I_B = (150)(25\ \mu A) = 3.75$ mA

   (b) $\beta = \dfrac{I_C}{I_B} = \dfrac{1.5\ \text{mA}}{75\ \mu A} = 20$

   (c) $I_C = \beta I_B = (240)(100\ \mu A) = 24$ mA

   (d) $I_B = \dfrac{I_C}{\beta} = \dfrac{20\ \text{mA}}{325} = 61.5\ \mu A$

8. (a) $\beta = \dfrac{I_C}{I_B} = \dfrac{12\ \text{mA}}{50\ \mu A} = 240$

   (b) $I_B = \dfrac{I_C}{\beta} = \dfrac{2\ \text{mA}}{440} = 79.5\ \mu A$

   (c) $I_C = \beta I_B = (175)(45\ \mu A) = 7.88$ mA

   (d) $\beta = \dfrac{I_C}{I_B} = \dfrac{84\ \text{mA}}{120\ \mu A} = 700$

9. (a) $I_E = I_C + I_B = 1$ mA $+ 25\ \mu A \cong 1.03$ mA
   (b) $I_B = I_E - I_C = 1.98$ mA $- 1.8$ mA $= 180\ \mu A$
   (c) $I_C = I_E - I_B = 3$ mA $- 120\ \mu A = 2.88$ mA
   (d) $I_B = I_E - I_C = 8$ mA $- 7.5$ mA $= 500\ \mu A$

(e) $I_C = I_E - I_B = 20$ mA $- 50\ \mu A = 19.95$ mA
(f) $I_E = I_C + I_B = 9.825$ mA $+ 175\ \mu A = 10$ mA

10. $I_C = \beta I_B = (100)(35\ \mu A) = 3.5$ mA
    $I_E = I_C + I_B = 3.5$ mA $+ 35\ \mu A \cong 3.54$ mA
11. $I_C = \beta I_B = (400)(150\ \mu A) = 60$ mA
    $I_E = I_C + I_B = 60$ mA $+ 150\ \mu A \cong 60.2$ mA
12. $I_C = \beta I_B = (120)(48\ \mu A) = 5.76$ mA
    $I_E = I_C + I_B = 5.76$ mA $+ 48\ \mu A = 5.81$ mA
13. $I_B = \dfrac{I_C}{\beta} = \dfrac{12\ \text{mA}}{440} = 27.3\ \mu A$

    $I_E = I_C + I_B = 12$ mA $+ 27.3\ \mu A \cong 12.03$ mA
14. $I_B = \dfrac{I_C}{\beta} = \dfrac{50\ \text{mA}}{400} = 125\ \mu A$

    $I_E = I_C + I_B = 50$ mA $+ 125\ \mu A \cong 50.1$ mA
15. $I_B = \dfrac{I_E}{\beta+1} = \dfrac{65\ \text{mA}}{381} = 171\ \mu A$

    $I_C = I_E - I_B = 65$ mA $- 171\ \mu A \cong 64.8$ mA
16. $I_B = \dfrac{I_E}{\beta+1} = \dfrac{120\ \text{mA}}{61} = 1.97$ mA

    $I_C = I_E - I_B = 120$ mA $- 1.97$ mA $\cong 118$ mA
17. $\alpha = \dfrac{\beta}{\beta+1} = \dfrac{426}{427} \cong 0.9977$

18. $\alpha = \dfrac{\beta}{\beta+1} = \dfrac{350}{351} = 0.9972$

19. $I_{B(\text{max})} = \dfrac{I_{C(\text{max})}}{\beta_{(\text{max})}} = \dfrac{120\ \text{mA}}{120} = 1$ mA

20. $I_{B(\text{max})} = \dfrac{I_{C(\text{max})}}{\beta_{(\text{max})}} = \dfrac{250\ \text{mA}}{100} = 2.5$ mA

21. Breakdown is measured at the point where all the
    curves go vertical (to the right of the active region).
    This occurs at approximately $V_{CE} = 30$ to 32 V.
22. The $I_B = 40\ \mu A$ line is centered on $I_C = 8$ mA .
23. The maximum value of $V_{CE(\text{sat})}$ would equal the
    knee voltage of the $I_B = 40\ \mu A$ curve. The value of
    V_K for this curve is approximately 2 V .

24. Conventional-flow version:

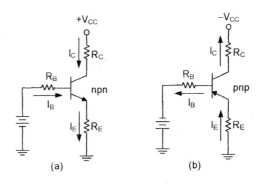

13

24. (Continued)

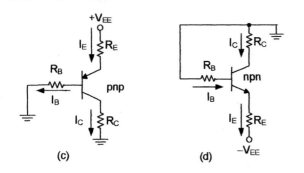

(c)　　　　　　(d)

Electron-flow version:

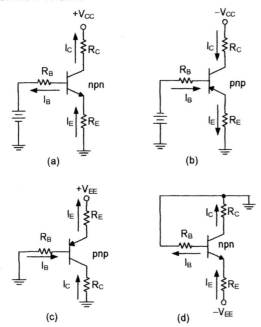

(a)　　　　　　(b)

(c)　　　　　　(d)

25. (a) The high forward resistance of the C-B junction indicates that it is *open*. (b) The low reverse C-B resistance indicates that the junction is *partially shorted*. (c) The transistor is good. (d) The high forward resistance of the B-E junction indicates that the junction is *open*.

26.

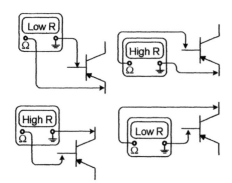

27. $\alpha = \dfrac{I_C}{I_E} = \dfrac{\beta I_B}{(\beta+1)I_B} = \dfrac{\beta}{\beta+1}$

28. $\beta = \dfrac{I_C}{I_B} = \dfrac{\alpha I_B}{(1-\alpha)I_B} = \dfrac{\alpha}{1-\alpha}$

29. The equation is used to determine the maximum allowable value of I_B, based on the maximum rated transistor collector current. If we were to use β_{min} in the denominator of the equation, we would obtain a value of $I_{B(max)} = \dfrac{500\,\text{mA}}{50} = 10\,\text{mA}$. Now, assume for a moment that we designed a circuit for a base current of 10 mA, based on this value of $I_{B(max)}$. As you know, the transistor beta can fall anywhere between 50 and 250 (as defined in the problem). If the transistor we placed in the circuit has a value of $\beta = 100$, then the collector current will have the value of $I_C = \beta I_B = (100)(10\,\text{mA}) = 1\,\text{A}$. This clearly exceeds the limit on the collector current (500 mA). However, if we limit the base current to the value found using

$$I_{B(max)} = \dfrac{500\,\text{mA}}{250} = 2\,\text{mA},$$

the maximum collector current rating will not be exceeded, regardless of the beta of the transistor being used.

30. The 2N4401 is the only transistor that can be used in the circuit. The $V_{BR(CBO)}$ rating for the 2N4124 is too low (30 V), and the 2N5087 is a PNP transistor.

CHAPTER 7

EXAMPLE PRACTICE PROBLEMS (CH 7)

7-1. $V_{CE(off)} = V_{CC} = +8\,\text{V}$, $I_{C(sat)} = \dfrac{V_{CC}}{R_C} = \dfrac{8\,\text{V}}{1.1\,\text{k}\Omega} \cong$

7.27 mA. Using these values, the dc load line for the circuit is drawn as shown.

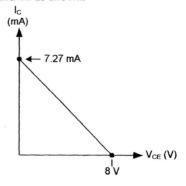

7-2. $V_{CE(off)} = V_{CC} = +16\text{ V}$, $I_{C(sat)} = \dfrac{V_{CC}}{R_C} = \dfrac{16\text{ V}}{2\text{ k}\Omega} = 8\text{ mA}$

Using these values, the dc load line for the circuit is plotted. According to the load line, $V_{CE} = 12$ V at $I_C = 2$ mA, $V_{CE} = 8$ V at $I_C = 4$ mA, and $V_{CE} = 4$ V at $I_C = 6$ mA.

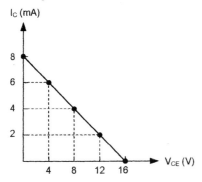

Verifications:
$V_{CE} = V_{CC} - I_C R_C = 16\text{ V} - (2\text{ mA})(2\text{ k}\Omega) = 12\text{ V}$
$V_{CE} = V_{CC} - I_C R_C = 16\text{ V} - (4\text{ mA})(2\text{ k}\Omega) = 8\text{ V}$
$V_{CE} = V_{CC} - I_C R_C = 16\text{ V} - (6\text{ mA})(2\text{ k}\Omega) = 4\text{ V}$

7-3. $I_B = \dfrac{V_{CC} - V_{BE}}{R_B} = \dfrac{14\text{ V} - 0.7\text{ V}}{270\text{ k}\Omega} = 49.3\text{ }\mu A$

$I_C = h_{FE}I_B = (200)(49.3\text{ }\mu A) = 9.86\text{ mA}$, $V_{CE} = V_{CC} - I_C R_C = 14\text{ V} - (9.86\text{ mA})(720\text{ }\Omega) = 6.9\text{ V}$

7-4. *Load line method:* The endpoints for the dc load line are $V_{CE(off)} = V_{CC} = +12\text{ V}$ and $I_{C(sat)} = \dfrac{V_{CC}}{R_C} =$

$\dfrac{12\text{ V}}{1\text{ k}\Omega} = 12\text{ mA}$. Using these values the load line is plotted as shown. The Q-point values of I_C and V_{CE} are found as follows:

$I_B = \dfrac{V_{CC} - V_{BE}}{R_B} = \dfrac{11.3\text{ V}}{500\text{ k}\Omega} = 22.6\text{ }\mu A$

$I_C = h_{FE}I_B = (150)(22.6\text{ }\mu A) = 3.39\text{ mA}$, $V_{CE} = V_{CC} - I_C R_C = 12\text{ V} - (3.39\text{ mA})(1\text{ k}\Omega) = 8.61\text{ V}$

Plotting the point that corresponds to these values of I_C and V_{CE} shows that the circuit is *not* midpoint biased.

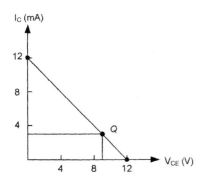

7-5. From Practice Problem 7-3: $I_C = 9.86$ mA and $V_{CE} = 6.91$ V. *The load line method:* The endpoints of the dc load line for this circuit are

$V_{CE(off)} = V_{CC} = +14\text{ V}$ and $I_{C(sat)} = \dfrac{V_{CC}}{R_C} = \dfrac{14\text{ V}}{720\text{ }\Omega} =$

19.4 mA. Using the current and voltage values listed here, the load line and Q-point for the circuit are plotted as shown. The Q-point falls approximately halfway between the ends of the load line, indicating that the circuit is midpoint biased.

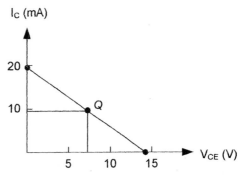

The observation method: The circuit has a value of $V_{CE(off)} = 14$ V and a Q-point value of $V_{CE} = 6.91$ V. Since $V_{CE} = 6.91\text{ V} \cong \dfrac{V_{CC}}{2}$, we know that the circuit is midpoint biased.

7-6. From practice problem 7-3: $I_B = 49.3\text{ }\mu A$. At 100°C: $I_C = h_{FE}I_B = (380)(49.3\text{ }\mu A) = 18.7\text{ mA}$
$V_{CE} = V_{CC} - I_C R_C = 14\text{ V} - (18.7\text{ mA})(720\text{ }\Omega) = 536\text{ mV}$

7-7. $V_B = V_{CC}\dfrac{R_2}{R_1 + R_2} = (10\text{ V})\dfrac{2.7\text{ k}\Omega}{14.7\text{ k}\Omega} = 1.84\text{ V}$

$V_E = V_B - 0.7\text{ V} = 1.84\text{ V} - 0.7\text{ V} = 1.14\text{ V}$

$I_{CQ} \cong I_E = \dfrac{V_E}{R_E} = \dfrac{1.14\text{ V}}{180\text{ }\Omega} = 6.33\text{ mA}$,

$V_{CEQ} = V_{CC} - I_{CQ}(R_C + R_E)$
$\qquad = 10\text{ V} - (6.33\text{ mA})(800\text{ }\Omega) = 4.94\text{ V}$

7-8. In practice problem 7-7, the emitter current was found to be 6.33 mA. Using this value and $h_{FE} =$

200, $I_B = \dfrac{I_E}{h_{FE} + 1} = \dfrac{6.33\text{ mA}}{201} = 31.5\text{ }\mu A$

7-9. $R_{base} = h_{FE}R_E = (80)(1.1\text{ k}\Omega) = 88\text{ k}\Omega$
Since this is less than 10 times R_2 we must determine R_{EQ} as

$V_{TH} = V_{CC}\dfrac{R_2}{R_1 + R_2} = (20\text{ V})\dfrac{1\text{ k}\Omega}{7.8\text{ k}\Omega} = 2.56\text{ V}$

$R_{TH} = R_1 \parallel R_2 = 6.8\text{ k}\Omega \parallel 1\text{ k}\Omega = 872\text{ }\Omega$

7-9. (Continued)

$$I_{CQ} = \frac{V_{TH} - V_{BE}}{\dfrac{R_{TH}}{h_{FE}} + R_E} = \frac{1.86\,\text{V}}{\dfrac{872\,\Omega}{75} + 1\,\text{k}\Omega} = 1.84\ \text{mA}$$

$$V_{CEQ} = V_{CC} - I_{CQ}(R_C + R_E)$$
$$= 20\ \text{V} - (1.84\ \text{mA})(5.7\ \text{k}\Omega) = 9.5\ \text{V}$$

7-10. $I_{CQ} = \dfrac{|V_{EE} + 0.7\,\text{V}|}{R_E} = \dfrac{|-15\,\text{V} + 0.7\,\text{V}|}{3\,\text{k}\Omega} = 4.77\ \text{mA}$

$$V_{CEQ} \cong V_{CC} - I_{CQ}R_C + 0.7\ \text{V}$$
$$= 15\ \text{V} - (4.77\ \text{mA})(1.5\ \text{k}\Omega) + 0.7\ \text{V}$$
$$= 8.55\ \text{V}$$

7-11. $I_{C(\text{sat})} = \dfrac{2V_{CC}}{R_C + R_E} = \dfrac{30\,\text{V}}{4.5\,\text{k}\Omega} = 6.67\ \text{mA}$ and

$$V_{CE(\text{off})} = 2V_{CC} = 30\ \text{V}$$

7-12. $I_B = \dfrac{V_{CC} - V_{BE}}{R_B + h_{FE}R_C} = \dfrac{12\,\text{V} - 0.7\,\text{V}}{240\,\text{k}\Omega + (120)(2\,\text{k}\Omega)} =$

$23.5\ \mu\text{A}, \quad I_{CQ} = h_{FE}I_B = (120)(23.5\ \mu\text{A}) =$
$2.82\ \text{mA}, \quad V_{CEQ} = V_{CC} - I_{CQ}R_C =$
$12\ \text{V} - (2.82\ \text{mA})(2\ \text{k}\Omega) = 6.36\ \text{V}$

7-13. $I_B = \dfrac{V_{CC} - V_{BE}}{R_B + (h_{FE} + 1)R_E}$

$$= \frac{16\ \text{V} - 0.7\ \text{V}}{470\ \text{k}\Omega + (101)(910\,\Omega)} = 27.2\ \mu\text{A}$$

$I_{CQ} = h_{FE}I_B = (100)(27.2\ \mu\text{A}) = 2.72\ \text{mA}$
$V_{CEQ} = V_{CC} - I_{CQ}(R_C + R_E) =$
$16\ \text{V} - (2.72\ \text{mA})(2.71\ \text{k}\Omega) = 8.63\ \text{V}$

PRACTICE PROBLEMS (CH 7)

1. $V_{CE(\text{off})} = V_{CC} = 8\ \text{V}, \quad I_{C(\text{sat})} = \dfrac{V_{CC}}{R_C} = \dfrac{8\,\text{V}}{3.3\,\text{k}\Omega} =$

2.42 mA. These values are used to plot the load line shown.

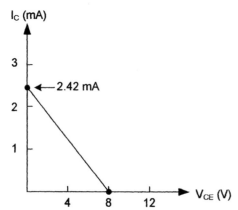

2. $V_{CE(\text{off})} = V_{CC} = 24\ \text{V}, \quad I_{C(\text{sat})} = \dfrac{V_{CC}}{R_C} = \dfrac{24\,\text{V}}{9.1\,\text{k}\Omega} =$

2.64 mA. These values are used to plot the load line shown.

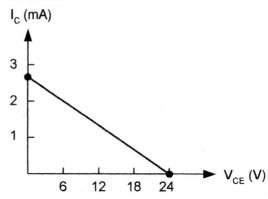

3. $V_{CE(\text{off})} = V_{CC} = 14\ \text{V}$ and $I_{C(\text{sat})} = \dfrac{V_{CC}}{R_C} = \dfrac{14\,\text{V}}{1\,\text{k}\Omega} =$

14 mA. These values are used to plot the load line shown. The load line shows that $V_{CE} = 12\ \text{V}$ @ $I_C = 2\ \text{mA}$, $V_{CE} = 6\ \text{V}$ @ $I_C = 8\ \text{mA}$, and $V_{CE} = 4\ \text{V}$ @ $I_C = 10\ \text{mA}$.

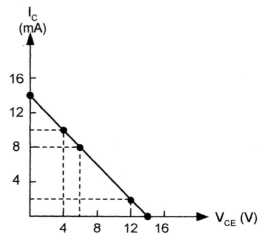

Verifications:
$V_{CE} = V_{CC} - I_C R_C = 14\ \text{V} - (2\ \text{mA})(1\ \text{k}\Omega) = 12\ \text{V}$
$V_{CE} = V_{CC} - I_C R_C = 14\ \text{V} - (8\ \text{mA})(1\ \text{k}\Omega) = 6\ \text{V}$
$V_{CE} = V_{CC} - I_C R_C = 14\ \text{V} - (10\ \text{mA})(1\ \text{k}\Omega) = 4\ \text{V}$

4. $V_{CE(\text{off})} = V_{CC} = 20\ \text{V}, \quad I_{C(\text{sat})} = \dfrac{V_{CC}}{R_C} = \dfrac{20\,\text{V}}{2.4\,\text{k}\Omega} =$

8.33 mA. These values are used to plot the dc load line shown (at the top of page 17). The load line is used to estimate the following values: $V_{CE} = 17.5\ \text{V}$ @ $I_C = 1\ \text{mA}$, $V_{CE} = 8\ \text{V}$ @ $I_C = 5\ \text{mA}$, and $V_{CE} = 3\ \text{V}$ @ $I_C = 7\ \text{mA}$.

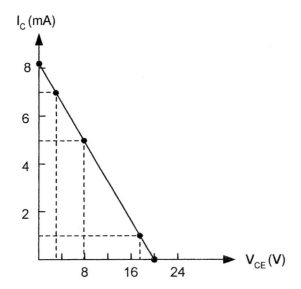

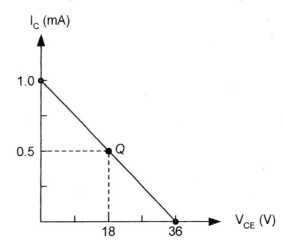

Verifications:

$V_{CE} = V_{CC} - I_C R_C = 20\ \text{V} - (1\ \text{mA})(2.4\ \text{k}\Omega) = 17.6\text{V}$

$V_{CE} = V_{CC} - I_C R_C = 20\ \text{V} - (5\ \text{mA})(2.4\ \text{k}\Omega) = 8\ \text{V}$

$V_{CE} = V_{CC} - I_C R_C = 20\ \text{V} - (7\ \text{mA})(2.4\ \text{k}\Omega) = 3.2\ \text{V}$

5. $V_{CE(\text{off})} = V_{CC} = 8\ \text{V}, \quad I_{C(\text{sat})} = \dfrac{V_{CC}}{R_C} = \dfrac{8\ \text{V}}{1\ \text{k}\Omega} = 8\ \text{mA}.$

These values are used to plot the dc load line shown.

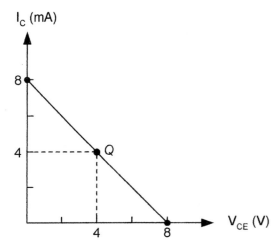

Plotting the Q-point at the center of the load line gives us midpoint values of $I_C = 4$ mA and $V_{CE} = 4$ V.

6. $V_{CE(\text{off})} = V_{CC} = 36\ \text{V}, \quad I_{C(\text{sat})} = \dfrac{V_{CC}}{R_C} = \dfrac{36\ \text{V}}{36\ \text{k}\Omega} = 1\ \text{mA}$

These values are used to plot the dc load line shown.

Plotting the Q-point at the center of the load line gives us midpoint values of $I_C = 500\ \mu\text{A}$ (0.5 mA) and $V_{CE} = 18$ V.

7. $I_B = \dfrac{V_{CC} - V_{BE}}{R_B} = \dfrac{10\ \text{V} - 0.7\ \text{V}}{186\ \text{k}\Omega} = 50\ \mu\text{A}$

$I_C = h_{FE} I_B = (80)(50\ \mu\text{A}) = 4\ \text{mA}, \quad V_{CE} = V_{CC} - I_C R_C = 10\ \text{V} - (4\ \text{mA})(1.25\ \text{k}\Omega) = 5\ \text{V}.$

8. $I_B = \dfrac{V_{CC} - V_{BE}}{R_B} = \dfrac{8\ \text{V} - 0.7\ \text{V}}{750\ \text{k}\Omega} = 9.73\ \mu\text{A}$

$I_C = h_{FE} I_B = (100)(9.73\ \mu\text{A}) = 973\ \mu\text{A}$

$V_{CE} = V_{CC} - I_C R_C = 8\ \text{V} - (973\ \mu\text{A})(6\ \text{k}\Omega) = 2.16\ \text{V}$

9. $I_B = \dfrac{V_{CC} - V_{BE}}{R_B} = \dfrac{12\ \text{V} - 0.7\ \text{V}}{360\ \text{k}\Omega} = 31.4\ \mu\text{A}$

$I_C = h_{FE} I_B = (150)(31.4\ \mu\text{A}) = 4.71\ \text{mA}$

$V_{CE} = V_{CC} - I_C R_C = 12\ \text{V} - (4.71\ \text{mA})(1\ \text{k}\Omega) = 7.29\ \text{V}.$ Since it is a *pnp* circuit with a negative supply voltage, the actual value of V_{CE} is -7.29 V.

10. $I_B = \dfrac{V_{CC} - V_{BE}}{R_B} = \dfrac{18\ \text{V} - 0.7\ \text{V}}{900\ \text{k}\Omega} = 19.2\ \mu\text{A}$

$I_C = h_{FE} I_B = (100)(19.2\ \mu\text{A}) = 1.92\ \text{mA} \quad V_{CE} = V_{CC} - I_C R_C = 18\ \text{V} - (1.92\ \text{mA})(4.7\ \text{k}\Omega) = 8.98\ \text{V}.$ Since it is a *pnp* circuit with a negative supply voltage, the actual value of V_{CE} is -8.98 V.

11. $V_{CE(\text{off})} = V_{CC} = 20\ \text{V}, \quad I_{C(\text{sat})} = \dfrac{V_{CC}}{R_C} = \dfrac{10\ \text{V}}{1.25\ \text{k}\Omega} =$

8 mA. These values are used to plot the dc load line shown (at the top of page 18). From problem 7, $V_{CE} = 5$ V at $I_C = 4$ mA. Using these values, the Q-point is plotted as shown. The circuit is midpoint-biased.

17

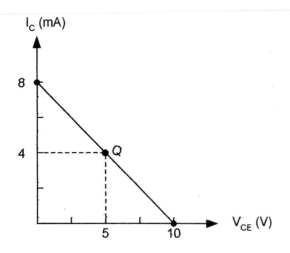

12. $V_{CE(off)} = V_{CC} = 8$ V, $I_{C(sat)} = \dfrac{V_{CC}}{R_C} = \dfrac{8\text{ V}}{6\text{ k}\Omega} =$

1.33 mA. These values are used to plot the dc load line shown. From problem 8, $V_{CE} = 2.16$ V at $I_C =$ 973 µA. Using these values, the Q-point is plotted as shown. The circuit is *not* midpoint biased.

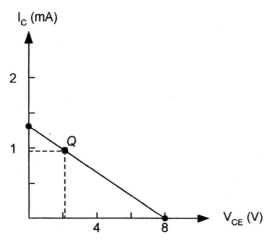

13. From problem 9: $V_{CC} = -12$ V and $V_{CE} = -7.29$ V.
Since $V_{CE} \neq \dfrac{V_{CC}}{2}$, the circuit is *not* midpoint biased.

14. From problem 10: $V_{CC} = -18$ V and $V_{CE} = -8.98$V.
Since $V_{CE} \cong \dfrac{V_{CC}}{2}$, the circuit is midpoint biased.

15. From problem 7: $I_B = 50$ µA.
$I_C = h_{FE}I_B = (120)(50\ \mu\text{A}) = 6$ mA
$V_{CE} = V_{CC} - I_C R_C = 10$ V $- (6\text{ mA})(1.25\text{ k}\Omega) = 2.5$ V

16. From problem 8: $I_B = 9.73$ µA.
$I_C = h_{FE}I_B = (120)(9.73\ \mu\text{A}) = 1.17$ mA, $V_{CE} =$
$V_{CC} - I_C R_C = 8$ V $- (1.17\text{ mA})(6\text{ k}\Omega) = 980$ mV

17. $h_{FE}R_E > 10R_2$, so we proceed as follows:
$$V_B = V_{CC}\frac{R_2}{R_1 + R_2} = (30\text{ V})\frac{5\text{ k}\Omega}{55\text{ k}\Omega} = 2.73\text{ V}$$
$$V_E = V_B - 0.7\text{ V} = 2.03\text{ V}, \quad I_{CQ} \cong I_E = \frac{V_E}{R_E} =$$
$$\frac{2.03\text{ V}}{1\text{ k}\Omega} = 2.03\text{ mA}, \quad V_{CEQ} = V_{CC} - I_{CQ}(R_C + R_E) =$$
30 V $- (2.03\text{ mA})(6\text{ k}\Omega) = 17.8$ V
$$I_B = \frac{I_E}{h_{FE} + 1} = \frac{2.03\text{ mA}}{151} = 13.4\ \mu\text{A}$$

18. $h_{FE}R_E > 10R_2$, so we proceed as follows:
$$V_B = V_{CC}\frac{R_2}{R_1 + R_2} = (10\text{ V})\frac{10\text{ k}\Omega}{50\text{ k}\Omega} = 2\text{ V}$$
$$V_E = V_B - 0.7\text{ V} = 1.3\text{ V}, \quad I_{CQ} \cong I_E = \frac{V_E}{R_E} =$$
$$\frac{1.3\text{ V}}{2\text{ k}\Omega} = 650\ \mu\text{A}, \quad V_{CEQ} = V_{CC} - I_{CQ}(R_C + R_E) =$$
10 V $- (650\ \mu\text{A})(8\text{ k}\Omega) = 4.8$ V
$$I_B = \frac{I_E}{h_{FE} + 1} = \frac{650\ \mu\text{A}}{81} = 8.02\ \mu\text{A}$$

19. $h_{FE}R_E < 10R_2$, so we proceed as follows:
$$V_{TH} = V_{CC}\frac{R_2}{R_1 + R_2} = (20\text{ V})\frac{1.8\,k\Omega}{11.8\,k\Omega} = 3.05\text{ V}$$
$$R_{TH} = R_1 \parallel R_2 = 10\text{ k}\Omega \parallel 1.8\text{ k}\Omega = 1.53\text{ k}\Omega$$
$$I_{CQ} = \frac{V_{TH} - V_{BE}}{\dfrac{R_{TH}}{h_{FE}} + R_E} = \frac{3.05\text{ V} - 0.7\text{ V}}{\dfrac{1.53\text{ k}\Omega}{80} + 200\ \Omega} = 10.7\text{ mA}$$
$$V_{CEQ} = V_{CC} - I_{CQ}(R_C + R_E)$$
$$= 20\text{ V} - (10.7\text{ mA})(1.2\text{ k}\Omega) = 7.16\text{ V}$$
Since this is a *pnp* circuit with a negative supply voltage, $V_{CEQ} = -7.16$ V. Finally,
$$I_B = \frac{I_C}{h_{FE}} = \frac{10.7\text{ mA}}{80} = 134\ \mu\text{A}$$

20. $h_{FE}R_E > 10R_2$, so we proceed as follows:
$$V_B = V_{CC}\frac{R_2}{R_1 + R_2} = (14\text{ V})\frac{2.4\text{ k}\Omega}{15.4\text{ k}\Omega} = 2.18\text{ V}$$
$$V_E = V_B - 0.7\text{ V} = 1.48\text{ V}, \quad I_{CQ} \cong I_E = \frac{V_E}{R_E} =$$
$$\frac{1.48\text{ V}}{140\ \Omega} = 10.6\text{ mA}, \quad V_{CEQ} = V_{CC} - I_{CQ}(R_C + R_E) =$$
14 V $- (10.6\text{ mA})(700\ \Omega) = 6.58$ V
$$I_B = \frac{I_E}{h_{FE} + 1} = \frac{10.6\text{ mA}}{221} = 48\ \mu\text{A}.$$ Since this is a
pnp circuit with a negative supply voltage,
$V_B = -2.18$ V, $V_E = -1.48$ V, and $V_{CEQ} = -6.58$ V

21. The circuit analysis is performed using the *typical* value: $h_{FE} = 75$.

22. The *geometric average* of the min and max values is used: $h_{FE(ave)} = \sqrt{h_{FE(min)} \times h_{FE(max)}} = \sqrt{(80)(200)} \cong 126$

23. $I_{C(sat)} = \dfrac{V_{CC}}{R_C + R_E} = \dfrac{30\,\text{V}}{6\,\text{k}\Omega} = 5\,\text{mA}$, $V_{CE(off)} = V_{CC} = 30\,\text{V}$. From problem 17: $V_{CEQ} = 17.8\,\text{V}$. Since $V_{CEQ} \neq \dfrac{V_{CC}}{2}$, the circuit is *not* midpoint biased.

24. $I_{C(sat)} = \dfrac{V_{CC}}{R_C + R_E} = \dfrac{10\,\text{V}}{8\,\text{k}\Omega} = 1.25\,\text{mA}$, $V_{CE(off)} = V_{CC} = 10\,\text{V}$. From problem 18: $V_{CEQ} = 4.8\,\text{V}$. Since $V_{CEQ} \cong \dfrac{V_{CC}}{2}$, the circuit is midpoint biased.

25. $I_{C(sat)} = \dfrac{V_{CC}}{R_C + R_E} = \dfrac{20\,\text{V}}{1.2\,\text{k}\Omega} = 16.7\,\text{mA}$, $V_{CE(off)} = V_{CC} = -20\,\text{V}$. From problem 19: $V_{CEQ} = -5.84\,\text{V}$. Since $V_{CEQ} \neq \dfrac{V_{CC}}{2}$, the circuit is *not* midpoint biased.

26. $I_{C(sat)} = \dfrac{V_{CC}}{R_C + R_E} = \dfrac{14\,\text{V}}{700\,\Omega} = 20\,\text{mA}$, $V_{CE(off)} = V_{CC} = -14\,\text{V}$. From problem 20: $V_{CEQ} = -6.58\,\text{V}$. Since $V_{CEQ} \cong \dfrac{V_{CC}}{2}$, the circuit is midpoint biased.

27. To determine the value of h_{FE}, assume that $I_{CQ} \cong \dfrac{1}{2} I_{C(sat)} = \dfrac{V_{CC}}{2(R_C + R_E)} = \dfrac{30\,\text{V}}{1.5\,\text{k}\Omega} = 20\,\text{mA}$. For $I_{CQ} = 20\,\text{mA}$, $h_{FE(ave)} = \sqrt{h_{FE(min)} \times h_{FE(max)}} = \sqrt{(100)(400)} = 200$. Since $h_{FE}R_E > 10R_2$, we proceed as follows:

$V_B = V_{CC} \dfrac{R_2}{R_1 + R_2} = (30\,\text{V})\left(\dfrac{2\,\text{k}\Omega}{14\,\text{k}\Omega}\right) = 4.29\,\text{V}$

$V_E = V_B - 0.7\,\text{V} = 3.59\,\text{V}$

$I_{CQ} \cong \dfrac{V_E}{R_E} = \dfrac{3.59\,\text{V}}{130\,\Omega} = 27.6\,\text{mA}$ and $V_{CEQ} = V_{CC} - I_{CQ}(R_C + R_E) = 30\,\text{V} - (27.6\,\text{mA})(750\,\Omega) = 9.3\,\text{V}$. $V_{CEQ} \neq \dfrac{V_{CC}}{2}$, so the circuit is not midpoint biased.

28. To determine the value of h_{FE}, assume that $I_{CQ} \cong \dfrac{1}{2} I_{C(sat)} = \dfrac{V_{CC}}{2(R_C + R_E)} = \dfrac{24\,\text{V}}{2.4\,\text{k}\Omega} = 10\,\text{mA}$. For $I_{CQ} = 10\,\text{mA}$, $h_{FE(ave)} = \sqrt{h_{FE(min)} \times h_{FE(max)}}$

$= \sqrt{(50)(400)} = 141$. Since $h_{FE}R_E > 10R_2$, we proceed as follows:

$V_B = V_{CC} \dfrac{R_2}{R_1 + R_2} = (24\,\text{V})\left(\dfrac{1.3\,\text{k}\Omega}{11.3\,\text{k}\Omega}\right) = 2.76\,\text{V}$

$V_E = V_B - 0.7\,\text{V} = 2.06\,\text{V}$

$I_{CQ} \cong \dfrac{V_E}{R_E} = \dfrac{2.06\,\text{V}}{200\,\Omega} = 10.3\,\text{mA}$ and $V_{CEQ} = V_{CC} - I_{CQ}(R_C + R_E) = 24\,\text{V} - (10.3\,\text{mA})(1.2\,\text{k}\Omega) = 11.6\,\text{V}$. $V_{CEQ} \cong \dfrac{V_{CC}}{2}$, so the circuit is considered to be midpoint biased.

29. $I_{CQ} = \dfrac{|V_{EE} + 0.7\,\text{V}|}{R_E} = \dfrac{|-12\,\text{V} + 0.7\,\text{V}|}{6\,\text{k}\Omega} = 1.88\,\text{mA}$

$V_{CEQ} \cong V_{CC} - I_{CQ}R_C + 0.7\,\text{V}$
$= 12\,\text{V} - (1.88\,\text{mA})(3\,\text{k}\Omega) + 0.7\,\text{V} = 7.06\,\text{V}$

30. $I_{CQ} = \dfrac{|V_{EE} + 0.7\,\text{V}|}{R_E} = \dfrac{|-12\,\text{V} + 0.7\,\text{V}|}{12\,\text{k}\Omega} = 942\,\mu\text{A}$

$V_{CEQ} \cong V_{CC} - I_{CQ}R_C + 0.7\,\text{V}$
$= 12\,\text{V} - (942\,\mu\text{A})(6\,\text{k}\Omega) + 0.7\,\text{V} = 7.05\,\text{V}$

The value of I_{CQ} dropped by half and the value of V_{CEQ} remained the same (for all practical purposes).

31. $I_{C(sat)} = \dfrac{2V_{CC}}{R_C + R_E} = \dfrac{24\,\text{V}}{9\,\text{k}\Omega} = 2.67\,\text{mA}$ and $V_{CE(off)} = 2V_{CC} = 24\,\text{V}$

32. $I_{C(sat)} = \dfrac{2V_{CC}}{R_C + R_E} = \dfrac{24\,\text{V}}{18\,\text{k}\Omega} = 1.33\,\text{mA}$ and $V_{CE(off)} = 2V_{CC} = 24\,\text{V}$. The value of $I_{C(sat)}$ dropped by half and the value of $V_{CE(off)}$ did not change.

33. $I_{CQ} = \dfrac{|V_{EE} + 0.7\,\text{V}|}{R_E} = \dfrac{|-15\,\text{V} + 0.7\,\text{V}|}{3\,\text{k}\Omega} = 4.77\,\text{mA}$

$V_{CEQ} \cong V_{CC} - I_{CQ}R_C + 0.7\,\text{V}$
$= 15\,\text{V} - (4.77\,\text{mA})(1.6\,\text{k}\Omega) = 8.07\,\text{V}$

$I_{C(sat)} = \dfrac{2V_{CC}}{R_C + R_E} = \dfrac{30\,\text{V}}{4.6\,\text{k}\Omega} = 6.52\,\text{mA}$ and $V_{CE(off)} = 2V_{CC} = 30\,\text{V}$

34. $I_{CQ} = \dfrac{|V_{EE} + 0.7\,\text{V}|}{R_E} = \dfrac{|-8\,\text{V} + 0.7\,\text{V}|}{360\,\Omega} = 20.3\,\text{mA}$

$V_{CEQ} = V_{CC} - I_{CQ}R_C + 0.7\,\text{V}$
$= 8\,\text{V} - (20.3\,\text{mA})(200\,\Omega) + 0.7\,\text{V} = 4.64\,\text{V}$

$I_{C(sat)} = \dfrac{2V_{CC}}{R_C + R_E} = \dfrac{16\,\text{V}}{560\,\Omega} = 28.6\,\text{mA}$

$V_{CE(off)} = 2V_{CC} = 16\,\text{V}$

35. $R_{\text{base}} = h_{FE}R_E = (220)(3 \text{ k}\Omega) = 660 \text{ k}\Omega$

36. $R_{\text{base}} = h_{FE}R_E = (160)(360 \, \Omega) = 57.6 \text{ k}\Omega$

37. $I_B = \dfrac{V_{CC} - V_{BE}}{R_B + h_{FE}R_C} = \dfrac{8 \text{ V} - 0.7 \text{ V}}{200 \text{ k}\Omega + (100)(2 \text{ k}\Omega)} =$

18.3 µA, $I_{CQ} = h_{FE}I_B = (100)(18.3 \text{ µA}) = 1.83$ mA, $V_{CEQ} = V_{CC} - I_{CQ}R_C = 8 \text{ V} - (1.83 \text{ mA})(2 \text{ k}\Omega) = 4.34$ V

38. $I_B = \dfrac{V_{CC} - V_{BE}}{R_B + h_{FE}R_C} = \dfrac{12 \text{ V} - 0.7 \text{ V}}{1 \text{M}\Omega + (80)(12 \text{ k}\Omega)} = 5.77 \text{ µA},$

$I_{CQ} = h_{FE}I_B = (80)(5.77 \text{ µA}) = 462 \text{ µA},$ $V_{CEQ} = V_{CC} - I_{CQ}R_C = 12 \text{ V} - (462 \text{ µA})(12 \text{ k}\Omega) = 6.46 \text{ V}$

39. $I_B = \dfrac{V_{CC} - V_{BE}}{R_B + h_{FE}R_C} = \dfrac{10 \text{ V} - 0.7 \text{ V}}{620 \text{ k}\Omega + (200)(3 \text{ k}\Omega)} =$

7.62 µA, $I_{CQ} = h_{FE}I_B = (200)(7.62 \text{ µA}) = 1.52$ mA, $V_{CEQ} = V_{CC} - I_{CQ}R_C = 10 \text{ V} - (1.52 \text{ mA})(3 \text{ k}\Omega) = 5.44$ V. Since this is a *pnp* circuit with a negative supply voltage, $V_{CEQ} = -5.44$ V.

40. $I_B = \dfrac{V_{CC} - V_{BE}}{R_B + h_{FE}R_C} = \dfrac{14 \text{ V} - 0.7 \text{ V}}{560 \text{ k}\Omega + (120)(4.7 \text{ k}\Omega)} =$

11.8 µA, $I_{CQ} = h_{FE}I_B = (120)(11.8 \text{ µA}) = 1.42$ mA, $V_{CEQ} = V_{CC} - I_{CQ}R_C = 14 \text{ V} - (1.42 \text{ mA})(4.7 \text{ k}\Omega) = 7.33$ V. Since this is a *pnp* circuit with a negative supply voltage, $V_{CEQ} = -7.33$ V.

41. $I_B = \dfrac{V_{CC} - V_{BE}}{R_B + (h_{FE} + 1)R_E} = \dfrac{60 \text{ V} - 0.7 \text{ V}}{2.7 \text{M}\Omega + (51)(5 \text{ k}\Omega)} =$

20.1 µA, $I_{CQ} = h_{FE}I_B = (50)(20.1 \text{ µA}) = 1$ mA, $V_{CEQ} = V_{CC} - I_{CQ}(R_C + R_E) = 60 \text{ V} - (1 \text{ mA})(30 \text{ k}\Omega) = 30$ V

42. $I_B = \dfrac{V_{CC} - V_{BE}}{R_B + (h_{FE} + 1)R_E} = \dfrac{28 \text{ V} - 0.7 \text{ V}}{1 \text{M}\Omega + (81)(200 \, \Omega)} =$

26.9 µA, $I_{CQ} = h_{FE}I_B = (80)(26.9 \text{ µA}) = 2.15$ mA, $V_{CEQ} = V_{CC} - I_{CQ}(R_C + R_E) = 28 \text{ V} - (2.15 \text{ mA})(7 \text{ k}\Omega) \cong 13$ V

43. $I_B = \dfrac{V_{CC} - V_{BE}}{R_B + (h_{FE} + 1)R_E} = \dfrac{15 \text{ V} - 0.7 \text{ V}}{39 \text{ k}\Omega + (36)(150 \, \Omega)} =$

322 µA, $I_{CQ} = h_{FE}I_B = (35)(322 \text{ µA}) = 11.3$ mA, $V_{CEQ} = V_{CC} - I_{CQ}(R_C + R_E) = 15 \text{ V} - (11.3 \text{ mA})(770 \, \Omega) = 6.3$ V. Since this is a *pnp* circuit with a negative supply voltage, $V_{CEQ} = -6.3$ V.

44. $I_B = \dfrac{V_{CC} - V_{BE}}{R_B + (h_{FE} + 1)R_E} = \dfrac{12 \text{ V} - 0.7 \text{ V}}{10 \text{ k}\Omega + (101)(13 \, \Omega)} \cong$

1 mA, $I_{CQ} = h_{FE}I_B = (100)(1 \text{ mA}) = 100$ mA, $V_{CEQ} = V_{CC} - I_{CQ}(R_C + R_E) = 12 \text{ V} - (100 \text{ mA})(60 \, \Omega) = 6$ V. Since this is a *pnp* circuit with a negative supply voltage, $V_{CEQ} = -6$ V.

45. The values of V_B and V_E are normal for the base-emitter circuit. The fact that $V_C = V_{CC}$ indicates that the transistor collector is open or $R_C = 0 \, \Omega$. Most likely, the transistor collector is open.

46. This combination of meter readings indicates that R_1 is open or R_2 is shorted (which is highly unlikely).

47. The $V_B = 5$ V reading is much higher than normal, and $V_E \cong V_C$, indicating that the transistor is in saturation. The most likely cause of the combination of readings is R_2 open (which, in effect, changes the circuit to an emitter feedback bias circuit).

48. V_C indicates that the transistor is not conducting. V_E indicates that there is conduction through the base-emitter circuit. The most likely cause of these readings is an open transistor collector terminal.

49. For the circuit shown, the load line is plotted using

$I_{C(\text{sat})} \cong \dfrac{V_{CC}}{R_C} = \dfrac{20 \text{ V}}{5.1 \text{ k}\Omega} = 3.92$ mA and $V_{CE(\text{off})} = 20$

V. The curves are derived using I_C values of 1, 2, 3, 4, and 5 mA. The values of I_B are calculated using $I_B = \dfrac{I_C}{200}$, where $h_{FE} = 200$. As shown, $I_B = 10$ µA for midpoint bias.

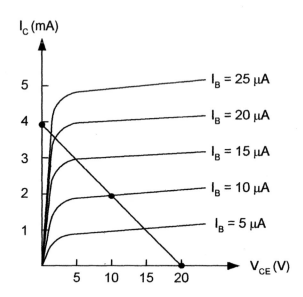

50. $I_{CQ} \cong \dfrac{|V_{EE} + 0.7 \text{ V}|}{R_E} = \dfrac{|-3.3 \text{ V}|}{330 \, \Omega} = 10$ mA, $V_{CEQ} = V_{CC} - I_{CQ}R_C + 0.7 \text{ V} = 8 \text{ V} - (10 \text{ mA})(390 \, \Omega) + 0.7 \text{ V} = 4.8$ V. At $I_{CQ} = 10$ mA, the 2N4013 has a minimum value of $h_{FE} = 30$.

$I_B = \dfrac{I_E}{h_{FE} + 1} = \dfrac{10 \text{ mA}}{31} = 323$ µA and $V_B = I_BR_B = (323 \text{ µA})(100 \, \Omega) = 32.3$ mV. Finally,

$I_{C(\text{sat})} = \dfrac{V_{CC} - V_{EE}}{R_C + R_E} = \dfrac{8 \text{ V} + 4 \text{ V}}{720 \, \Omega} = 16.7$ mA and

$V_{CE(\text{off})} = V_{CC} - V_{EE} = 8 \text{ V} - (-4 \text{ V}) = 12$ V

51. Assuming an ideal value of $V_{BE} = 0$ V, eq. (7.23) can be written as $I_B = \dfrac{V_{CC}}{R_B + h_{FE}R_C}$. If $R_B = h_{FE}R_C$, then $I_B = \dfrac{V_{CC}}{2h_{FE}R_C}$, or $h_{FE}I_B = \dfrac{1}{2}\left(\dfrac{V_{CC}}{R_C}\right)$.

$I_{C(\text{sat})} = \dfrac{V_{CC}}{R_C}$ and $I_C = h_{FE}I_B$, so the equation for $h_{FE}I_B$ (above) shows that $I_C = \dfrac{1}{2} I_{C(\text{sat})}$ when $R_B = h_{FE}R_C$.

52. The 2N3904 has a breakdown rating of $V_{BR(CEO)} = 40$ V. If the amplifier is driven into cutoff, the transistor is exposed to $V_{CE(\text{off})} = 48$ V, which will destroy a 2N3904.

CHAPTER 8

EXAMPLE PRACTICE PROBLEMS   (CH 8)

8-1. $A_v = \dfrac{v_{\text{out}}}{v_{\text{in}}} = \dfrac{72\,\text{mV}}{300\,\mu\text{V}} = 240$

8-2. $v_{\text{out}} = A_v v_{\text{in}} = (240)(360\,\mu\text{V}) = 86.4\,\text{mV}$

8-3. $v_{\text{in}} = v_S \dfrac{Z_{\text{in}}}{R_S + Z_{\text{in}}} = (800\,\mu\text{V})\dfrac{750\,\Omega}{820\,\Omega} = 732\,\mu\text{V}$

8-4. For $v_S = v_{\text{in}} = 800\,\mu\text{V}$: $v_{\text{out}} = A_v v_{\text{in}} = (480)(800\,\mu\text{V}) = 384$ mV. For $v_S = 732\,\mu\text{V}$:
$v_{\text{out}} = A_v v_{\text{in}} = (480)(732\,\mu\text{V}) = 351\,\text{mV}$

8-5. $v_L = v_{\text{out}} \dfrac{R_L}{Z_{\text{out}} + R_L} = (480\,\text{mV})\dfrac{1.5\,\text{k}\Omega}{1.74\,\text{k}\Omega} = 414\,\text{mV}$

8-6. $\eta = \dfrac{P_L}{P_{\text{dc}}} \times 100 = \dfrac{450\,\text{mW}}{3.3\,\text{W}} \times 100 = 13.6\,\%$

8-7. $A_{p(\text{dB})} = 10 \log \dfrac{P_{\text{out}}}{P_{\text{in}}} = 10 \log \dfrac{6\,\text{W}}{420\,\mu\text{W}} = 41.5\,\text{dB}$

8-8. $A_p = \log^{-1} \dfrac{A_{p(\text{dB})}}{10} = \log^{-1} \dfrac{20\,\text{dB}}{10} = 100$

8-9. $A_p = \log^{-1} \dfrac{A_{p(\text{dB})}}{10} = \log^{-1} \dfrac{5.2\,\text{dB}}{10} = 3.31$
$P_{\text{out}} (3.31)(40\,\mu\text{W}) = 132\,\mu\text{W}$

8-10. $A_p = \log^{-1} \dfrac{A_{p(\text{dB})}}{10} = \log^{-1} \dfrac{12.4\,\text{dB}}{10} = 17.4$

$P_{\text{in}} = \dfrac{2.2\,\text{W}}{17.4} = 126\,\text{mW}$

8-11.   [This example has no practice problem.]

8-12. $P_{\text{out}} = \log^{-1} \dfrac{32\,\text{dB}}{10} \times 1\,\text{mW} = (1585)(1\,\text{mW}) = 1.59\,\text{W}$

8-13. $A_{v(\text{dB})} = 20 \log \dfrac{v_{\text{out}}}{v_{\text{in}}} = 20 \log \dfrac{7.8\,\text{V}}{25\,\text{mV}} = 49.9\,\text{dB}$

8-14. $A_v = \log^{-1} \dfrac{A_{v(\text{dB})}}{20} = \log^{-1} \dfrac{12\,\text{dB}}{20} = 3.98$

8-15. $A_v = \log^{-1} \dfrac{A_{v(\text{dB})}}{20} = \log^{-1} \dfrac{-12\,\text{dB}}{20} = 0.25$

PRACTICE PROBLEMS   (CH 8)

1. $A_v = \dfrac{300\,\text{mV}}{1.2\,\text{mV}} = 250 \qquad A_v = \dfrac{18\,\text{mV}}{200\,\mu\text{V}} = 90$

$A_v = \dfrac{2.2\,\text{V}}{24\,\text{mV}} = 91.7 \qquad A_v = \dfrac{140\,\text{mV}}{800\,\mu\text{V}} = 175$

2. $A_v = \dfrac{600\,\text{mV}}{38\,\text{mV}} = 15.8 \qquad A_v = \dfrac{9.2\,\text{V}}{6\,\text{mV}} = 1.53 \times 10^3$

$A_v = \dfrac{88\,\text{mV}}{500\,\mu\text{V}} = 176 \qquad A_v = \dfrac{48\,\text{mV}}{48\,\text{mV}} = 1$

3. $v_{\text{out}} = A_v v_{\text{in}} = (540)(240\,\mu\text{V}) = 130\,\text{mV}$
$v_{\text{out}} = A_v v_{\text{in}} = (300)(1.4\,\text{mV}) = 420\,\text{mV}$
$v_{\text{out}} = A_v v_{\text{in}} = (440)(24\,\text{mV}) = 10.6\,\text{V}$
$v_{\text{out}} = A_v v_{\text{in}} = (720)(800\,\mu\text{V}) = 576\,\text{mV}$

4. $v_{\text{out}} = A_v v_{\text{in}} = (90)(40\,\text{mV}) = 3.6\,\text{V}$
$v_{\text{out}} = A_v v_{\text{in}} = (650)(250\,\mu\text{V}) = 163\,\text{mV}$
$v_{\text{out}} = A_v v_{\text{in}} = (420)(1.5\,\text{mV}) = 630\,\text{mV}$

5. $v_{\text{in}} = v_S \dfrac{Z_{\text{in}}}{R_S + Z_{\text{in}}} = (600\,\mu\text{V})\dfrac{1.2\,\text{k}\Omega}{1.38\,\text{k}\Omega} = 522\,\mu\text{V}$

6. $v_{\text{in}} = v_S \dfrac{Z_{\text{in}}}{R_S + Z_{\text{in}}} = (18\,\text{mV})\dfrac{720\,\Omega}{780\,\Omega} = 16.6\,\text{mV}$

7. $v_L = v_{\text{out}} \dfrac{R_L}{Z_{\text{out}} + R_L} = (8.8\,\text{V})\dfrac{3\,\text{k}\Omega}{3.12\,\text{k}\Omega} = 8.46\,\text{V}$

8. $v_L = v_{\text{out}} \dfrac{R_L}{Z_{\text{out}} + R_L} = (12\,\text{V})\dfrac{5.2\,\text{k}\Omega}{5.28\,\text{k}\Omega} = 11.8\,\text{V}$

9. $v_{\text{in}} = v_S \dfrac{Z_{\text{in}}}{R_S + Z_{\text{in}}} = (12\,\text{mV})\dfrac{800\,\Omega}{850\,\Omega} = 11.3\,\text{mV}$
$v_{\text{out}} = A_v v_{\text{in}} = (400)(11.3\,\text{mV}) = 4.52\,\text{V}$
$v_L = v_{\text{out}} \dfrac{R_L}{Z_{\text{out}} + R_L} = (4.52\,\text{V})\dfrac{3\,\text{k}\Omega}{3.3\,\text{k}\Omega} = 4.11\,\text{V}$
$A_{v(\text{eff})} = \dfrac{v_L}{v_S} = \dfrac{4.11\,\text{V}}{12\,\text{mV}} \cong 343$

10. $v_{\text{in}} = v_S \dfrac{Z_{\text{in}}}{R_S + Z_{\text{in}}} = (800\,\mu\text{V})\dfrac{600\,\Omega}{620\,\Omega} = 774\,\mu\text{V}$

$v_{\text{out}} = A_v v_{\text{in}} = (850)(774\,\mu\text{V}) = 658\,\text{mV}$

$$v_L = v_{out} \frac{R_L}{Z_{out} + R_L} = (658 \text{ mV}) \frac{1 \text{k}\Omega}{1.15 \text{k}\Omega} = 572 \text{ mV}$$

$$A_{v(eff)} = \frac{v_L}{v_S} = \frac{572 \text{ mV}}{800 \,\mu\text{V}} = 715$$

11. $v_{in} = v_S \frac{Z_{in}}{R_S + Z_{in}} = (24 \text{ mV}) \frac{600 \,\Omega}{680 \,\Omega} = 21.2 \text{ mV}$

$v_{out} = A_v v_{in} = (280)(21.2 \text{ mV}) = 5.94 \text{ V}$

$v_L = v_{out} \frac{R_L}{Z_{out} + R_L} = (5.94 \text{ V}) \frac{2 \text{k}\Omega}{2.12 \text{k}\Omega} = 5.6 \text{ V}$

$A_{v(eff)} = \frac{v_L}{v_S} = \frac{5.6 \text{ V}}{24 \text{ mV}} = 233$

12. $v_{in} = v_S \frac{Z_{in}}{R_S + Z_{in}} = (100 \text{ mV}) \frac{300 \,\Omega}{360 \,\Omega} = 83.3 \text{ mV}$

$v_{out} = A_v v_{in} = (140)(83.3 \text{ mV}) = 11.7 \text{ V}$

$v_L = v_{out} \frac{R_L}{Z_{out} + R_L} = (11.7 \text{ V}) \frac{12 \text{k}\Omega}{12.3 \text{k}\Omega} = 11.4 \text{ V}$

$A_{v(eff)} = \frac{v_L}{v_S} = \frac{11.4 \text{ mV}}{100 \,\mu\text{V}} = 114$

13. $\eta = \frac{P_{out}}{P_{in}} \times 100 = \frac{1.2 \text{ W}}{8.8 \text{ W}} \times 100 = 13.6 \,\%$

14. $\eta = \frac{P_{out}}{P_{in}} \times 100 = \frac{300 \text{ mW}}{2 \text{ W}} \times 100 = 15 \,\%$

15. $\eta = \frac{P_L}{P_{dc}} \times 100 = \frac{200 \text{ mW}}{1.4 \text{ W}} \times 100 = 14.3 \,\%$

16. $\eta = \frac{P_L}{P_{dc}} \times 100 = \frac{115 \text{ mW}}{3 \text{ W}} \times 100 = 3.83 \,\%$

17. $A_{p(dB)} = 10 \log \frac{P_{out}}{P_{in}} = 10 \log \frac{5 \text{ W}}{10 \text{ mW}} = 27 \text{ dB}$

$A_{p(dB)} = 10 \log \frac{P_{out}}{P_{in}} = 10 \log \frac{1 \text{ W}}{100 \text{ mW}} = 10 \text{ dB}$

$A_{p(dB)} = 10 \log \frac{P_{out}}{P_{in}} = 10 \log \frac{4 \text{ W}}{1.25 \text{ mW}} = 35.1 \text{ dB}$

$A_{p(dB)} = 10 \log \frac{P_{out}}{P_{in}} = 10 \log \frac{6 \text{ W}}{12 \text{ W}} = -3.01 \text{ dB}$

18. $A_{p(dB)} = 10 \log \frac{P_{out}}{P_{in}} = 10 \log \frac{1 \text{ W}}{500 \,\mu\text{W}} = 33 \text{ dB}$

$A_{p(dB)} = 10 \log \frac{P_{out}}{P_{in}} = 10 \log \frac{1.4 \text{ W}}{22 \text{ W}} = -12 \text{ dB}$

$A_{p(dB)} = 10 \log \frac{P_{out}}{P_{in}} = 10 \log \frac{2.64 \text{ W}}{33 \text{ mW}} = 19 \text{ dB}$

$A_{p(dB)} = 10 \log \frac{P_{out}}{P_{in}} = 10 \log \frac{2.2 \text{ W}}{120 \text{ mW}} = 12.6 \text{ dB}$

19. $A_p = \log^{-1} \frac{A_{p(dB)}}{10} = \log^{-1} \frac{48 \text{ dB}}{10} = 63.1 \times 10^3$

20. $A_p = \log^{-1} \frac{A_{p(dB)}}{10} = \log^{-1} \frac{-18 \text{ dB}}{10} = 15.8 \times 10^{-3}$

21. $A_p = \log^{-1} \frac{A_{p(dB)}}{10} = \log^{-1} \frac{12 \text{ dB}}{10} = 15.8$

$P_{out} = A_p P_{in} = (15.8)(30 \text{ mW}) = 474 \text{ mW}$

22. $A_p = \log^{-1} \frac{A_{p(dB)}}{10} = \log^{-1} \frac{3 \text{ dB}}{10} = 2$

$P_{out} = A_p P_{in} = (2)(400 \text{ mW}) = 800 \text{ mW}$

23. $A_p = \log^{-1} \frac{A_{p(dB)}}{10} = \log^{-1} \frac{-12 \text{ dB}}{10} = 0.063$

$P_{out} = A_p P_{in} = (0.063)(800 \text{ mW}) = 50.4 \text{ mW}$

24. $A_p = \log^{-1} \frac{A_{p(dB)}}{10} = \log^{-1} \frac{-6 \text{ dB}}{10} = 0.251$

$P_{out} = A_p P_{in} = (0.251)(1.2 \text{ mW}) = 301 \,\mu\text{W}$

25. $A_p = \log^{-1} \frac{A_{p(dB)}}{10} = \log^{-1} \frac{5 \text{ dB}}{10} = 3.16$

$P_{in} = \frac{P_{out}}{A_p} = \frac{2.2 \text{ W}}{3.16} = 696 \text{ mW}$

26. $A_p = \log^{-1} \frac{A_{p(dB)}}{10} = \log^{-1} \frac{-12 \text{ dB}}{10} = 0.063$

$P_{in} = \frac{P_{out}}{A_p} = \frac{600 \,\mu\text{W}}{0.063} = 9.52 \text{ mW}$

27. $A_p = \log^{-1} \frac{A_{p(dB)}}{10} = \log^{-1} \frac{40 \text{ dB}}{10} = 1 \times 10^4$

$P_{out} = A_p P_{in} = (1 \times 10^4)(1 \text{ mW}) = 10 \text{ W}$

28. $A_p = \log^{-1} \frac{A_{p(dB)}}{10} = \log^{-1} \frac{22 \text{ dB}}{10} = 158$

$P_{out} = A_p P_{in} = (158)(1 \text{ mW}) = 158 \text{ mW}$

29. $A_p = \log^{-1} \frac{A_{p(dB)}}{10} = \log^{-1} \frac{-1.2 \text{ dB}}{10} = 0.759$

$P_{out} = A_p P_{in} = (0.759)(1 \text{ mW}) = 759 \,\mu\text{W}$

30. $A_p = \log^{-1} \frac{A_{p(dB)}}{10} = \log^{-1} \frac{60 \text{ dB}}{10} = 1 \times 10^6$

$P_{out} = A_p P_{in} = (1 \times 10^6)(1 \text{ mW}) = 1 \text{ kW}$

31. $A_{v(dB)} = 20 \log \frac{v_{out}}{v_{in}} = 20 \log \frac{3.6 \text{ V}}{120 \text{ mV}} = 29.5 \text{ dB}$

$A_{v(dB)} = 20 \log \frac{v_{out}}{v_{in}} = 20 \log \frac{800 \text{ mV}}{50 \,\mu\text{V}} = 84.1 \text{ dB}$

$A_{v(dB)} = 20 \log \frac{v_{out}}{v_{in}} = 20 \log \frac{14 \text{ V}}{200 \text{ mV}} = 36.9 \text{ dB}$

$A_{v(dB)} = 20 \log \frac{v_{out}}{v_{in}} = 20 \log \frac{300 \text{ mV}}{150 \text{ mV}} = 6.02 \text{ dB}$

32. $\dfrac{v_{\text{out}}}{v_{\text{in}}} = A_v = \log^{-1} \dfrac{A_{v(\text{dB})}}{20} = \log^{-1} \dfrac{22\,\text{dB}}{20} = 12.6$

33. $\dfrac{v_{\text{out}}}{v_{\text{in}}} = A_v = \log^{-1} \dfrac{A_{v(\text{dB})}}{20} = \log^{-1} \dfrac{12\,\text{dB}}{20} = 3.98$

34. $\dfrac{v_{\text{out}}}{v_{\text{in}}} = A_v = \log^{-1} \dfrac{A_{v(\text{dB})}}{20} = \log^{-1} \dfrac{-3\,\text{dB}}{20} = 0.708$

35. $\dfrac{v_{\text{out}}}{v_{\text{in}}} = A_v = \log^{-1} \dfrac{A_{v(\text{dB})}}{20} = \log^{-1} \dfrac{-14\,\text{dB}}{20} = 0.1995$

36. $v_{\text{in}} = v_S \dfrac{Z_{\text{in}}}{R_S + Z_{\text{in}}} = (480\ \mu\text{V}) \dfrac{600\ \Omega}{700\ \Omega} = 411\ \mu\text{V}$

$A_v = \log^{-1} \dfrac{A_{v(\text{dB})}}{20} = \log^{-1} \dfrac{30.8\ \text{dB}}{20} = 34.7$

$v_{\text{out}} = A_v v_{\text{in}} = (34.7)(411\ \mu\text{V}) = 14.3\ \text{mV}$

$v_L = v_{\text{out}} \dfrac{R_L}{Z_{\text{out}} + R_L} = (14.3\ \text{mV}) \dfrac{120\ \Omega}{130\ \Omega} = 13.2\ \text{mV}$

$A_{v(\text{eff})} = 20 \log \dfrac{v_L}{v_S} = 20 \log \dfrac{13.2\ \text{mV}}{480\ \mu\text{V}} = 28.8\ \text{dB}$

$P_L = \dfrac{v_L^2}{R_L} = \dfrac{(13.2\ \text{mV})^2}{120\ \Omega} = 1.45\ \mu\text{W}$

$P_{L(\text{dBm})} = 10 \log \dfrac{1.45\ \mu\text{W}}{1\ \text{mW}} \cong -28.4\ \text{dBm}$

37. $v_{\text{in}} = v_S \dfrac{Z_{\text{in}}}{R_S + Z_{\text{in}}} = (1\ \text{mV}) \dfrac{190\ \Omega}{200\ \Omega} = 950\ \mu\text{V}$

$P_S = \dfrac{v_S^2}{R_S + Z_{\text{in}}} = \dfrac{(1\ \text{mV})^2}{200\ \Omega} = 5\ \text{nW}$

$v_{\text{out}} = A_v v_{\text{in}} = (1000)(950\ \mu\text{V}) = 950\ \text{mV}$

$v_L = v_{\text{out}} \dfrac{R_L}{Z_{\text{out}} + R_L} = (950\ \text{mV}) \dfrac{550\ \Omega}{600\ \Omega} = 871\ \text{mV}$

$P_L = \dfrac{v_L^2}{R_L} = \dfrac{(871\ \text{mV})^2}{550\ \Omega} = 1.38\ \text{mW}$

$A_{p(\text{eff})} = 10 \log \dfrac{P_L}{P_S} = 10 \log \dfrac{1.38\ \text{mW}}{5\ \text{nW}} = 54.4\ \text{dB}$

CHAPTER 9

EXAMPLE PRACTICE PROBLEMS   (CH 9)

9-1. $V_B = V_{CC} \dfrac{R_2}{R_1 + R_2} = (10\ \text{V}) \dfrac{10\ \text{k}\Omega}{50\ \text{k}\Omega} = 2\ \text{V}$

$V_E = V_B - 0.7\ \text{V} = 2\ \text{V} - 0.7\ \text{V} = 1.3\ \text{V}$

$I_E = \dfrac{V_E}{R_E} = \dfrac{1.3\ \text{V}}{2\ \text{k}\Omega} = 650\ \mu\text{A}$

$r'_e = \dfrac{25\ \text{mV}}{I_E} = \dfrac{25\ \text{mV}}{650\ \mu\text{A}} = 38.5\ \Omega$

9-2.

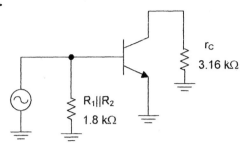

9-3. $A_v = \dfrac{v_{\text{out}}}{v_{\text{in}}} = \dfrac{14.2\ \text{V}}{120\ \text{mV}} = 118$

9-4. $V_B = V_{CC} \dfrac{R_2}{R_1 + R_2} = (30\ \text{V}) \dfrac{5.1\ \text{k}\Omega}{56.1\ \text{k}\Omega} = 2.73\ \text{V}$

$V_E = V_B - 0.7\ \text{V} = 2.73\ \text{V} - 0.7\ \text{V} = 2.03\ \text{V}$

$I_E = \dfrac{V_E}{R_E} = \dfrac{2.03\ \text{V}}{910\ \Omega} = 2.23\ \text{mA}$

$r'_e = \dfrac{25\ \text{mV}}{I_E} = \dfrac{25\ \text{mV}}{2.23\ \text{mA}} = 11.2\ \Omega$

$r_C = R_C \parallel R_L = (5.1\ \text{k}\Omega) \parallel (10\ \text{k}\Omega) = 3.38\ \text{k}\Omega$

$A_v = \dfrac{r_C}{r'_e} = \dfrac{3.38\ \text{k}\Omega}{11.2\ \Omega} = 302$

9-5. Since $h_{FE} R_E < 10 R_2$, we proceed as follows:

$V_{TH} = V_{CC} \dfrac{R_2}{R_1 + R_2} = (10\ \text{V}) \dfrac{10\ \text{k}\Omega}{49\ \text{k}\Omega} = 2.04\ \text{V}$

$R_{TH} = R_1 \parallel R_2 = 39\ \text{k}\Omega \parallel 10\ \text{k}\Omega = 7.96\ \text{k}\Omega$

$I_{CQ} = \dfrac{V_{TH} - V_{BE}}{\dfrac{R_{TH}}{h_{FE}} + R_E} = \dfrac{2.04\ \text{V} - 0.7\ \text{V}}{\dfrac{7.96\ \text{k}\Omega}{40} + 2.2\ \text{k}\Omega} = 559\ \mu\text{A}$

We assume that $I_{CQ} \cong I_E$, therefore:

$r'_e = \dfrac{25\ \text{mV}}{I_E} = \dfrac{25\ \text{mV}}{559\ \mu\text{A}} = 44.7\ \Omega$

$r_C = R_C \parallel R_L = (6.2\ \text{k}\Omega) \parallel (10\ \text{k}\Omega) = 3.83\ \text{k}\Omega$

$A_v = \dfrac{r_C}{r'_e} = \dfrac{3.83\ \text{k}\Omega}{44.7\ \Omega} = 85.7$

9-6. From Practice Problem 9-5: $A_v = 85.7$

$v_{\text{out}} = A_v v_{\text{in}} = (85.7)(20\ \text{mV}) = 1.71\ \text{V}$

9-7. From Practice Problem 9-5: $A_v = 85.7$

$A_p = A_i A_v = (20)(85.7) = 1714$

$P_{\text{out}} = A_p P_{\text{in}} = 1714 \times 60\ \mu\text{W} = 103\ \text{mW}$

9-8. From Example 9.5: $r'_e = 24.3\ \Omega$

$r_C = R_C = 1.5\ \text{k}\Omega$, $A_{vo} = \dfrac{r_C}{r'_e} = \dfrac{1.5\ \text{k}\Omega}{24.3\ \Omega} = 61.7$

9-9. From Practice Problem 9-5: $r'_e = 44.7\ \Omega$

$Z_{\text{base}} = h_{fe} r'_e = (200)(44.7\ \Omega) = 8.94\ \text{k}\Omega$

$Z_{\text{in}} = R_1 \parallel R_2 \parallel Z_{\text{base}}$
$=$
$(39\ \text{k}\Omega) \parallel (10\ \text{k}\Omega) \parallel (8.94\ \text{k}\Omega) = 4.21\ \text{k}\Omega$

9-10. $A_i = h_{fe} \dfrac{Z_{in} r_C}{Z_{in(base)} R_L}$

$= (300) \dfrac{(3.8\,\text{k}\Omega)(2.15\,\text{k}\Omega)}{(8.2\,\text{k}\Omega)(6.2\,\text{k}\Omega)} = 48.2$

9-11. All values used in this problem can be found in the example. For the second stage:

$Z_{base} = h_{fe} r'_e = (280)(17.4\,\Omega) = 4.87\,\text{k}\Omega$

$Z_{in} = R_5 \| R_6 \| Z_{base}$
$= (15\,\text{k}\Omega) \| (2.5\,\text{k}\Omega) \| (4.87\,\text{k}\Omega) = 1.49\,\text{k}\Omega$

For the first stage:

$r_C = R_3 \| Z_{in} = (5\,\text{k}\Omega) \| (1.49\,\text{k}\Omega) = 1.15\,\text{k}\Omega$

$A_v = \dfrac{r_C}{r'_e} = \dfrac{1.15\ \text{k}\Omega}{19.8\,\Omega} = 58.1$

9-12. From Example 9.10: $r'_{e1} = 19.8\,\Omega$

and $r'_{e2} = 17.4\,\Omega$. For Stage 2,

$r_C = R_7 \| R_L = (5\,\text{k}\Omega)\|(22\,\text{k}\Omega) = 4.07\,\text{k}\Omega$,

$Z_{base} = h_{fe} r'_{e2} = (240)(17.4\,\Omega) = 4.18\,\text{k}\Omega$,

$Z_{in2} = R_5\|R_6\|Z_{base} = (15\,\text{k}\Omega)\|(2.5\,\text{k}\Omega)\|(4.18\,\text{k}\Omega)$

$= 1.42\,\text{k}\Omega$, $\quad A_v = \dfrac{r_C}{r'_e} = \dfrac{4.07\,\text{k}\Omega}{17.4\,\Omega} = 234$

For Stage 1, $r_C = R_3 \| Z_{in2} = (5\,\text{k}\Omega)\|(1.42\,\text{k}\Omega) =$

$1.11\,\text{k}\Omega$ and $A_v = \dfrac{r_C}{r'_e} = \dfrac{1.11\,\text{k}\Omega}{19.8\,\Omega} = 56.1$.

Overall, $A_{vT} = A_{v1} A_{v2} = (56.1)(234) = 13.1 \times 10^3$

9-13. From the example, $V_E = 1.37\,\text{V}$ and $r_C =$

$1.3\,\text{k}\Omega$. $I_E = \dfrac{V_E}{R_E + r_E} = \dfrac{1.37\,\text{V}}{1.15\,\text{k}\Omega} = 1.19\,\text{mA}$,

$r'_e = \dfrac{25\,\text{mV}}{I_E} = 21\,\Omega$

$A_v = \dfrac{r_C}{r'_e + r_E} = \dfrac{1.3\,\text{k}\Omega}{351\,\Omega} = 3.7$

9-14. [This example has no practice problem.]
9-15. [This example has no practice problem.]
9-16. From Example 9.13: $r'_e = 22.1\,\Omega$

$Z_{base} = h_{fe}(r'_e + r_E) = (150)(322.1\,\Omega) = 48.3\,\text{k}\Omega$

$Z_{in} = R_1 \| R_2 \| Z_{base}$
$= (18\,\text{k}\Omega) \| (4.7\,\text{k}\Omega) \| (48.3\,\text{k}\Omega) = 3.46\,\text{k}\Omega$

9-17. [This example has no practice problem.]

9-18. $h_{ie} = \sqrt{h_{ie(min)} \times h_{ie(max)}} = \sqrt{(1\,\text{k}\Omega)(5\,\text{k}\Omega)} =$

$2.24\,\text{k}\Omega$, $h_{fe} = \sqrt{h_{fe(min)} \times h_{fe(max)}} = \sqrt{(70)(350)} \cong$

157, $Z_{base} = h_{ie} = 2.24\,\text{k}\Omega$, $Z_{in} = R_1\|R_2\|Z_{base}$
$= (33\,\text{k}\Omega) \| (4.7\,\text{k}\Omega) \| (2.24\,\text{k}\Omega) = 1.45\,\text{k}\Omega$,

$r_C = R_C \| R_L = (12\,\text{k}\Omega) \| (4.7\,\text{k}\Omega) = 3.38\,\text{k}\Omega$

$A_v = \dfrac{h_{fe} r_C}{h_{ie}} = \dfrac{(157)(3.38\,\text{k}\Omega)}{2.24\,\text{k}\Omega} = 237$

9-19. From Figure 9.26: $h_{ie} \cong 2.2\,\text{k}\Omega$ to $3.1\,\text{k}\Omega$ and $h_{fe} \cong 170$ to 220 at $I_{CQ} = 2\,\text{mA}$. Using these ranges,

$h_{ie} = \sqrt{h_{ie(min)} h_{ie(max)}} = \sqrt{(2.2\,\text{k}\Omega)(3.1\,\text{k}\Omega)} =$

$2.61\,\text{k}\Omega$, $h_{fe} = \sqrt{h_{fe(min)} h_{fe(max)}} = \sqrt{(170)(220)} =$

193, and $A_{vL} = \dfrac{h_{fe} r_C}{h_{ie}} = \dfrac{(193)(1.64\,\text{k}\Omega)}{2.61\,\text{k}\Omega} = 121$

PRACTICE PROBLEMS (CH 9)

1. $r'_e = \dfrac{25\,\text{mV}}{I_E} = \dfrac{25\,\text{mV}}{12\,\text{mA}} = 2.08\,\Omega$

2. $r'_e = \dfrac{25\,\text{mV}}{I_E} = \dfrac{25\,\text{mV}}{10\,\text{mA}} = 2.5\,\Omega$

3. $I_E = \dfrac{V_E}{R_E} = \dfrac{2.2\,\text{V}}{910\,\Omega} = 2.42\,\text{mA}$

$r'_e = \dfrac{25\,\text{mV}}{I_E} = \dfrac{25\,\text{mV}}{2.42\,\text{mA}} = 10.3\,\Omega$

4. $I_E = \dfrac{V_E}{R_E} = \dfrac{12\,\text{V}}{4.7\,\text{k}\Omega} = 2.55\,\text{mA}$

$r'_e = \dfrac{25\,\text{mV}}{I_E} = \dfrac{25\,\text{mV}}{2.55\,\text{mA}} = 9.8\,\Omega$

5. $V_E = V_B - 0.7\,\text{V} = 3.2\,\text{V} - 0.7\,\text{V} = 2.5\,\text{V}$

$I_E = \dfrac{V_E}{R_E} = \dfrac{2.5\,\text{V}}{1.2\,\text{k}\Omega} = 2.08\,\text{mA}$

$r'_e = \dfrac{25\,\text{mV}}{I_E} = \dfrac{25\,\text{mV}}{2.08\,\text{mA}} = 12\,\Omega$

6. $V_E = V_B - 0.7\,\text{V} = 4.8\,\text{V} - 0.7\,\text{V} = 4.1\,\text{V}$

$I_E = \dfrac{V_E}{R_E} = \dfrac{4.1\,\text{V}}{3.9\,\text{k}\Omega} = 1.05\,\text{mA}$

$r'_e = \dfrac{25\,\text{mV}}{I_E} = \dfrac{25\,\text{mV}}{1.05\,\text{mA}} = 23.8\,\Omega$

7. $V_B = V_{CC} \dfrac{R_2}{R_1 + R_2} = (12\,\text{V}) \dfrac{2.2\,\text{k}\Omega}{14.2\,\text{k}\Omega} = 1.86\text{V}$

$V_E = V_B - 0.7\,\text{V} = 1.86\,\text{V} - 0.7\,\text{V} = 1.16\,\text{V}$

$I_E = \dfrac{V_E}{R_E} = \dfrac{1.16\,\text{V}}{1.5\,\text{k}\Omega} = 773\,\mu\text{A}$

$r'_e = \dfrac{25\,\text{mV}}{I_E} = \dfrac{25\,\text{mV}}{773\,\mu\text{A}} = 32.3\,\Omega$

8. $V_B = V_{CC} \dfrac{R_2}{R_1 + R_2} = (16\,\text{V}) \dfrac{1.2\,\text{k}\Omega}{8.7\,\text{k}\Omega} = 2.21\,\text{V}$

$V_E = V_B - 0.7\,\text{V} = 2.21\,\text{V} - 0.7\,\text{V} = 1.51\,\text{V}$

$I_E = \dfrac{V_E}{R_E} = \dfrac{1.51\,\text{V}}{820\,\Omega} = 1.84\,\text{mA}$

$r'_e = \dfrac{25\,\text{mV}}{I_E} = \dfrac{25\,\text{mV}}{1.84\,\text{mA}} = 13.6\,\Omega$

9.

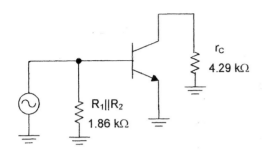

10.

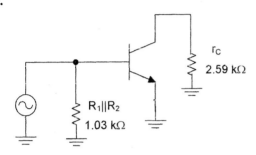

11.

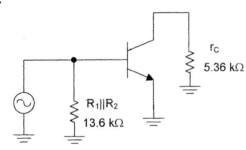

12.

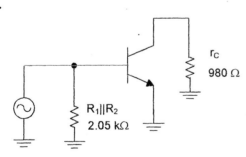

13. $A_v = \dfrac{v_{out}}{v_{in}} = \dfrac{4\,V}{120\,mV} = 33.3$

14. $A_v = \dfrac{v_{out}}{v_{in}} = \dfrac{6.4\,V}{82\,mV} = 78$

15. $A_v = \dfrac{r_C}{r'_e} = \dfrac{2.2\,k\Omega}{22.8\,\Omega} = 96.5$

16. $A_v = \dfrac{r_C}{r'_e} = \dfrac{4.7\,k\Omega}{32\,\Omega} = 147$

17. $r'_e = \dfrac{25\,mV}{I_E} = \dfrac{25\,mV}{1\,mA} = 25\,\Omega$

$A_v = \dfrac{r_C}{r'_e} = \dfrac{2.7\,k\Omega}{25\,\Omega} = 108$

18. $r'_e = \dfrac{25\,mV}{I_E} = \dfrac{25\,mV}{2\,mA} = 12.5\,\Omega$

$A_v = \dfrac{r_C}{r'_e} = \dfrac{3.3\,k\Omega}{12.5\,\Omega} = 264$

19. From problem 7: $r'_e = 32.3\,\Omega$. From problem 9:

$r_C = 4.29\,k\Omega.$ $\quad A_v = \dfrac{r_C}{r'_e} = \dfrac{4.29\,k\Omega}{32.3\,\Omega} = 133$

20. From problem 8: $r'_e = 13.6\,\Omega$. From problem 10:

$r_C = 2.59\,k\Omega.$ $\quad A_v = \dfrac{r_C}{r'_e} = \dfrac{2.59\,k\Omega}{13.6\,\Omega} = 190$

21. From problem 11: $r_C = 5.36\,k\Omega$.

$V_B = V_{CC}\dfrac{R_2}{R_1 + R_2} = (18\,V)\dfrac{16\,k\Omega}{107\,k\Omega} = 2.69V$

$V_E = V_B - 0.7\,V = 2.69\,V - 0.7\,V = 1.99\,V$

$I_E = \dfrac{V_E}{R_E} = \dfrac{1.99\,V}{1.8\,k\Omega} = 1.11\,mA$

$r'_e = \dfrac{25\,mV}{I_E} = \dfrac{25\,mV}{1.11\,mA} = 22.5\,\Omega$

$A_v = \dfrac{r_C}{r'_e} = \dfrac{5.36\,k\Omega}{22.5\,\Omega} = 238$

22. From Problem 12: $r_C = 980\,\Omega$. $h_{FE}R_E < 10R_2$, so

$V_{TH} = V_{CC}\dfrac{R_2}{R_1 + R_2} = (9\,V)\dfrac{2.4\,k\Omega}{16.4\,k\Omega} = 1.32\,V$

$R_{TH} = R_1 \parallel R_2 = 14\,k\Omega \parallel 2.4\,k\Omega = 2.05\,k\Omega$

$I_{CQ} = \dfrac{V_{TH} - V_{BE}}{\dfrac{R_{TH}}{h_{FE}} + R_E} = \dfrac{1.32\,V - 0.7\,V}{\dfrac{2.05\,k\Omega}{100} + 180\,\Omega} = 3.09\,mA$

We assume that $I_{CQ} \cong I_E$, therefore:

$r'_e = \dfrac{25\,mV}{I_E} = \dfrac{25\,mV}{3.09\,mA} = 8.09\,\Omega$

$r_C = 980\,\Omega, A_v = \dfrac{r_C}{r'_e} = \dfrac{980\,\Omega}{8.09\,\Omega} = 121$

23. From Problem 21: $A_v = 238$

$v_{out} = A_v v_{in} = (238)(12\,mV) = 2.86\,V$

24. From Problem 20: $A_v = 190$

$v_{out} = A_v v_{in} = (190)(22\,mV) = 4.18\,V$

25. From Problem 19: $A_v = 133$

$A_p = A_i A_v = (14)(133) = 1.86 \times 10^3$

26. From Problem 20: $A_v = 190$

$A_p = A_i A_v = (11)(190) = 2.09 \times 10^3$

27. From Problem 21: $A_v = 238$

$A_p = A_i A_v = (31)(238) = 7.38 \times 10^3$

28. From Problem 22: $A_v = 121$

$A_p = A_i A_v = (7.5)(121) = 908$

29. $A_p = A_i A_v = (40)(110) = 4.4 \times 10^3$

$P_{out} = A_p P_{in} = (4.4 \times 10^3)(10 \text{ mW}) = 44 \text{ W}$

30. $A_p = A_i A_v = (1.44)(68.8) = 99.1$

$P_{out} = A_p P_{in} = (99.1)(240 \text{ mW}) = 23.8 \text{ W}$

31. From problem 7: $r'_e = 32.3 \ \Omega$. $r_C = R_C = 6 \text{ k}\Omega$

$A_v = \dfrac{r_C}{r'_e} = \dfrac{6 \text{ k}\Omega}{32.3 \ \Omega} = 186$

32. From problem 8: $r'_e = 13.6 \ \Omega$. $r_C = R_C = 3.3 \text{ k}\Omega$

$A_v = \dfrac{r_C}{r'_e} = \dfrac{3.3 \text{ k}\Omega}{13.6 \ \Omega} = 243$

33. From problem 21: $r'_e = 22.5 \ \Omega$. $r_C = R_C = 7.2 \text{ k}\Omega$

$A_v = \dfrac{r_C}{r'_e} = \dfrac{7.2 \text{ k}\Omega}{22.5 \ \Omega} = 320$

34. From problem 22: $r'_e = 8.09 \ \Omega$. $r_C = R_C = 1.1 \text{ k}\Omega$

$A_v = \dfrac{r_C}{r'_e} = \dfrac{1.1 \text{ k}\Omega}{8.09 \ \Omega} = 136$

35. From Problem 7: $r'_e = 32.3 \ \Omega$

$Z_{base} = h_{fe} r'_e = (150)(32.3 \ \Omega) = 4.85 \text{ k}\Omega$

$Z_{in} = R_1 \| R_2 \| Z_{base}$

$= (12 \text{ k}\Omega) \| (2.2 \text{ k}\Omega) \| (4.85 \text{ k}\Omega) = 1.34 \text{ k}\Omega$

36. From Problem 8: $r'_e = 13.6 \ \Omega$

$Z_{base} = h_{fe} r'_e = (120)(13.6 \ \Omega) = 1.63 \text{ k}\Omega$

$Z_{in} = R_1 \| R_2 \| Z_{base}$

$= (7.5 \text{ k}\Omega) \| (1.2 \text{ k}\Omega) \| (1.63 \text{ k}\Omega) = 633 \ \Omega$

37. From Problem 21: $r'_e = 22.5 \ \Omega$

$Z_{base} = h_{fe} i'_e = (150)(22.5 \ \Omega) = 3.38 \text{ k}\Omega$

$Z_{in} = R_1 \| R_2 \| Z_{base}$

$= (91 \text{ k}\Omega) \| (16 \text{ k}\Omega) \| (3.38 \text{ k}\Omega) = 2.71 \text{ k}\Omega$

38. From Problem 22: $r'_e = 8.09 \ \Omega$

$Z_{base} = h_{fe} r'_e = (100)(8.09 \ \Omega) = 809 \ \Omega$

$Z_{in} = R_1 \| R_2 \| Z_{base}$

$= (14 \text{ k}\Omega) \| (2.4 \text{ k}\Omega) \| (809 \ \Omega) = 580 \ \Omega$

39. From Problem 35: $r'_e = 32.3 \ \Omega$, $Z_{base} = h_{fe} r'_e = 4.85 \text{ k}\Omega$, and $Z_{in} = R_1 \| R_2 \| Z_{base} = 1.34 \text{ k}\Omega$.

$r_C = R_C \| R_L = (6 \text{ k}\Omega) \| (15 \text{ k}\Omega) = 4.29 \text{ k}\Omega$

$A_i = h_{fe} \dfrac{Z_{in} r_C}{Z_{base} R_L} = (150) \dfrac{(1.34 \text{ k}\Omega)(4.29 \text{ k}\Omega)}{(4.85 \text{ k}\Omega)(15 \text{ k}\Omega)} = 11.9$

The assumed value of $A_i = 14$ is *incorrect*.

40. From Problem 36: $r'_e = 13.6 \ \Omega$, $Z_{base} = h_{fe} r'_e = 1.63 \text{ k}\Omega$, and $Z_{in} = R_1 \| R_2 \| Z_{base} = 633 \ \Omega$.

$r_C = R_C \| R_L = (3.3 \text{ k}\Omega) \| (12 \text{ k}\Omega) = 2.59 \text{ k}\Omega$

$A_i = h_{fe} \dfrac{Z_{in} r_C}{Z_{base} R_L} = (120) \dfrac{(633 \ \Omega)(2.59 \text{ k}\Omega)}{(1.63 \text{ k}\Omega)(12 \text{ k}\Omega)} = 10.1$

The assumed value of $A_i = 11$ is *incorrect* (though an argument can be made that it is within a 10% tolerance).

41. From Problem 37: $r'_e = 22.5 \ \Omega$, $Z_{base} = h_{fe} r'_e = 3.38 \text{ k}\Omega$, and $Z_{in} = R_1 \| R_2 \| Z_{base} = 2.71 \text{ k}\Omega$.

$r_C = R_C \| R_L = (7.2 \text{ k}\Omega) \| (21 \text{ k}\Omega) = 5.36 \text{ k}\Omega$

$A_i = h_{fe} \dfrac{Z_{in} r_C}{Z_{base} R_L} = (150) \dfrac{(2.71 \text{ k}\Omega)(5.36 \text{ k}\Omega)}{(3.38 \text{ k}\Omega)(21 \text{ k}\Omega)} = 30.7$

The assumed value of $A_i = 31$ is *correct* (within tolerance).

42. From Problem 38: $r'_e = 8.09 \ \Omega$, $Z_{base} = h_{fe} r'_e = 809 \ \Omega$, and $Z_{in} = R_1 \| R_2 \| Z_{base} = 580 \ \Omega$.

$r_C = R_C \| R_L = (1.1 \text{ k}\Omega) \| (9 \text{ k}\Omega) = 980 \ \Omega$

$A_i = h_{fe} \dfrac{Z_{in} r_C}{Z_{base} R_L} = (100) \dfrac{(580 \ \Omega)(980 \ \Omega)}{(809 \ \Omega)(9 \text{ k}\Omega)} = 7.81$

The assumed value of $A_i = 7.5$ is *correct* (within tolerance).

43. $h_{FE} R_8 < 10 R_6$, so we proceed as follows:

$V_{TH} = V_{CC} \dfrac{R_5}{R_6 + R_5} = (15 \text{ V}) \dfrac{11 \text{ k}\Omega}{58 \text{ k}\Omega} = 2.84 \text{ V}$

$R_{TH} = R_5 \| R_6 = 47 \text{ k}\Omega \| 11 \text{ k}\Omega = 8.91 \text{ k}\Omega$

$I_{CQ} = \dfrac{V_{TH} - V_{BE}}{\dfrac{R_{TH}}{h_{FE}} + R_8} = \dfrac{2.84 \text{ V} - 0.7 \text{ V}}{\dfrac{8.91 \text{ k}\Omega}{100} + 600 \ \Omega} = 3.11 \text{ mA}$

We assume that $I_{CQ} \cong I_E$, therefore:

$r'_{e2} = \dfrac{25 \text{ mV}}{I_E} = \dfrac{25 \text{ mV}}{3.11 \text{ mA}} = 8.04 \ \Omega$

$r_{C2} = R_7 \| R_L = (2.2 \text{ k}\Omega) \| (3 \text{ k}\Omega) = 1.27 \text{ k}\Omega$

$A_{v2} = \dfrac{r_C}{r'_e} = \dfrac{1.27 \text{ k}\Omega}{8.04 \ \Omega} = 158$

44. From Problem 43: $r'_{e2} = 8.04 \ \Omega$.

$V_{B1} = V_{CC} \dfrac{R_2}{R_1 + R_2} = (15 \text{ V}) \dfrac{12 \text{ k}\Omega}{59 \text{ k}\Omega} = 3.05 \text{ V}$,

$V_{E1} = V_B - 0.7 \text{ V} = 2.35 \text{ V}$, $\quad I_{E2} = \dfrac{V_E}{R_4} = 1.96 \text{ mA}$

$r'_{e1} = \dfrac{25 \text{ mV}}{1.96 \text{ mA}} = 12.8 \ \Omega$, $\quad Z_{in2} = R_5 \| R_6 \| h_{fe} r'_{e2} =$

$(47 \text{ k}\Omega) \| (11 \text{ k}\Omega) \| 965 \ \Omega = 871 \ \Omega$,

$r_{C1} = R_3 \| Z_{in2} = (5.6 \text{ k}\Omega)(871 \ \Omega) = 754 \ \Omega$,

$A_{v1} = \dfrac{r_{C1}}{r'_{e1}} = \dfrac{754 \ \Omega}{12.8 \ \Omega} = 58.9$

45. The second stage of this circuit is the same as the first stage of the circuit from Figure 9.34, therefore:

$r'_{e2} = 8.04 \ \Omega$. $r_{C2} = R_7 \| R_L = (5.6 \text{ k}\Omega) \| (3.9 \text{ k}\Omega)$

$= 2.3 \text{ k}\Omega$, and $A_{v2} = \dfrac{r_{C2}}{r'_{e2}} = \dfrac{2.3 \text{ k}\Omega}{8.04 \ \Omega} = 286$

$V_{B1} = V_{CC} \dfrac{R_2}{R_1 + R_2} = (15 \text{ V}) \dfrac{10 \text{ k}\Omega}{57 \text{ k}\Omega} = 2.63 \text{ V}$

$V_{E1} = V_B - 0.7 \text{ V} = 1.93 \text{ V}, \qquad I_{E1} = \dfrac{V_E}{R_6} = 1.93 \text{ mA},$

$r'_{e1} = \dfrac{25 \text{ mV}}{1.93 \text{ mA}} = 13 \ \Omega, \quad Z_{in2} = R_5 \| R_6 \| h_{fe}r'_{e2}$

$\quad = (47 \text{ k}\Omega) \| (12 \text{ k}\Omega) \| 804 \text{ k}\Omega = 742 \ \Omega,$

$r_{C1} = R_3 \| Z_{in2} = (3.9 \text{ k}\Omega) \| (742 \ \Omega) = 623 \ \Omega,$

$A_{v1} = \dfrac{r_{C1}}{r'_{e1}} = \dfrac{623 \ \Omega}{13 \ \Omega} = 47.9,$

$A_{vT} = A_{v1} \times A_{v2} = (47.9)(286) = 13.7 \times 10^3$

46. $A_{vT} = A_{v1} \times A_{v2} = (23.8)(122) = 2.9 \times 10^3$

$A_{iT} = A_{i1} \times A_{i2} = (24)(38) = 912$

$A_{pT} = A_{vT} \times A_{iT} = (2.9 \times 10^3)(912) = 2.64 \times 10^6$

47. $A_{vT} = A_{v1} \times A_{v2} = (88.6)(90.3) = 8.0 \times 10^3$

$A_{iT} = A_{i1} \times A_{i2} = (11)(21) = 231$

$A_{pT} = A_{vT} \times A_{iT} = (8.0 \times 10^3)(231) = 1.85 \times 10^6$

48. $A_{vT} = A_{v1} \times A_{v2} = (24.8)(77.1) = 1.91 \times 10^3$

$A_{iT} = A_{i1} \times A_{i2} = (30)(9) = 270$

$A_{pT} = A_{vT} \times A_{iT} = (1.91 \times 10^3)(270) = 5.16 \times 10^5$

49. From Problem 43: $r'_{e3} = 8.04 \ \Omega, \ r_{C3} = 1.27 \text{ k}\Omega,$ and $A_{v3} = 158$. From Problem 44: $Z_{in3} = 871 \ \Omega$ and $Z_{base} = h_{fe}r'_{e3} = 965 \ \Omega.$

$A_{i3} = h_{fe}\dfrac{Z_{in3}r_{C3}}{Z_{base}R_L} = (120)\dfrac{(871 \ \Omega)(1.27 \text{ k}\Omega)}{(965 \ \Omega)(3 \text{ k}\Omega)} = 45.9.$

From Problem 44: $r'_{e2} = 12.8 \ \Omega, \ r_{C2} = 54 \ \Omega, \ Z_{in3} = 871 \ \Omega$ and $A_{v2} = 58.9$. From Problem 45: $Z_{in2} = 1.12 \text{ k}\Omega$ and $Z_{base} = h_{fe}r'_{e2} = 1.28 \text{ k}\Omega$. Using $R_L = Z_{in3},$

$A_i = h_{fe}\dfrac{Z_{in2}r_{C2}}{Z_{base}R_L} = (100)\dfrac{(1.12 \text{ k}\Omega)(754 \ \Omega)}{(1.28 \text{ k}\Omega)(871 \ \Omega)} = 75.7$

From Problem 45: $r'_{e1} = 13 \ \Omega, \ r_{C1} = 870 \ \Omega, \ Z_{in2} = 1.12 \text{ k}\Omega$ and $A_{v1} = 66.9$. $Z_{base} = h_{fe}r'_{e1} = (100)(13 \ \Omega) = 1.3 \text{ k}\Omega, \ Z_{in} = R_1 \| R_2 \| Z_{base} = (47 \text{ k}\Omega) \| (10 \text{ k}\Omega) \| (1.3 \text{ k}\Omega) = 1.12 \text{ k}\Omega.$
Using $R_L = Z_{in2},$

$A_{i1} = h_{fe}\dfrac{Z_{in1}r_{C1}}{Z_{base}R_L} = (100)\dfrac{(1.12 \text{ k}\Omega)(876 \ \Omega)}{(1.3 \text{ k}\Omega)(1.12 \text{ k}\Omega)} = 67.4$

$A_{vT} = A_{v1}A_{v2}A_{v3} = (67.4)(58.9)(158) = 6.27 \times 10^5$

$A_{iT} = A_{i1}A_{i2}A_{i3} = (67.4)(75.7)(45.9) = 2.34 \times 10^5$

$A_{pT} = A_{iT}A_{vT} = (2.34 \times 10^5)(6.27 \times 10^5) = 1.47 \times 10^{11}$

50. $V_B = V_{CC}\dfrac{R_2}{R_1 + R_2} = (12 \text{ V})\dfrac{2.2 \text{ k}\Omega}{14.2 \text{ k}\Omega} = 1.86 \text{ V}$

$V_E = V_B - 0.7 \text{ V} = 1.16 \text{ V},$

$I_E = \dfrac{V_E}{r_E + R_E} = \dfrac{1.16 \text{ V}}{1.49 \text{ k}\Omega} = 779 \ \mu\text{A},$

$r'_e = \dfrac{25 \text{ mV}}{I_E} = \dfrac{25 \text{ mV}}{779 \ \mu\text{A}} = 32.1 \ \Omega$

$r_C = R_C \| R_L = (6.2 \text{ k}\Omega) \| (18 \text{ k}\Omega) = 4.61 \text{ k}\Omega$

$A_v = \dfrac{r_C}{r'_e + r_E} = \dfrac{4.61 \text{ k}\Omega}{32.1 \ \Omega + 390 \ \Omega} = 10.9$

51. $V_B = V_{CC}\dfrac{R_2}{R_1 + R_2} = (16 \text{ V})\dfrac{1.2 \text{ k}\Omega}{8.7 \text{ k}\Omega} = 2.21 \text{ V}$

$V_E = V_B - 0.7 \text{ V} = 1.51 \text{ V},$

$I_E = \dfrac{V_E}{r_E + R_E} = \dfrac{1.51 \text{ V}}{820 \ \Omega} = 1.84 \text{ mA},$

$r'_e = \dfrac{25 \text{ mV}}{I_E} = \dfrac{25 \text{ mV}}{1.84 \text{ mA}} = 13.6 \ \Omega$

$r_C = R_C \| R_L = (3.3 \text{ k}\Omega) \| (10 \text{ k}\Omega) = 2.84 \text{ k}\Omega$

$A_v = \dfrac{r_C}{r'_e + r_E} = \dfrac{2.48 \text{ k}\Omega}{13.6 \ \Omega + 140 \ \Omega} = 16.1$

52. $V_B = V_{CC}\dfrac{R_2}{R_1 + R_2} = (18 \text{ V})\dfrac{16 \text{ k}\Omega}{107 \text{ k}\Omega} = 2.69 \text{ V}$

$V_E = V_B - 0.7 \text{ V} = 1.99 \text{ V},$

$I_E = \dfrac{V_E}{r_E + R_E} = \dfrac{1.99 \text{ V}}{1.8 \text{ k}\Omega} = 1.11 \text{ mA},$

$r'_e = \dfrac{25 \text{ mV}}{I_E} = \dfrac{25 \text{ mV}}{1.11 \text{ mA}} = 22.5 \ \Omega$

$r_C = R_C \| R_L = (7.2 \text{ k}\Omega) \| (5 \text{ k}\Omega) = 2.95 \text{ k}\Omega$

$A_v = \dfrac{r_C}{r'_e + r_E} = \dfrac{2.95 \text{ k}\Omega}{22.5 \ \Omega + 300 \ \Omega} = 9.15$

53. From Problem 50: $r'_e = 32.1 \ \Omega$
$Z_{base} = h_{fe}(r'_e + r_E) = (150)(422.1 \ \Omega) = 63.3 \text{ k}\Omega$
$Z_{in} = R_1 \| R_2 \| Z_{base}$
$\quad = (12 \text{ k}\Omega) \| (2.2 \text{ k}\Omega) \| (63.3 \text{ k}\Omega) = 1.81 \text{ k}\Omega$

54. From Problem 51: $r'_e = 13.6 \ \Omega$
$Z_{base} = h_{fe}(r'_e + r_E) = (120)(153.6 \ \Omega) = 18.4 \text{ k}\Omega$
$Z_{in} = R_1 \| R_2 \| Z_{base}$
$\quad = (7.5 \text{ k}\Omega) \| (1.2 \text{ k}\Omega) \| (18.4 \text{ k}\Omega) = 979 \ \Omega$

55. $Z_{base} = h_{ie} = 5 \text{ k}\Omega, \qquad r'_e = \dfrac{h_{ie}}{h_{fe}} = \dfrac{5 \text{ k}\Omega}{100} = 50 \ \Omega,$

$A_v = \dfrac{h_{fe}r_C}{h_{ie}} = \dfrac{(100)(3.8 \text{ k}\Omega)}{5 \text{ k}\Omega} = 76$

56. $Z_{base} = h_{ie} = 4 \text{ k}\Omega, \qquad r'_e = \dfrac{h_{ie}}{h_{fe}} = \dfrac{4 \text{ k}\Omega}{120} = 33.3 \ \Omega,$

$A_v = \dfrac{h_{fe}r_C}{h_{ie}} = \dfrac{(120)(3.8 \text{ k}\Omega)}{4 \text{ k}\Omega} = 114$

57. From the curves, the following are estimated at $I_{CQ} = 1 \text{ mA}$: $h_{ie} = 2.75 \text{ k}\Omega$ to $4.75 \text{ k}\Omega$ and $h_{fe} = 95$ to 175. Using the geometric averages of these ratings: $h_{ie} = \sqrt{(2.75 \text{ k}\Omega)(4.75 \text{ k}\Omega)} = 3.61 \text{ k}\Omega$

$h_{fe} = \sqrt{(95)(175)} = 129$, $Z_{base} = h_{ie} = 3.61\ k\Omega$, and

$$A_v = \frac{h_{fe}r_C}{h_{ie}} = \frac{(129)(2.48\ k\Omega)}{3.61\ k\Omega} = 88.6$$

58. From the curves, the following are estimated at $I_{CQ} = 2\ mA$: $h_{ie} = 1.5\ k\Omega$ to $2.5\ k\Omega$ and $h_{fe} = 120$ to 190. Using the geometric averages of these ratings:

$$h_{ie} = \sqrt{(1.5\ k\Omega)(2.5\ k\Omega)} = 1.94\ k\Omega$$

$$h_{fe} = \sqrt{(120)(190)} = 151, \quad Z_{base} = h_{ie} = 1.94\ k\Omega,$$

and $A_v = \dfrac{h_{fe}r_C}{h_{ie}} = \dfrac{(151)(1.18\ k\Omega)}{1.94\ k\Omega} = 91.8$

59. From the curves, the following are estimated at $I_{CQ} = 5\ mA$: $h_{ie} = 750\ \Omega$ to $1.25\ k\Omega$ and $h_{fe} = 140$ to 220. Using the geometric averages of these ratings: $h_{ie} = \sqrt{(750\ \Omega)(1.25\ k\Omega)} = 968\ \Omega$

$$h_{fe} = \sqrt{(140)(220)} = 175, \quad Z_{base} = h_{ie} = 968\ \Omega, \text{ and}$$

$$A_v = \frac{h_{fe}r_C}{h_{ie}} = \frac{(175)(878\ \Omega)}{968\ \Omega} = 159$$

60. From the curves, the following are estimated at $I_{CQ} = 10\ mA$: $h_{ie} = 500\ \Omega$ to $750\ \Omega$ and $h_{fe} = 150$ to 225. Using the geometric averages of these ratings:

$$h_{ie} = \sqrt{(500\ \Omega)(750\ \Omega)} = 612\ \Omega$$

$$h_{fe} = \sqrt{(150)(225)} = 184, \quad Z_{base} = h_{ie} = 612\ \Omega, \text{ and}$$

$$A_v = \frac{h_{fe}r_C}{h_{ie}} = \frac{(184)(1.05\ k\Omega)}{612\ \Omega} = 316$$

61. Row 1: TP-2 indicates that Q_1 is in cutoff, but TP-1 indicates that the biasing circuit is operating normally. The problem is most likely caused by Q_1, R_4, and/or R_5 being open. **Row 2**: TP-5 and TP-6 are identical, indicating that Q_3 is shorted (base-to-collector). **Row 3**: TP-5 shows a loss of signal amplitude and biasing potential (V_B). The most likely cause of this display is R_{10} open. **Row 4**: TP-5 shows no signal, but a proper biasing (dc) potential. The most likely problem is C_4 open.

62. a. The readings indicate that the transistor is open.
b. The 4 V reading at the load indicates that the output coupling capacitor is shorted. c. V_C is low by several volts (should be $-10.8\ V$). Q_1 is leaky.

63. The circuit is emitter-feedback biased.
$R_E = R_3 + R_4 = 1.8\ k\Omega,$

$$I_B = \frac{V_{CC} - 0.7\ V}{R_B + (h_{FE} + 1)R_E} = \frac{20\ V - 0.7\ V}{1.6\ M\Omega + 182\ k\Omega} =$$

$10.8\ \mu A$, and $I_{CQ} = h_{FE}I_B = (101)(10.8\ \mu A) = 1.08\ mA$. Assuming $I_{CQ} = 1\ mA$, the 2N3251 curves provide *estimated* values of $h_{fe} = 250$ and

$h_{ie} = 7.5\ k\Omega$. $r'_e = \dfrac{h_{ie}}{h_{fe}} = 30\ \Omega,$

$Z_{base} = h_{fe}(r'_e + R_4) = (250)(230\ \Omega) = 57.5\ k\Omega,$
$Z_{in} = R_1 \| Z_{base} = (1.6\ M\Omega)\|(57.5\ k\Omega) = 55.5\ k\Omega$
$r_C = R_C \| R_L = (8.2\ k\Omega)\|(10\ k\Omega) = 4.51\ k\Omega$

$$A_v = \frac{r_C}{r'_e + R_4} = \frac{4.51\ k\Omega}{230\ \Omega} = 19.6,$$

$$A_i = h_{fe}\frac{Z_{in}r_C}{Z_{base}R_L} = (250)\frac{(55.5\ k\Omega)(4.51\ k\Omega)}{(57.5\ k\Omega)(10\ k\Omega)} = 109,$$

and $A_p = A_iA_v = (109)(19.6) = 2.14 \times 10^3$

64. From Problem 63: $r'_e = 30\ \Omega$ and $A_v = 19.6$. Normally, $v_{out} = A_vv_{in} = (19.6)(100\ mV_{pp}) = 1.96\ V_{pp}$ With an open load, $r_C = R_C = 8.2\ k\Omega,$

$$A_v = \frac{r_C}{r'_e + R_4} = \frac{8.2\ k\Omega}{230\ \Omega} = 35.7, \quad v_{out} = A_vv_{in} =$$

$(35.7)(100\ mV_{pp}) = 3.57\ V_{pp}$, and
$\Delta v_{out} = 3.57\ V_{pp} - 1.96\ V_{pp} = 1.61\ V_{pp}$

65. For Stage 2, $h_{FE}R_E < 10R_2$ so we proceed as

$$V_{TH} = V_{CC}\frac{R_2}{R_1 + R_2} = (12\ V)\frac{11 k\Omega}{58 k\Omega} = 2.28\ V$$

$R_{TH} = R_1 \| R_2 = 47\ k\Omega \| 11\ k\Omega = 8.91\ k\Omega$

$$I_{CQ} = \frac{V_{TH} - V_{BE}}{\dfrac{R_{TH}}{h_{FE}} + R_E} = \frac{2.28\ V - 0.7\ V}{\dfrac{8.91 k\Omega}{100} + 620\ \Omega} = 2.23\ mA$$

Assume $I_{CQ} \cong 2\ mA$. Using the curves in Figure 9.38, $h_{ie} = 1.5\ k\Omega$ to $2.5\ k\Omega$. $h_{fe} = 120$ to 180. Since $A_v = \dfrac{h_{fe}r_C}{h_{ie}}$, for the minimum value of A_v, we use

the lowest value of h_{fe} and the highest value of h_{ie}. Since $r_C = 2.4\ k\Omega\|5\ k\Omega = 1.62\ k\Omega$, therefore,

$$A_{v2} = \frac{h_{fe}r_C}{h_{ie}} = \frac{(120)(1.62\ k\Omega)}{2.5\ k\Omega} = 77.8.$$

For Stage 1, $h_{FE}R_E < 10R_2$ so we proceed as

$$V_{TH} = V_{CC}\frac{R_2}{R_1 + R_2} = (12\ V)\frac{3.9 k\Omega}{21.9 k\Omega} = 2.14\ V$$

$R_{TH} = R_1 \| R_2 = 18\ k\Omega \| 3.9\ k\Omega = 3.21\ k\Omega$

$$I_{CQ} = \frac{V_{TH} - V_{BE}}{\dfrac{R_{TH}}{h_{FE}} + R_E} = \frac{2.14\ V - 0.7\ V}{\dfrac{3.21 k\Omega}{100} + 240\ \Omega} = 5.29\ mA$$

Assuming $I_{CQ} \cong 5\ mA$, $h_{ie} = 750\ \Omega$ to $1.2\ k\Omega$. $h_{fe} = 130$ to 210. For Stage 2, $Z_{base} = h_{ie} = 2.5\ k\Omega$, so $Z_{in2} = 47\ k\Omega\|11\ k\Omega\|2.5\ k\Omega = 1.95\ k\Omega$. This means $r_C = R_3\|Z_{in2} = 910\ \Omega\|1.95\ k\Omega = 620\ \Omega$. As we did for Stage 2, we use the lowest value of h_{fe} and the highest value of h_{ie}, therefore

$A_{v1} = \dfrac{h_{fe}r_C}{h_{ie}} = \dfrac{(130)(620\ \Omega)}{1.2\ k\Omega} = 67.2$. Finally, the

minimum overall voltage gain is found as
$A_{vT} = A_{v1} \times A_{v2} = 67.2 \times 77.8 = 5.23 \times 10^3$.

66. The 2N3904 curves show the component to have values of $h_{fe} = 150$ and $h_{ie} = 900\ \Omega$ at $I_{CQ} = 5$ mA. Using these values,

$$A_v = \frac{h_{fe}r_C}{h_{ie}} = \frac{(150)(2.4\ \text{k}\Omega)}{900\ \Omega} = 400$$

67. The 2N5089 spec sheet lists values of $h_{fe} = 450$ (minimum) and $h_{fe} = 1800$ (maximum). Using these values, the geometric average of h_{fe} is found

as $h_{fe} = \sqrt{h_{fe(\text{min})} \times h_{fe(\text{max})}} = \sqrt{(450)(1800)} \cong 900$

CHAPTER 10

EXAMPLE PRACTICE PROBLEMS (CH 10)

10-1. $h_{FC}R_E < 10R_2$, so we proceed as follows:

$$V_{TH} = V_{CC}\frac{R_2}{R_1 + R_2} = (18\ \text{V})\frac{22\ \text{k}\Omega}{38\ \text{k}\Omega} = 10.4\ \text{V}$$

$$R_{TH} = R_1\|R_2 = 16\ \text{k}\Omega\|22\ \text{k}\Omega = 9.26\ \text{k}\Omega$$

$$I_{CQ} = \frac{V_{TH} - V_{BE}}{\dfrac{R_{TH}}{h_{FC}} + R_E} = \frac{10.4\ \text{V} - 0.7\ \text{V}}{\dfrac{9.26\ \text{k}\Omega}{200} + 910\ \Omega} = 10.1\text{mA}$$

Assuming $I_E \cong I_{CQ}$ we solve for V_{CEQ} as
$$V_{CEQ} = V_{CC} - I_E R_E = 18\ \text{V} - 9.19\ \text{V} = 8.81\ \text{V}$$

10-2. $V_{CE(\text{off})} = V_{CC} = 18$ V and $I_{C(\text{sat})} = \dfrac{V_{CC}}{R_C} =$

$$\frac{18\ \text{V}}{910\ \Omega} = 19.8\ \text{mA. The load line is drawn below.}$$

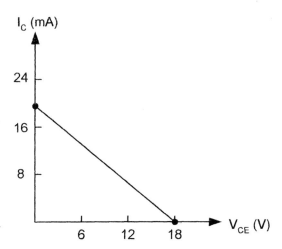

10-3. From Problem 10-1: $I_E = 10.1$ mA

$$r'_e = \frac{25\ \text{mV}}{I_E} = \frac{25\ \text{mV}}{10.1\ \text{mA}} = 2.48\ \Omega$$

$$r_E = R_E\|R_L = (910\ \Omega)\|(4\ \text{k}\Omega) = 741\ \Omega$$

$$A_v = \frac{r_E}{r'_e + r_E} = \frac{741\ \Omega}{2.48\ \Omega + 741\ \Omega} = 0.997$$

10-4. From Problem 10-3: $A_v = 0.997$.
$$A_p = A_i A_v = (24)(0.997) = 23.9$$

10-5. From Problem 10-3: $r'_e = 2.48\ \Omega$

$$r_E = R_E\|R_L = (910\ \Omega)\|(2\ \text{k}\Omega) = 625\ \Omega$$

$$Z_{\text{base}} = h_{fc}(r'_e + r_E) = (240)(627.5\ \Omega)$$

$$= 151\ \text{k}\Omega,\ Z_{\text{in}} = R_1\|R_2\|Z_{\text{base}} =$$

$$(16\ \text{k}\Omega)\|(22\ \text{k}\Omega)\|(151\ \text{k}\Omega) = 8.73\ \text{k}\Omega$$

10-6. $r'_e = \dfrac{h_{ic}}{h_{fc}} = \dfrac{3\ \text{k}\Omega}{200} = 15\ \Omega,\quad R_{th} = R_1\|R_2\|R_S =$

$$(2.5\ \text{k}\Omega)\|(3.3\ \text{k}\Omega)\|(500\ \Omega) \cong 370\ \Omega,\ Z_{\text{out}} =$$

$$R_E\left\|\left(r'_e + \frac{R_{th}}{h_{fc}}\right)\right. = (200\ \Omega)\left\|\left(15\ \Omega + \frac{370\ \Omega}{200}\right)\right.$$

$$= 15.5\ \Omega$$

10-7. $r'_e = \dfrac{h_{ic}}{h_{fc}} = \dfrac{540\ \Omega}{120} = 4.5\ \Omega,\ r_E = R_E\|R_L =$

$$(1.5\ \text{k}\Omega)\|(2.7\ \text{k}\Omega) = 964\ \Omega,\ Z_{\text{base}} = h_{fc}(r'_e + r_E) =$$

$(120)(968.5\ \Omega) \cong 116\ \text{k}\Omega$. For emitter-feedback bias: $Z_{\text{in}} = R_1\|Z_{\text{base}} = (180\ \text{k}\Omega)\|(116\ \text{k}\Omega) = 70.5\ \text{k}\Omega$.

For voltage-divider bias: $Z_{\text{in}} = R_1\|R_2\|Z_{\text{base}} = (6.2\ \text{k}\Omega)\|(9.1\ \text{k}\Omega)\|(116\ \text{k}\Omega) = 3.57\ \text{k}\Omega$

10-8. $R_{IN(1)} = h_{FC1}h_{FC2}R_E = (240)(240)(390\ \Omega) = 22.5\ \text{M}\Omega$

10-9. $r_E = R_E\|R_L = (510\ \Omega)\|(100\ \Omega) = 83.6\ \Omega,\ Z_{\text{base}} = h_{ic1} + h_{fc1}(h_{ic2} + h_{fc2}r_E) = 38\ \text{k}\Omega + (80)[4\ \text{k}\Omega + (180)(83.6\ \Omega)] = 1.56\ \text{M}\Omega,\ Z_{\text{in}} = R_1\|R_2\|Z_{\text{base}} = (240\ \text{k}\Omega)\|(240\ \text{k}\Omega)\|(1.56\ \text{M}\Omega) = 111\ \text{k}\Omega,\ r'_{e1} =$

$$\frac{h_{ic1}}{h_{fc1}} = \frac{38\ \text{k}\Omega}{80} = 475\ \Omega,\ r'_{e2} = \frac{h_{ic2}}{h_{fc2}} = \frac{4\ \text{k}\Omega}{180} = 22.2\ \Omega$$

$$R_{th} = R_1\|R_2\|R_S = (240\ \text{k}\Omega)\|(240\ \text{k}\Omega)\|(6\ \text{k}\Omega)$$

$$= 5.71\ \text{k}\Omega,\qquad Z_{\text{out}} \cong r'_{e2} + \frac{r'_{e1} + (R_{th}/h_{fc1})}{h_{fc2}}$$

$$= 22.2\ \Omega + \frac{475\ \Omega + (5.71\ \text{k}\Omega/80)}{180} = 25.2\ \Omega,\ A_i =$$

$$h_{fc1}h_{fc2}\frac{Z_{\text{in}}r_E}{Z_{\text{in(base)}}R_L} = (80)(180)\frac{(111\ \text{k}\Omega)(83.6\ \Omega)}{(1.56\ \text{M}\Omega)(100\ \Omega)}$$

$$= 857$$

10-10. $I_E = \dfrac{|V_{EE} + V_{BE}|}{R_E} = \dfrac{|-15\ \text{V} + 0.7\ \text{V}|}{30\ \text{k}\Omega} = 477\ \mu\text{A}$

$$r'_e = \frac{25\ \text{mV}}{I_E} = \frac{25\ \text{mV}}{477\ \mu\text{A}} = 52.4\ \Omega,\quad Z_{\text{in}} \cong r'_e =$$

$52.4\ \Omega,\quad Z_{\text{out}} \cong R_C = 15\ \text{k}\Omega,\quad r_C = R_C\|R_L =$

$$(15\ \text{k}\Omega)\|(3\ \text{k}\Omega) = 2.5\ \text{k}\Omega,\quad A_v = \frac{r_C}{r'_e} = \frac{2.5\ \text{k}\Omega}{52.4\ \Omega} =$$

$47.7,\quad A_i \cong \dfrac{r_C}{R_L} = \dfrac{2.5\ \text{k}\Omega}{3\ \text{k}\Omega} = 0.833$

PRACTICE PROBLEMS (CH 10)

1. $h_{FE}R_E < 10R_2$, so we proceed as follows:

$$V_{TH} = V_{CC}\frac{R_2}{R_1 + R_2} = (12\,\text{V})\frac{100\text{k}\Omega}{200\text{k}\Omega} = 6\,\text{V}$$

$$R_{TH} = R_1 \parallel R_2 = 100\,\text{k}\Omega \parallel 100\,\text{k}\Omega = 50\,\text{k}\Omega$$

$$I_{CQ} = \frac{V_{TH} - V_{BE}}{\dfrac{R_{TH}}{h_{FC}} + R_E} = \frac{6\,\text{V} - 0.7\,\text{V}}{\dfrac{50\,\text{k}\Omega}{150} + 2\text{k}\Omega} = 2.27\,\text{mA}$$

Assuming $I_E \cong I_{CQ}$ we solve for V_{CE} as
$$V_{CE} = V_{CC} - I_E R_E = 12\,\text{V} - 4.54\,\text{V} = 7.46\,\text{V}$$

2. $V_B = V_{CC}\dfrac{R_2}{R_1 + R_2} = (8\,\text{V})\dfrac{2\,\text{k}\Omega}{3.3\,\text{k}\Omega} = 4.85\,\text{V}$

$$V_E = V_B - 0.7\,\text{V} = 4.15\,\text{V}$$

$$I_E = \frac{V_E}{R_E} = \frac{4.15\,\text{V}}{220\,\Omega} = 18.9\,\text{mA}$$

3. $V_{CE(\text{off})} = V_{CC} = 12\,\text{V}$, $I_{C(\text{sat})} = \dfrac{V_{CC}}{R_E} = \dfrac{12\,\text{V}}{2\,\text{k}\Omega} = 6\,\text{mA}$

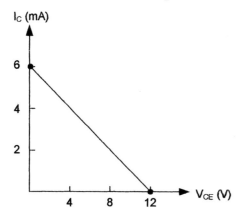

4. $V_{CE(\text{off})} = V_{CC} = 8\,\text{V}$, $I_{C(\text{sat})} = \dfrac{V_{CC}}{R_E} = \dfrac{8\,\text{V}}{220\,\Omega} = $

36.4 mA

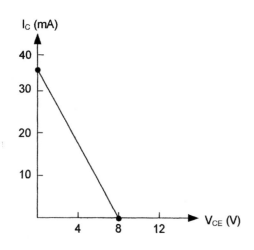

5. $r'_e = \dfrac{h_{ic}}{h_{fc}} = \dfrac{2\,\text{k}\Omega}{100} = 20\,\Omega$, $r_E = R_E \parallel R_L =$

$(2\,\text{k}\Omega)\parallel(5\,\text{k}\Omega) = 1.43\,\text{k}\Omega$, $Z_{\text{base}} = h_{fc}(r'_e + r_E) =$
$(100)(1.45\,\text{k}\Omega) = 145\,\text{k}\Omega$, $Z_{\text{in}} = R_1 \parallel R_2 \parallel Z_{\text{base}} =$
$(100\,\text{k}\Omega) \parallel (100\,\text{k}\Omega) \parallel (145\,\text{k}\Omega) = 37.2\,\text{k}\Omega$

6. $r'_e = \dfrac{h_{ic}}{h_{fc}} = \dfrac{1\text{k}\Omega}{80} = 12.5\,\Omega$, $r_E = R_E \parallel R_L =$

$(220\,\Omega)\parallel(100\,\Omega) = 68.8\,\Omega$, $Z_{\text{base}} = h_{fc}(r'_e + r_E) =$
$(80)(81.3\,\Omega) = 6.5\,\text{k}\Omega$, $Z_{\text{in}} = R_1 \parallel R_2 \parallel Z_{\text{base}} =$
$(1.3\,\text{k}\Omega) \parallel (2\,\text{k}\Omega) \parallel (6.5\,\text{k}\Omega) = 703\,\Omega$.

7. Using values calculated in Problem 5:

$$A_v = \frac{r_E}{r'_e + r_E} = \frac{1.43\,\text{k}\Omega}{1.45\,\text{k}\Omega} = 0.986$$

$$A_i = h_{fc}\frac{Z_{\text{in}}r_E}{Z_{\text{base}}R_L} = (100)\frac{(37.2\,\text{k}\Omega)(1.43\,\text{k}\Omega)}{(145\,\text{k}\Omega)(5\,\text{k}\Omega)}$$
$= 7.34$, $A_p = A_i A_v = (7.34)(0.986) = 7.24$

8. Using values calculated in Problem 6:

$$A_v = \frac{r_E}{r'_e + r_E} = \frac{68.8\,\Omega}{81.3\,\Omega} = 0.846$$

$$A_i = h_{fc}\frac{Z_{\text{in}}r_E}{Z_{\text{base}}R_L} = (80)\frac{(703\,\Omega)(68.8\,\Omega)}{(6.5\,\text{k}\Omega)(100\,\Omega)} = 5.95$$
$A_p = A_i A_v = (5.95)(0.846) = 5.03$

9. From problem 5: $r'_e = 20\,\Omega$. $R_{th} = R_1 \parallel R_2 \parallel R_S =$ $(100\,\text{k}\Omega) \parallel (100\,\text{k}\Omega) \parallel (100\,\Omega) = 99.8\,\Omega$,

$$Z_{\text{out}} \cong r'_e + \frac{R_{th}}{h_{fc}} = 20\,\Omega + \frac{99.8\,\Omega}{100} = 21.0\,\Omega$$

10. From problem 6: $r'_e = 12.5\,\Omega$. $R_{th} = R_1 \parallel R_2 \parallel R_S =$ $(1.3\,\text{k}\Omega) \parallel (2\,\text{k}\Omega) \parallel (600\,\Omega) \cong 341\,\Omega$

$$Z_{\text{out}} \cong r'_e + \frac{R_{th}}{h_{fc}} = 12.5\,\Omega + \frac{341\,\Omega}{80} = 16.8\,\Omega$$

11. $r'_e = \dfrac{h_{ic}}{h_{fc}} = \dfrac{1\,\text{k}\Omega}{80} = 12.5\,\Omega$

$r_E = R_E \parallel R_L = (1\,\text{k}\Omega) \parallel (500\,\Omega) = 333\,\Omega$,
$Z_{\text{base}} = h_{fc}(r'_e + r_E) = (80)(345.5\,\Omega) = 27.6\,\text{k}\Omega$
$Z_{\text{in}} = R_1 \parallel R_2 \parallel Z_{\text{base}} =$
$(6.2\,\text{k}\Omega) \parallel (9.1\,\text{k}\Omega) \parallel (27.6\,\text{k}\Omega) = 3.25\,\text{k}\Omega$
$R_{th} = R_1 \parallel R_2 \parallel R_S = (6.2\,\text{k}\Omega) \parallel (9.1\,\text{k}\Omega) \parallel (800\,\Omega)$
$= 657\,\Omega$, $Z_{\text{out}} \cong r'_e + \dfrac{R_{th}}{h_{fc}} = 12.5\,\Omega + \dfrac{657\,\Omega}{80} =$

$20.7\,\Omega$, $A_v = \dfrac{r_E}{r'_e + r_E} = \dfrac{333\,\Omega}{345.5\,\Omega} = 0.964$

$A_i = h_{fc}\dfrac{Z_{\text{in}}r_E}{Z_{\text{base}}R_L} = (80)\dfrac{(3.25\,\text{k}\Omega)(333\,\Omega)}{(27.6\,\text{k}\Omega)(500\,\Omega)} = 6.27$
$A_p = A_i A_v = (6.27)(0.964) = 6.04$

12. $r'_e = \dfrac{h_{ic}}{h_{fc}} = \dfrac{2\ \text{k}\Omega}{140} = 14.3\ \Omega$

$r_E = R_E \parallel R_L = (390\ \Omega) \parallel (390\ \Omega) = 195\ \Omega$
$Z_{\text{base}} = h_{fc}\,(r'_e + r_E) = (140)(209.3\ \Omega) = 29.3\ \text{k}\Omega$
$Z_{\text{in}} = R_1 \parallel R_2 \parallel Z_{\text{base}} =$
$(3.3\ \text{k}\Omega) \parallel (3.9\ \text{k}\Omega) \parallel (29.3\ \text{k}\Omega) = 1.68\ \text{k}\Omega$
$R_{th} = R_1 \parallel R_2 \parallel R_S = (3.3\ \text{k}\Omega) \parallel (3.9\ \text{k}\Omega) \parallel (800\ \Omega)$
$= 553\ \Omega, \quad Z_{\text{out}} \cong r'_e + \dfrac{R_{th}}{h_{fc}} = 14.3\ \Omega + \dfrac{553\ \Omega}{140} =$

$18.3\ \Omega, \quad A_v = \dfrac{r_E}{r'_e + r_E} = \dfrac{195\ \Omega}{209.3\ \Omega} = 0.9317$

$A_i = h_{fc}\dfrac{Z_{\text{in}}r_E}{Z_{\text{base}}R_L} = (140)\dfrac{(1.68\ \text{k}\Omega)(195\ \Omega)}{(29.3\ \text{k}\Omega)(390\ \Omega)} = 4.01$
$A_p = A_i A_v = (4.01)(0.9317) = 3.74$

13. $r'_e = \dfrac{h_{ic}}{h_{fc}} = \dfrac{2\ \text{k}\Omega}{100} = 20\ \Omega, \quad r_E = R_E \parallel R_L =$

$(3\ \text{k}\Omega) \parallel (1.5\ \text{k}\Omega) = 1\ \text{k}\Omega, \ Z_{\text{base}} = h_{fc}(r'_e + r_E) =$
$(100)(1.02\ \text{k}\Omega) = 102\ \text{k}\Omega, \quad Z_{\text{in}} = R_1 \parallel Z_{\text{base}} =$
$(510\ \text{k}\Omega) \parallel (102\ \text{k}\Omega) = 85\ \text{k}\Omega$

14. $r'_e = \dfrac{h_{ic}}{h_{fc}} = \dfrac{3\ \text{k}\Omega}{180} = 16.7\ \Omega, \ r_E = R_E \parallel R_L =$

$(1.5\ \text{k}\Omega) \parallel (10\ \text{k}\Omega) = 1.3\ \text{k}\Omega, \ Z_{\text{base}} = h_{fc}(r'_e + r_E) =$
$(180)(1.317\ \text{k}\Omega) = 237\ \text{k}\Omega, \quad Z_{\text{in}} = R_1 \parallel Z_{\text{base}} =$
$(290\ \text{k}\Omega) \parallel (237\ \text{k}\Omega) = 130\ \text{k}\Omega$

15. $V_B = V_{CC}\dfrac{R_2}{R_1 + R_2} = (18\ \text{V})\dfrac{300\ \text{k}\Omega}{600\ \text{k}\Omega} = 9\ \text{V}$

$I_E = \dfrac{V_B - 2V_{BE}}{R_E} = \dfrac{9\ \text{V} - 1.4\ \text{V}}{750\ \Omega} = 10.1\ \text{mA}$

$R_{\text{IN}1} = h_{FC1}h_{FC2}R_E = (60)(140)(750\ \Omega) = 6.3\ \text{M}\Omega$

16. $V_B = V_{CC}\dfrac{R_2}{R_1 + R_2} = (10\ \text{V})\dfrac{80\ \text{k}\Omega}{160\ \text{k}\Omega} = 5\ \text{V}$

$I_E = \dfrac{V_B - 2V_{BE}}{R_E} = \dfrac{5\ \text{V} - 1.4\ \text{V}}{360\ \Omega} = 10\ \text{mA}$

$R_{\text{IN}1} = h_{FC1}h_{FC2}R_E = (50)(110)(360\ \Omega) = 1.98\ \text{M}\Omega$

17. $r_E = R_E \parallel R_L = (750\ \Omega) \parallel (2\ \text{k}\Omega) = 545\ \Omega$
$Z_{\text{base}} = h_{ic1} + h_{fc1}(h_{ic2} + h_{fc2}r_E) =$
$40\ \text{k}\Omega + (40)[2\ \text{k}\Omega + (160)(545\ \Omega)] =$
$40\ \text{k}\Omega + (40)(89.2\ \text{k}\Omega) = 3.61\ \text{M}\Omega$
$Z_{\text{in}} = R_1 \parallel R_2 \parallel Z_{\text{base}} =$
$(300\ \text{k}\Omega) \parallel (300\ \text{k}\Omega) \parallel (3.61\ \text{M}\Omega) = 144\ \text{k}\Omega$

$r'_{e1} = \dfrac{h_{ic1}}{h_{fc1}} = \dfrac{40\ \text{k}\Omega}{40} = 1\ \text{k}\Omega$

$r'_{e2} = \dfrac{h_{ic2}}{h_{fc2}} = \dfrac{2\ \text{k}\Omega}{160} = 12.5\ \Omega$

$R_{th} = R_1 \parallel R_2 \parallel R_S = (300\ \text{k}\Omega) \parallel (300\ \text{k}\Omega) \parallel (1\ \text{k}\Omega) = 993\ \Omega,$

$Z_{\text{out}} \cong r'_{e2} + \dfrac{r'_{e1} + (R_{th}/h_{fc1})}{h_{fc2}} = 12.5\ \Omega +$

$\dfrac{1\ \text{k}\Omega + (993\ \Omega/40)}{160} = 12.5\ \Omega + 6.4\ \Omega = 18.9\ \Omega$

18. $r_E = R_E \parallel R_L = (360\ \Omega) \parallel (2\ \text{k}\Omega) = 305\ \Omega$
$Z_{\text{base}} = h_{ic1} + h_{fc1}(h_{ic2} + h_{fc2}r_E) =$
$32\ \text{k} + (20)[4\ \text{k}\Omega + (100)(305\ \Omega)] =$
$32\ \text{k}\Omega + (20)(34.51\ \text{k}\Omega) = 722\ \text{k}\Omega$
$Z_{\text{in}} = R_1 \parallel R_2 \parallel Z_{\text{base}} =$
$(80\ \text{k}\Omega) \parallel (80\ \text{k}\Omega) \parallel (722\ \text{k}\Omega) = 37.9\ \text{k}\Omega$

$r'_{e1} = \dfrac{h_{ic1}}{h_{fc1}} = \dfrac{32\ \text{k}\Omega}{20} = 1.6\ \text{k}\Omega$

$r'_{e2} = \dfrac{h_{ic2}}{h_{fc2}} = \dfrac{4\ \text{k}\Omega}{100} = 40\ \Omega$

$R_{th} = R_1 \parallel R_2 \parallel R_S =$
$(80\ \text{k}\Omega) \parallel (80\ \text{k}\Omega) \parallel (2\ \text{k}\Omega) = 1.9\ \text{k}\Omega$

$Z_{\text{out}} \cong r'_{e2} + \dfrac{r'_{e1} + (R_{th}/h_{fc1})}{h_{fc2}} = 40\ \Omega +$

$\dfrac{1.6\ \text{k}\Omega + (1.9\ \text{k}\Omega/20)}{100} = 40\ \Omega + 17\ \Omega = 57\ \Omega$

19. Using the values calculated in problem 17:
$A_i = h_{fc1}h_{fc2}\dfrac{Z_{\text{in}}r_E}{Z_{\text{base}}R_L} =$

$(40)(160)\dfrac{(144\ \text{k}\Omega)(545\ \Omega)}{(3.61\ \text{M}\Omega)(2\ \text{k}\Omega)} = 69.6$

20. Using the values calculated in problem 18:
$A_i = h_{fc1}h_{fc2}\dfrac{Z_{\text{in}}r_E}{Z_{\text{base}}R_L} =$

$(20)(100)\dfrac{(37.9\ \text{k}\Omega)(305\ \Omega)}{(722\ \text{k}\Omega)(2\ \text{k}\Omega)} = 16$

21. From Problem 17: $r'_{e1} = 1\ \text{k}\Omega$, $r'_{e2} = 12.5\ \Omega$, and
$r_E = 545\ \Omega$. $Z_{\text{base}} \cong h_{fc1}h_{fc2}r_E = (40)(160)(545\ \Omega) =$
$3.49\ \text{M}\Omega, \quad Z_{\text{in}} \cong R_1 \parallel R_2 \parallel Z_{\text{base}} =$
$(300\ \text{k}\Omega) \parallel (300\ \text{k}\Omega) \parallel (3.49\ \text{M}\Omega) = 144\ \text{k}\Omega, \quad Z_{\text{out}} \cong$
$r'_{e2} + \dfrac{r'_{e1}}{h_{fc2}} = 12.5\ \Omega + \dfrac{1\ \text{k}\Omega}{160} = 18.8\ \Omega, \quad A_i =$

$h_{fc1}h_{fc2}\dfrac{Z_{\text{in}}r_E}{Z_{\text{base}}R_L} = (40)(160)\dfrac{(144\ \text{k}\Omega)(545\ \Omega)}{(3.49\ \text{M}\Omega)(2\ \text{k}\Omega)} \cong 72$

22. From Problem 18: $r'_{e1} = 1.6\ \text{k}\Omega$, $r'_{e2} = 40\ \Omega$, and
$r_E = 305\ \Omega$. $Z_{\text{base}} \cong h_{fc1}h_{fc2}r_E = (20)(100)(305\ \Omega) =$
$610\ \text{k}\Omega, \quad Z_{\text{in}} \cong R_1 \parallel R_2 \parallel Z_{\text{base}} =$
$(80\ \text{k}\Omega) \parallel (80\ \text{k}\Omega) \parallel (610\ \text{k}\Omega) = 37.5\ \text{k}\Omega, \quad Z_{\text{out}} \cong$
$r'_{e2} + \dfrac{r'_{e1}}{h_{fc2}} = 40\ \Omega + \dfrac{1.6\ \text{k}\Omega}{100} = 56\ \Omega, \quad A_i =$

$h_{fc1}h_{fc2}\dfrac{Z_{\text{in}}r_E}{Z_{\text{base}}R_L} = (20)(100)\dfrac{(37.5\ \text{k}\Omega)(305\ \Omega)}{(610\ \text{k}\Omega)(2\ \text{k}\Omega)}$

$\cong 18.8$

23. $I_E = \dfrac{\left|V_{EE} + V_{BE}\right|}{R_E} = \dfrac{\left|-2\,\text{V} + 0.7\,\text{V}\right|}{910\,\Omega} = 1.43\,\text{mA}$

$r'_e = \dfrac{25\,\text{mV}}{I_E} = \dfrac{25\,\text{mV}}{1.43\,\text{mA}} = 17.5\,\Omega$

$r_C = R_C \parallel R_L = (5.1\,\text{k}\Omega)\|(10\,\text{k}\Omega) = 3.38\,\text{k}\Omega$

$A_v = \dfrac{r_C}{r'_e} = \dfrac{3.38\,\text{k}\Omega}{17.5\,\Omega} = 193$

24. $I_E = \dfrac{\left|V_{EE} + V_{BE}\right|}{R_E} = \dfrac{\left|-1\,\text{V} + 0.7\,\text{V}\right|}{560\,\Omega} = 536\,\mu\text{A}$

$r'_e = \dfrac{25\,\text{mV}}{I_E} = \dfrac{25\,\text{mV}}{536\,\mu\text{A}} = 46.6\,\Omega$

$r_C = R_C \parallel R_L = (5.6\,\text{k}\Omega)\|(10\,\text{k}\Omega) = 3.59\,\text{k}\Omega$

$A_v = \dfrac{r_C}{r'_e} = \dfrac{3.59\,\text{k}\Omega}{46.6\,\Omega} = 77$

25. From problem 23: $r'_e = 17.5\,\Omega$. $Z_{in} \cong r'_e = 17.5\,\Omega$ and $Z_{out} \cong R_C = 5.1\,\text{k}\Omega$

26. From problem 24: $r'_e = 46.6\,\Omega$. $Z_{in} \cong r'_e = 46.6\,\Omega$ and $Z_{out} \cong R_C = 5.6\,\text{k}\Omega$

27. Assuming the dc power supply is operating normally, the problem could be caused by any of the following: Q_1 open, R_1 open, R_2 shorted, or R_E shorted. (The shorted component problems are unlikely.)

28. The 1.5 V reading is caused by a shorted base-emitter junction. The transistor CB junction cuts off, and the reading results from the R_1 and $(R_2 \parallel R_E)$ voltage divider.

29. The negative alternation of the waveform from TP-2 on is being clipped. The dc voltage reading (3.5 V) indicates that V_B of Q_1 is too high. This would most likely be caused by R_2 open.

30. The transistor is in cutoff. Assuming that V_{EE} is good, we have two possible faults: Q_1 is bad or R_E is open.

31. V_B of Q_2 is at 0 V if Q_1 is in cutoff. Assuming that the dc power supply is operating normally, the problem could be caused by Q_1 open, R_1 open or R_2 shorted. (The shorted component is the least likely cause.)

32. The 7.6 V reference should be blocked by the output capacitor; it must be shorted.

33. The negative alternation of the waveform from TP-4 on is being clipped. The dc voltage reading (0 V) indicates that Q_2 is in cutoff. The low amplitude positive alternation is simply the result of the input turning on Q_2. This would most likely be caused by R_5 open.

34. The 0 V reference at the base of Q_1 indicates that R_1 is open.

35. *Stage 2:* $r'_e = \dfrac{h_{ic}}{h_{fc}} = \dfrac{1.8\,\text{k}\Omega}{120} = 15\,\Omega$

$r_E = R_E \parallel R_L = (470\,\Omega) \parallel (900\,\Omega) = 309\,\Omega$
$Z_{base} = h_{fc}(r'_e + r_E) = (120)(324\,\Omega) = 38.9\,\text{k}\Omega$
$Z_{in(2)} = R_5 \parallel R_6 \parallel Z_{base} = (40\,\text{k}\Omega)\|(30\,\text{k}\Omega)\|(38.9\,\text{k}\Omega)$

$= 11.9\,\text{k}\Omega, \qquad A_{v2} = \dfrac{r_E}{r'_e + r_E} = \dfrac{309\,\Omega}{324\,\Omega} = 0.9537$

$A_{i2} = h_{fc}\dfrac{Z_{in}r_E}{Z_{base}R_L} = (120)\dfrac{(11.9\,\text{k}\Omega)(309\,\Omega)}{(38.9\,\text{k}\Omega)(900\,\Omega)} = 12.6$

Stage 1: $Z_{base} = h_{ie} = 4\,\text{k}\Omega$
$Z_{in1} = R_1 \parallel R_2 \parallel Z_{base} = (62\,\text{k}\Omega) \parallel (12\,\text{k}\Omega) \parallel (4\,\text{k}\Omega)$
$= 2.86\,\text{k}\Omega, \qquad r_C = R_3 \parallel Z_{in2} = (4.7\,\text{k}\Omega) \parallel (11.9\,\text{k}\Omega)$

$= 3.37\,\text{k}\Omega, \qquad A_{v1} = \dfrac{h_{fe}r_C}{h_{ie}} = \dfrac{(120)(3.37\,\text{k}\Omega)}{4\,\text{k}\Omega} = 101$

Using $R_L = Z_{in\,2} = 11.9\,\text{k}\Omega$:

$A_{i1} = h_{fe}\dfrac{Z_{in}r_C}{Z_{base}R_L} = (120)\dfrac{(2.86\,\text{k}\Omega)(3.37\,\text{k}\Omega)}{(4\,\text{k}\Omega)(11.9\,\text{k}\Omega)}$

$= 24.3.$

Overall: $A_{vT} = A_{v1}A_{v2} = (101)(0.9537) = 96.3$
$A_{iT} = A_{i1}A_{i2} = (24.3)(12.6) = 306$
$A_{pT} = A_{iT}A_{vT} = (306)(96.3) = 2.95 \times 10^4,$ and
$Z_{in} = Z_{in1} = 2.86\,\text{k}\Omega$

36. To determine the *h*-parameter values for the circuit, we must determine the approximate values of collector current for the transistor, as follows:

$V_B = V_{CC}\dfrac{R_2}{R_1 + R_2} = (20\,\text{V})\dfrac{39\,\text{k}\Omega}{67\,\text{k}\Omega} = 11.6\,\text{V}$

$V_E = V_B - 1.4\,\text{V} = 11.6\,\text{V} - 1.4\,\text{V} = 10.2\,\text{V}$

$I_{E2} = \dfrac{V_E}{R_E} = \dfrac{10.2\,\text{V}}{1\,\text{k}\Omega} = 10.2\,\text{mA}$

$I_{E1} = I_{B2} = \dfrac{I_{E2}}{h_{FC2}} = \dfrac{10.2\,\text{mA}}{50} = 204\,\mu\text{A}$

$I_{CQ2} = I_{E2} - I_{B2} \cong 10\,\text{mA},$ and

$I_{CQ1} = I_{E1} - \dfrac{I_{E1}}{h_{FC1}} = 204\,\mu\text{A} - \dfrac{204\,\mu\text{A}}{50} \cong 200\,\mu\text{A}.$

Using these values of I_{CQ}, The following values are obtained from the curves:
$h_{ie1} \cong 12.5\,\text{k}\Omega$, $h_{fe1} \cong 72$, $h_{ie2} \cong 500\,\Omega$, $h_{fe2} \cong 160$.
Assuming that $h_{ic} = h_{ie}$ and $h_{fc} = h_{fe}$ for each transistor, the analysis proceeds as follows:

$r'_{e1} = \dfrac{h_{ic1}}{h_{fc1}} = \dfrac{12.5\,\text{k}\Omega}{72} = 174\,\Omega$

$r'_{e2} = \dfrac{h_{ic2}}{h_{fc2}} = \dfrac{500\,\Omega}{160} = 3.13\,\Omega$

$r_E = R_E \parallel R_L = (1\,\text{k}\Omega) \parallel (300\,\Omega) \cong 231\,\Omega$
$Z_{base} \cong h_{fc1}h_{fc2}r_E = (72)(160)(231\,\Omega) = 2.66\,\text{M}\Omega$
$Z_{in} \cong R_1 \parallel R_2 \parallel Z_{base} = (28\,\text{k}\Omega)(39\,\text{k}\Omega)(2.66\,\text{M}\Omega)$

$$=16.2 \text{ k}\Omega, \quad Z_{\text{out}} \cong r'_{e2} + \frac{r'_{e1}}{h_{fc2}} = 3.13 \ \Omega + \frac{174 \ \Omega}{160}$$

$$= 4.28 \ \Omega, \quad A_i = h_{fc1}h_{fc2}\frac{Z_{\text{in}}r_E}{Z_{\text{base}}R_L} =$$

$$(72)(160)\frac{(16.2 \text{ k}\Omega)(231 \ \Omega)}{(2.66 \text{ M}\Omega)(300 \ \Omega)} = 54.0$$

37. For the circuit shown:

$$V_B = V_{CC}\frac{R_2}{R_1 + R_2} = (28 \text{ V})\frac{150 \text{ k}\Omega}{270 \text{ k}\Omega} = 15.6 \text{ V}$$

$$V_E = V_B - 1.4 \text{ V} = 15.6 \text{ V} - 1.4 \text{ V} = 14.2 \text{ V}$$

$$I_E = \frac{V_E}{R_E} = \frac{14.2 \text{ V}}{1.4 \text{ k}\Omega} = 10.1 \text{ mA}$$

Assuming that $I_{CQ} \cong 10$ mA, the following values are obtained from the 2N6426 spec sheet: $h_{fe} = 20,000$ (minimum) and $h_{ie} = 100 \text{ k}\Omega$ to 2 MΩ. Based on these ratings, we will assume that

$$h_{fc} = 20,000 \text{ and } h_{ic} = \sqrt{(100 \text{ k}\Omega)(2 \text{ M}\Omega)} = 447 \text{ k}\Omega.$$

Using these values: $r'_e = \dfrac{h_{ic}}{h_{fc}} = \dfrac{447 \text{ k}\Omega}{20 \times 10^3} = 22.4 \ \Omega$

$r_E = R_E \| R_L = (1.4 \text{ k}\Omega) \| (5 \text{ k}\Omega) = 1.09 \text{ k}\Omega$
$Z_{\text{base}} \cong h_{fc}r_E = (20 \times 10^3)(1.09 \text{ k}\Omega) = 21.8 \text{ M}\Omega$
$Z_{\text{in}} \cong R_1 \| R_2 \| Z_{\text{base}} = (120 \text{ k}\Omega)(150 \text{ k}\Omega)(21.8 \text{ M}\Omega)$
$= 64.7 \text{ k}\Omega, \qquad R_{th} = R_1 \| R_2 = 66.7 \text{ k}\Omega$

$$Z_{\text{out}} \cong r'_e + \frac{R_{th}}{h_{fc}} = 22.4 \ \Omega + \frac{66.7 \text{ k}\Omega}{20 \times 10^3} = 25.7 \ \Omega$$

$$A_i = h_{fc}\frac{Z_{\text{in}}r_E}{Z_{\text{base}}R_L} = (20 \times 10^3)\frac{(64.7 \text{ k}\Omega)(1.09 \text{ k}\Omega)}{(21.8 \text{ M}\Omega)(5 \text{ k}\Omega)}$$

$$\cong 129$$

38. In Problem 37, the circuit is found to have a value of $I_E = 10.1$ mA. Assuming that $I_{CQ} = I_E = 10$ mA, The h_{FE} curve on the BC517 spec sheet indicates that the component has an h_{FE} of approximately 35,000 at $I_{CQ} = 10$ mA.

CHAPTER 11

EXAMPLE PRACTICE PROBLEMS   (CH 11)

11-1. $h_{FE}R_E < 10R_2$, so we proceed as follows:

$$V_{TH} = V_{CC}\frac{R_2}{R_1 + R_2} = (18 \text{ V})\frac{240 \ \Omega}{1.54 \text{ k}\Omega} = 2.81 \text{ V}$$

$$R_{TH} = R_1 \| R_2 = 1.3 \text{ k}\Omega \| 240 \ \Omega = 203 \ \Omega$$

$$I_{CQ} = \frac{V_{TH} - V_{BE}}{\dfrac{R_{TH}}{h_{FE}} + R_E} = \frac{2.81 \text{ V} - 0.7 \text{ V}}{\dfrac{203 \ \Omega}{80} + 30 \ \Omega} = 64.8 \text{ mA}$$

$r_C = R_C \| R_L = 110 \ \Omega \| 300 \ \Omega = 80.5 \ \Omega$
$2I_{CQ}r_C = (2)(64.8 \text{ mA})(80.5 \text{ k}\Omega) = 10.4 \text{ V}$
and $2V_{CEQ} = (2)(8.93 \text{ V}) = 17.9 \text{ V}$.
Since $2I_{CQ}r_C < 2V_{CEQ}$, the circuit has a value of
PP $= 2I_{CQ}r_C = 10.4 \text{ V}$

11-2. From Problem 11-1: $I_{CQ} \cong 64.8$ mA.

$$I_1 = \frac{V_{CC}}{R_1 + R_2} = \frac{18 \text{ V}}{1.54 \text{ k}\Omega} \cong 11.7 \text{ mA}$$

$$I_{CC} = I_1 + I_{CQ} = 11.7 \text{ mA} + 64.8 \text{ mA} = 76.5 \text{ mA}$$
$$P_S = V_{CC}I_{CC} = (18 \text{ V})(76.5 \text{ mA}) = 1.38 \text{ W}$$

11-3. $P_L = \dfrac{V_L^2}{R_L} = \dfrac{(4.62 \text{ V}_{\text{rms}})^2}{16 \ \Omega} = 1.33 \text{ W}$

11-4. $P_L = \dfrac{V_{\text{pk}}^2}{2R_L} = \dfrac{(8 \text{ V})^2}{64 \ \Omega} = 1 \text{ W}$

11-5. $P_{L(\text{max})} = \dfrac{\text{PP}^2}{8R_L} = \dfrac{(20 \text{ V}_{\text{PP}})^2}{128 \ \Omega} = 3.13 \text{ W}$

11-6. From problems 11-1 and 11-2:
PP $= 10.4$ V and $P_S = 1.38$ W.

$$P_{L(\text{max})} = \frac{\text{PP}^2}{8R_L} = \frac{(10.4 \text{ V}_{\text{PP}})^2}{2.4 \text{ k}\Omega} = 45.1 \text{ mW}$$

$$\eta = \frac{P_{L(\text{max})}}{P_S} \times 100 = \frac{45.1 \text{ mW}}{1.38 \text{ W}} \times 100 = 3.27 \text{ \%}$$

11-7. $P_S = V_{CC}I_{CC} = (12 \text{ V})(120 \text{ mA}) = 1.44 \text{ W}$

$$r_C = Z_P = \left(\frac{N_P}{N_S}\right)^2 R_L = \left(\frac{5}{1}\right)^2 (4 \ \Omega) = 100 \ \Omega$$

$$2V_{CEQ} = 20 \text{ V}, \quad 2I_{CQ}r_C = (2)(120 \text{ mA})(100 \ \Omega)$$
$$= 24 \text{ V}, \qquad \text{PP} = 2V_{CEQ} = 20 \text{ V},$$

$$V_{PP} = \left(\frac{N_S}{N_P}\right)PP = \left(\frac{1}{5}\right)(20 \text{ V}) = 4 \text{ V}$$

$$P_{L(\text{max})} = \frac{V_{PP}^2}{8R_L} = \frac{(4 \text{ V})^2}{(32 \ \Omega)} = 500 \text{ mW}, \text{ and}$$

$$\eta = \frac{P_{L(\text{max})}}{P_S} \times 100 = \frac{500 \text{ mW}}{1.44 \text{ W}} \times 100 = 34.7 \text{ \%}$$

11-8. $v_{ce(\text{off})} = \dfrac{V_{CC}}{2} = 6 \text{ V}$

$$i_{c(\text{sat})} = \frac{V_{CC}}{2R_L} = \frac{12 \text{ V}}{4.4 \text{ k}\Omega} = 2.73 \text{ mA}$$

11-9. PP $= V_{CC} = 12$ V

$$P_{L(\text{max})} = \frac{\text{PP}^2}{8R_L} = \frac{(12 \text{ V}_{\text{PP}})^2}{17.6 \text{ k}\Omega} = 8.18 \text{ mW}$$

11-10. $I_1 = \dfrac{V_{CC}}{R_1 + R_2 + R_3} = \dfrac{12 \text{ V}}{2.27 \text{ k}\Omega} = 5.29 \text{ mA}$

$$I_{C1(\text{ave})} = \frac{V_{CC}}{2\pi R_L} = \frac{12 \text{ V}}{2\pi(8 \ \Omega)} = 239 \text{ mA},$$

$$I_{CC} = I_{C1(ave)} + I_1 = 239 \text{ mA} + 5.29 \text{ mA} \cong 244 \text{ mA}$$
$$P_S = V_{CC}I_{CC} = (12 \text{ V})(245 \text{ mA}) = 2.93 \text{ W}$$

11-11. $PP = V_{CC} = 12 \text{ V}$

$$P_{L(max)} = \frac{PP^2}{8R_L} = \frac{(12 \text{ V}_{PP})^2}{(8)(8 \text{ }\Omega)} = 2.25 \text{ W}$$

11-12. From Problems 10 and 11: $P_S = 2.93 \text{ W}$ and $P_{L(max)} = 2.25 \text{ W}$. Using these values,

$$\eta = \frac{P_{L(max)}}{P_S} \times 100 = \frac{2.25 \text{ W}}{2.93 \text{ W}} \times 100 = 76.8\%$$

11-13. From the example: $I_1 = 6.91 \text{ mA}$

$$I_{C1(ave)} = \frac{V_{PP}}{2\pi R_L} = \frac{11 \text{ V}}{2\pi(10 \text{ }\Omega)} = 175 \text{ mA},$$

$$I_{CC} = I_{C1(ave)} + I_1 = 175 \text{ mA} + 6.91 \text{ mA} \cong 182 \text{ mA}$$
$$P_S = V_{CC}I_{CC} = (15 \text{ V})(182 \text{ mA}) = 2.73 \text{ W}$$

$$P_L = \frac{V_{PP}^2}{8R_L} = \frac{(11 \text{ V})^2}{(80 \text{ }\Omega)} = 1.51 \text{ W}, \text{ and}$$

$$\eta = \frac{P_L}{P_S} \times 100 = \frac{1.51 \text{ W}}{2.73 \text{ W}} \times 100 = 55.3\%$$

11-14. $I_{CQ} \cong \dfrac{V_E}{R_E} = \dfrac{2.4 \text{ V}}{1.2 \text{ k}\Omega} = 2 \text{ mA}$

$$V_{CEQ} = V_{CC} - I_{CQ}(R_C + R_E) =$$
$$16 \text{ V} - (2 \text{ mA})(3.9 \text{ k}\Omega) = 8.2 \text{ V}$$
$$P_D = V_{CEQ}I_{CQ} = (8.2 \text{ V})(2 \text{ mA}) = 16.4 \text{ mW}$$

11-15. $PP = V_{CC} = 15 \text{ V}$

$$P_D = \frac{PP^2}{40R_L} = \frac{(15 \text{ V}_{PP})^2}{480 \text{ }\Omega} \cong 469 \text{ mW}$$

PRACTICE PROBLEMS CH. 11

1. $h_{FE}R_E < 10R_2$, so we proceed as follows:
$$V_{TH} = V_{CC}\frac{R_2}{R_1 + R_2} = (16 \text{ V})\frac{1.1 \text{ k}\Omega}{5 \text{ k}\Omega} = 3.52 \text{ V}$$

$$R_{TH} = R_1 \| R_2 = 3.9 \text{ k}\Omega \| 1.1 \text{ k}\Omega = 858 \text{ }\Omega$$

$$I_{CQ} = \frac{V_{TH} - V_{BE}}{\dfrac{R_{TH}}{h_{FC}} + R_E} = \frac{3.52 \text{ V} - 0.7 \text{ V}}{\dfrac{858 \text{ }\Omega}{200} + 47 \text{ }\Omega} = 55 \text{ mA}$$

Assuming $I_{CQ} \cong I_E = 55 \text{ mA}$:
$V_{CEQ} = 16 \text{ V} - (55 \text{ mA})(157 \text{ }\Omega) = 7.37 \text{ V}$
$r_C = R_C \| R_L = (110 \text{ }\Omega) \| (300 \text{ }\Omega) = 80.5 \text{ }\Omega$
$2I_{CQ}r_C = (2)(55 \text{ mA})(80.5 \text{ }\Omega) = 8.86 \text{ V}$ and
$2V_{CEQ} = (2)(7.37 \text{ V}) = 14.7 \text{ V}$.
Since $2I_{CQ}r_C < 2V_{CEQ}$, the circuit has a value of
$PP = 2I_{CQ}r_C = 8.86 \text{ V}$.

2. $h_{FE}R_E < 10R_2$, so we proceed as follows:
$$V_{TH} = V_{CC}\frac{R_2}{R_1 + R_2} = (32 \text{ V})\frac{200 \text{ k}\Omega}{1.6 \text{ k}\Omega} = 4 \text{ V}$$

$$R_{TH} = R_1 \| R_2 = 1.4 \text{ k}\Omega \| 200 \text{ k}\Omega = 175 \text{ }\Omega$$

$$I_{CQ} = \frac{V_{TH} - V_{BE}}{\dfrac{R_{TH}}{h_{FC}} + R_E} = \frac{4 \text{ V} - 0.7 \text{ V}}{\dfrac{175 \text{ }\Omega}{80} + 22 \text{ }\Omega} = 136 \text{ mA}$$

Assuming $I_{CQ} \cong I_E = 136 \text{ mA}$:
$V_{CEQ} = 32 \text{ V} - (136 \text{ mA})(108 \text{ }\Omega) = 17.3 \text{ V}$
$r_C = R_C \| R_L = (86 \text{ }\Omega) \| (75 \text{ }\Omega) = 40.1 \text{ }\Omega$
$2I_{CQ}r_C = (2)(136 \text{ mA})(40.1 \text{ }\Omega) = 10.9 \text{ V}$ and
$2V_{CEQ} = (2)(17.3 \text{ V}) = 34.6 \text{ V}$.
Since $2I_{CQ}r_C < 2V_{CEQ}$, the circuit has a value of
$PP = 2I_{CQ}r_C = 10.9 \text{ V}$

3. $h_{FE}R_E < 10R_2$, so we proceed as follows:
$$V_{TH} = V_{CC}\frac{R_2}{R_1 + R_2} = (12 \text{ V})\frac{360 \text{ }\Omega}{2.16 \text{ k}\Omega} = 2 \text{ V}$$

$$R_{TH} = R_1 \| R_2 = 1.8 \text{ k}\Omega \| 360 \text{ }\Omega = 300 \text{ }\Omega$$

$$I_{CQ} = \frac{V_{TH} - V_{BE}}{\dfrac{R_{TH}}{h_{FC}} + R_E} = \frac{2 \text{ V} - 0.7 \text{ V}}{\dfrac{300 \text{ }\Omega}{50} + 47 \text{ }\Omega} = 24.5 \text{ mA}$$

Assuming $I_{CQ} \cong I_E = 24.5 \text{ mA}$:
$V_{CEQ} = 12 \text{ V} - (24.5 \text{ mA})(227 \text{ }\Omega) = 6.44 \text{ V}$
$r_C = R_C \| R_L = (180 \text{ }\Omega) \| (300 \text{ }\Omega) = 113 \text{ }\Omega$
$2I_{CQ}r_C = (2)(24.5 \text{ mA})(113 \text{ }\Omega) = 5.54 \text{ V}$ and
$2V_{CEQ} = (2)(6.44 \text{ V}) = 12.9 \text{ V}$.
Since $2I_{CQ}r_C < 2V_{CEQ}$, the circuit has a value of
$PP = 2I_{CQ}r_C = 5.54 \text{ V}$, and the circuit would most
likely experience *cutoff* clipping.

4. $V_B = V_{CC}\dfrac{R_2}{R_1 + R_2} = (4 \text{ V})\dfrac{1 \text{ k}\Omega}{2 \text{ k}\Omega} = 2 \text{ V}$

$V_E = V_B - 0.7 \text{ V} = 1.3 \text{ V}$

$I_E = \dfrac{V_E}{R_E} = \dfrac{1.3 \text{ V}}{470 \text{ }\Omega} = 2.77 \text{ mA}$.   Assuming

$I_{CQ} \cong I_E = 2.77 \text{ mA}$: $V_{CEQ} = V_{CC} - I_{CQ}(R_C + R_E) =$
$4 \text{ V} - (2.77 \text{ mA})(800 \text{ }\Omega) = 1.78 \text{ V}$
$r_C = R_C \| R_L = (330 \text{ }\Omega) \| (820 \text{ }\Omega) = 235 \text{ }\Omega$
$2I_{CQ}r_C = (2)(2.77 \text{ mA})(235 \text{ }\Omega) = 1.3 \text{ V}$ and
$2V_{CEQ} = (2)(1.78 \text{ V}) = 3.56 \text{ V}$.
Since $2I_{CQ}r_C < 2V_{CEQ}$, the circuit has a value of
$PP = 1.3 \text{ V}$ and would most likely experience
cutoff clipping.

5. From Problem 1: $I_{CQ} = 55 \text{ mA}$.
$$I_1 = \frac{V_{CC}}{R_1 + R_2} = \frac{16 \text{ V}}{4 \text{ k}\Omega} = 4 \text{ mA}$$

$I_{CC} = I_{CQ} + I_1 = 55 \text{ mA} + 4 \text{ mA} = 59 \text{ mA}$
$P_S = V_{CC}I_{CC} = (16 \text{ V})(59 \text{ mA}) = 944 \text{ mW}$

6. From Problem 2: $I_{CQ} = 136 \text{ mA}$.
$$I_1 = \frac{V_{CC}}{R_1 + R_2} = \frac{32 \text{ V}}{1.6 \text{ k}\Omega} = 20 \text{ mA}$$

$I_{CC} = I_{CQ} + I_1 = 136 \text{ mA} + 20 \text{ mA} = 156 \text{ mA}$
$P_S = V_{CC}I_{CC} = (32 \text{ V})(156 \text{ mA}) = 4.99 \text{ W}$

7. $P_L = \dfrac{V_L^2}{R_L} = \dfrac{(2.8 \text{ V}_{rms})^2}{300 \text{ }\Omega} = 26.1 \text{ mW}$

8. $P_L = \dfrac{V_L^2}{R_L} = \dfrac{(3.5\ \text{V}_{\text{rms}})^2}{75\ \Omega} = 163\ \text{mW}$

9. From Problem 1: $\text{PP} = 8.86\ \text{V}_{\text{PP}}$.

$P_{L(\text{max})} = \dfrac{\text{PP}^2}{8R_L} = \dfrac{(8.86\ \text{V}_{\text{PP}})^2}{(8)(300\ \Omega)} = 32.7\ \text{mW}$

10. From Problem 2: $\text{PP} = 10.9\ \text{V}_{\text{PP}}$.

$P_{L(\text{max})} = \dfrac{\text{PP}^2}{8R_L} = \dfrac{(10.9\ \text{V}_{\text{PP}})^2}{(8)(75\ \Omega)} = 198\ \text{mW}$

11. From Problems 5 and 9: $P_S = 944\ \text{mW}$ and $P_{L(\text{max})} = 32.7\ \text{mW}$.

$\eta = \dfrac{P_{L(\text{max})}}{P_S} \times 100 = \dfrac{32.7\ \mu\text{W}}{944\ \text{mW}} \times 100 = 3.46\ \%$

12. From Problems 6 and 10: $P_S = 4.99\ \text{W}$ and $P_{L(\text{max})} = 198\ \text{mW}$.

$\eta = \dfrac{P_{L(\text{max})}}{P_S} \times 100 = \dfrac{198\ m\text{W}}{4.99\ \text{W}} \times 100 = 3.97\ \%$

13. From Problem 3: $I_{CQ} = 24.5\ \text{mA}$ and $\text{PP} = 5.54\ \text{V}_{\text{pp}}$.

$I_1 = \dfrac{V_{CC}}{R_1 + R_2} = \dfrac{12\ \text{V}}{2.16\ \text{k}\Omega} = 5.56\ \text{mA}$

$I_{CC} = I_{CQ} + I_1 = 24.5\ \text{mA} + 5.56\ \text{mA} = 30.1\ \text{mA}$

$P_S = V_{CC} I_{CC} = (12\ \text{V})(30.1\ \text{mA}) = 361\ \text{mW}$

$P_{L(\text{max})} = \dfrac{\text{PP}^2}{8R_L} = \dfrac{(5.54\ \text{V}_{\text{PP}})^2}{(8)(300\ \Omega)} = 12.8\ \text{mW}$

$\eta = \dfrac{P_{L(\text{max})}}{P_S} \times 100 = \dfrac{12.8\ \text{mW}}{361\ \text{mW}} \times 100 = 3.55\ \%$

14. From Problem 4: $I_{CQ} = 2.77\ \text{mA}$ and $\text{PP} = 1.3\ \text{V}_{\text{PP}}$.

$I_1 = \dfrac{V_{CC}}{R_1 + R_2} = \dfrac{4\ \text{V}}{2\ \text{k}\Omega} = 2\ \text{mA}$

$I_{CC} = I_{CQ} + I_1 = 2.77\ \text{mA} + 2\ \text{mA} = 4.77\ \text{mA}$

$P_S = V_{CC} I_{CC} = (4\ \text{V})(4.77\ \text{mA}) = 19.1\ \text{mW}$

$P_{L(\text{max})} = \dfrac{\text{PP}^2}{8R_L} = \dfrac{(1.3\ \text{V}_{\text{PP}})^2}{(8)(820\ \Omega)} = 258\ \mu\text{W}$

$\eta = \dfrac{P_{L(\text{max})}}{P_S} \times 100 = \dfrac{258\ \mu\text{W}}{19.1\ \text{mW}} \times 100 = 1.35\%$

15. $V_B = V_{CC} \dfrac{R_2}{R_1 + R_2} = (20\ \text{V}) \dfrac{3.3\ \text{k}\Omega}{18.3\ \text{k}\Omega} = 3.61\ \text{V}$

$V_E = V_B - 0.7\ \text{V} = 2.91\ \text{V}$

$I_{CQ} \cong \dfrac{V_E}{R_E} = \dfrac{2.91\ \text{V}}{470\ \Omega} = 6.19\ \text{mA}$

$V_{CEQ} = V_{CC} - I_{CQ}(R_C + R_E) =$
$20\ \text{V} - (6.19\ \text{mA})(1.47\ \text{k}\Omega) = 10.9\ \text{V}$

$r_C = R_C \parallel R_L = (1\ \text{k}\Omega) \parallel (2.2\ \text{k}\Omega) \cong 688\ \Omega$

$2I_{CQ}r_C = (2)(6.19\ \text{mA})(688\ \Omega) = 8.52\ \text{V}$ and

$2V_{CEQ} = (2)(10.9\ \text{V}) = 21.8\ \text{V}$. (Use $\text{PP} = 8.52\ \text{V}_{\text{PP}}$)

$I_1 = \dfrac{V_{CC}}{R_1 + R_2} = \dfrac{20\ \text{V}}{18.3\ \text{k}\Omega} = 1.09\ \text{mA}$

$I_{CC} = I_{CQ} + I_1 = 6.19\ \text{mA} + 1.09\ \text{mA} = 7.28\ \text{mA}$

$P_S = V_{CC} I_{CC} = (20\ \text{V})(7.28\ \text{mA}) = 146\ \text{mW}$

$P_{L(\text{max})} = \dfrac{\text{PP}^2}{8R_L} = \dfrac{(8.52\ \text{V}_{\text{PP}})^2}{(8)(2.2\ \text{k}\Omega)} = 4.12\ \text{mW}$

$\eta = \dfrac{P_{L(\text{max})}}{P_S} \times 100 = \dfrac{4.12\ \text{mW}}{146\ \text{mW}} \times 100 = 2.82\%$

16. $V_B = V_{CC} \dfrac{R_2}{R_1 + R_2} = (40\ \text{V}) \dfrac{2.7\ \text{k}\Omega}{58.7\ \text{k}\Omega} = 1.84\ \text{V}$

$V_E = V_B - 0.7\ \text{V} = 1.14\ \text{V}$

$I_{CQ} \cong \dfrac{V_E}{R_E} = \dfrac{1.14\ \text{V}}{1\ \text{k}\Omega} = 1.14\ \text{mA}$.

$V_{CEQ} = V_{CC} - I_{CQ}(R_C + R_E) =$
$40\ \text{V} - (1.14\ \text{mA})(21\ \text{k}\Omega) = 16.1\ \text{V}$

$r_C = R_C \parallel R_L = (20\ \text{k}\Omega) \parallel (4.7\ \text{k}\Omega) = 3.81\ \text{k}\Omega$

$2I_{CQ}r_C = (2)(1.14\ \text{mA})(3.81\ \text{k}\Omega) = 8.69\ \text{V}$ and

$2V_{CEQ} = (2)(16.1\ \text{V}) = 32.2\ \text{V}$. (Use $\text{PP} = 8.69\ \text{V}_{\text{PP}}$)

$I_1 = \dfrac{V_{CC}}{R_1 + R_2} = \dfrac{40\ \text{V}}{58.7\ \text{k}\Omega} \cong 681\ \mu\text{A}$

$I_{CC} = I_{CQ} + I_1 = 1.14\ \text{mA} + 681\ \mu\text{A} \cong 1.82\ \text{mA}$

$P_S = V_{CC} I_{CC} = (40\ \text{V})(1.82\ \text{mA}) = 72.8\ \text{mW}$

$P_{L(\text{max})} = \dfrac{\text{PP}^2}{8R_L} = \dfrac{(8.69\ \text{V}_{\text{PP}})^2}{(8)(4.7\ \text{k}\Omega)} = 2.01\ \text{mW}$

$\eta = \dfrac{P_{L(\text{max})}}{P_S} \times 100 = \dfrac{2.01\ \text{mW}}{72.8\ \text{mW}} \times 100 = 2.76\%$

17. Since $h_{FE}R_E < 10R_2$, we proceed as follows:

$V_{TH} = V_{CC} \dfrac{R_2}{R_1 + R_2} = (22\ \text{V}) \dfrac{400\ \Omega}{3.1\ \text{k}\Omega} = 2.84\ \text{V}$

$R_{TH} = R_1 \parallel R_2 = 2.7\ \text{k}\Omega \parallel 400\ \Omega = 348\ \Omega$

$I_{CQ} = \dfrac{V_{TH} - V_{BE}}{\dfrac{R_{TH}}{h_{FC}} + R_E} = \dfrac{2.84\ \text{V} - 0.7\ \text{V}}{\dfrac{348\ \Omega}{40} + 80\ \Omega} = 24.1\ \text{mA}$

Assuming $I_E \cong I_{CQ}$ we solve for V_{CEQ} as

$V_{CEQ} = V_{CC} - I_{CQ}(R_W + R_E)$
$\qquad = 22\ \text{V} - (24.1\ \text{mA})(82\ \Omega) = 20\ \text{V}$

$r_C = Z_P = \left(\dfrac{N_P}{N_S}\right)^2 R_L = (10)^2(8\ \Omega) = 800\ \Omega$

$i_{c(\text{sat})} = I_{CQ} + \dfrac{V_{CEQ}}{r_C} = 20\ \text{mA} + \dfrac{20\ \text{V}}{800\ \Omega} = 45\ \text{mA}$

$v_{ce(\text{off})} = V_{CEQ} + I_{CQ}r_C = 20\ \text{V} + (24.1\ \text{mA})(800\ \Omega) = $
$39.3\ \text{V}$. The ac load line is a straight line with
endpoints of $i_{c(\text{sat})} = 45\ \text{mA}$ and $v_{ce(\text{off})} = 39.3\ \text{V}$.

18. $V_B = V_{CC} \dfrac{R_2}{R_1 + R_2} = (20\ \text{V}) \dfrac{51\ \Omega}{521\ \Omega} = 1.96\ \text{V}$

$V_E = V_B - 0.7\ \text{V} = 1.26\ \text{V}$

$I_{CQ} \cong I_E = \dfrac{V_E}{R_E} = \dfrac{1.26\ \text{V}}{20\ \Omega} = 63\ \text{mA}$

$$V_{CEQ} = V_{CC} - I_{CQ}(R_W + R_E)$$
$$= 20 \text{ V} - (63 \text{ mA})(24 \text{ }\Omega) = 18.5 \text{ V}$$

$$r_C = Z_P = \left(\frac{N_P}{N_S}\right)^2 R_L = (4)^2(19 \text{ }\Omega) = 304 \text{ }\Omega$$

$$i_{c(sat)} = I_{CQ} + \frac{V_{CEQ}}{r_C} = 63 \text{ mA} + \frac{18.5 \text{ V}}{304 \text{ }\Omega} = 124 \text{ mA},$$

$$v_{ce(off)} = V_{CEQ} + I_{CQ}r_C = 18.5 \text{ V} + (63 \text{ mA})(304 \text{ }\Omega)$$
$$= 37.7 \text{ V}. \quad \text{The ac load line has endpoint values of}$$
$$i_{c(sat)} = 124 \text{ mA and } v_{ce(off)} = 37.7 \text{ V}.$$

19. From Problem 17: $V_{CEQ} = 20$ V, $I_{CQ} = 24.1$ mA, and $r_C = 800$ Ω. $2V_{CEQ} = (2)(20 \text{ V}) = 40$ V
$2I_{CQ}r_C = (2)(24.1 \text{ mA})(800 \text{ }\Omega) = 38.6$ V,

$$PP = 38.6 \text{ V}, V_{pp} = \frac{N_S}{N_P}PP = \frac{1}{10}(38.6 \text{ V}) = 3.86 \text{ V},$$

$$P_{L(max)} = \frac{V_{pp}^2}{8R_L} = \frac{(3.86 \text{ V})^2}{(8)(8 \text{ }\Omega)} = 233 \text{ mW}$$

20. From Problem 18: $V_{CEQ} = 18.5$ V, $I_{CQ} = 63$ mA, and $r_C = 304$ Ω. $2V_{CEQ} = (2)(18.5 \text{ V}) = 37$ V
$2I_{CQ}r_C = (2)(63 \text{ mA})(304 \text{ }\Omega) = 38.3$ V,

$$PP = 37 \text{ V}, \quad V_{pp} = \frac{N_S}{N_P}PP = \frac{1}{4}(37 \text{ V}) = 9.25 \text{ V},$$

$$P_{L(max)} = \frac{V_{pp}^2}{8R_L} = \frac{(9.25 \text{ V})^2}{(8)(19 \text{ }\Omega)} = 563 \text{ mW}$$

21. From Problems 17 and 19: $I_{CQ} = 24.1$ mA and $P_{L(max)} = 233$ mW.

$$I_1 = \frac{V_{CC}}{R_1 + R_2} = \frac{22 \text{ V}}{3.1 \text{ k}\Omega} \cong 7.1 \text{ mA}$$

$I_{CC} = I_{CQ} + I_1 = 24.1 \text{ mA} + 7.1 \text{ mA} = 31.2 \text{ mA}$
$P_S = V_{CC}I_{CC} = (22 \text{ V})(31.2 \text{ mA}) = 686 \text{ mW}$

$$\eta = \frac{P_{L(max)}}{P_S} \times 100 = \frac{233 \text{ mW}}{686 \text{ mW}} \times 100 = 34 \text{ \%}$$

22. From Problems 18 and 20: $I_{CQ} = 63$ mA, and $P_{L(max)} = 563$ mW.

$$I_1 = \frac{V_{CC}}{R_1 + R_2} = \frac{20 \text{ V}}{521 \text{ }\Omega} = 38.4 \text{ mA}$$

$I_{CC} = I_{CQ} + I_1 = 63 \text{ mA} + 38.4 \text{ mA} \cong 101 \text{ mA}$
$P_S = V_{CC}I_{CC} = (20 \text{ V})(101 \text{ mA}) = 2.02 \text{ W}$

$$\eta = \frac{P_{L(max)}}{P_S} \times 100 = \frac{563 \text{ mW}}{2.02 \text{ W}} \times 100 = 27.9 \text{ \%}$$

23. $V_{CEQ} = \frac{V_{CC}}{2} = 9$ V. This value is used to plot the vertical dc load line shown. The endpoint values for the ac load line are $i_{c(sat)} = \frac{V_{CC}}{2R_L} = \frac{18 \text{ V}}{(2)(3 \text{ k}\Omega)}$

$$= 3 \text{ mA and } v_{ce(off)} = \frac{V_{CC}}{2} = 9 \text{ V}.$$

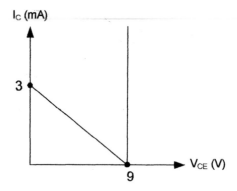

24. $V_{CEQ} = \frac{V_{CC}}{2} = 12$ V. This value is used to plot the vertical dc load line. The endpoint values for the ac load line are $i_{c(sat)} = \frac{V_{CC}}{2R_L} = \frac{24 \text{ V}}{(2)(200 \text{ }\Omega)} = 60$ mA

and $v_{ce(off)} = \frac{V_{CC}}{2} = 12$ V.

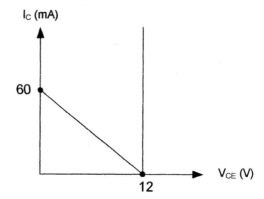

25. $PP \cong V_{CC} = 18$ V

$$P_{L(max)} = \frac{PP^2}{8R_L} = \frac{(18 \text{ V}_{PP})^2}{24 \text{ k}\Omega} = 13.5 \text{ mW}$$

26. $PP \cong V_{CC} = 24$ V

$$P_{L(max)} = \frac{PP^2}{8R_L} = \frac{(24 \text{ V}_{PP})^2}{1.6 \text{ k}\Omega} = 360 \text{ mW}$$

27. $I_1 = \frac{V_{CC}}{R_1 + R_2 + R_3} = \frac{48 \text{ V}}{9.68 \text{ k}\Omega} = 4.96$ mA

$$I_{C1(ave)} = \frac{V_{CC}}{2\pi R_L} = \frac{48 \text{ V}}{101 \text{ }\Omega} = 475 \text{ mA}$$

$I_{CC} = I_{C1(ave)} + I_1 = 475 \text{ mA} + 4.96 \text{ mA} \cong 480 \text{ mA}$
$P_S = V_{CC}I_{CC} = (48 \text{ V})(480 \text{ mA}) = 23$ W

28. $I_1 = \frac{V_{CC}}{R_1 + R_2 + R_3} = \frac{22 \text{ V}}{21.4 \text{ k}\Omega} = 1.03$ mA

$$I_{C1(ave)} = \frac{V_{CC}}{2\pi R_L} = \frac{22 \text{ V}}{75.4 \text{ }\Omega} = 292 \text{ mA}$$

$I_{CC} = I_{C1(ave)} + I_1 = 292 \text{ mA} + 1.03 \text{ mA} = 293 \text{ mA}$
$P_S = V_{CC}I_{CC} = (22 \text{ V})(293 \text{ mA}) = 6.45$ W

29. $\text{PP} \cong V_{CC} = 48 \text{ V}$

$$P_{L(\text{max})} = \frac{\text{PP}^2}{8R_L} = \frac{(48 \text{ V}_{\text{PP}})^2}{128 \, \Omega} = 18 \text{ W}$$

30. $\text{PP} \cong V_{CC} = 22 \text{ V}$

$$P_{L(\text{max})} = \frac{\text{PP}^2}{8R_L} = \frac{(22 \text{ V}_{\text{PP}})^2}{96 \, \Omega} = 5.04 \text{ W}$$

31. From Problems 27 and 29: $P_S = 23$ W, and $P_{L(\text{max})} = 18$ W

$$\eta = \frac{P_{L(\text{max})}}{P_S} \times 100 = \frac{18 \text{ W}}{23 \text{ W}} \times 100 = 78.3 \text{ \%}$$

32. From Problems 28 and 30: $P_S = 6.45$ W, and $P_{L(\text{max})} = 5.04$ W

$$\eta = \frac{P_{L(\text{max})}}{P_S} \times 100 = \frac{5.04 \text{ W}}{6.45 \text{ W}} \times 100 = 78.1 \text{ \%}$$

33. $V_{CEQ} = \dfrac{V_{CC}}{2} = 4 \text{ V}, \quad V_{B(Q1)} \cong V_{CEQ} + 0.7 \text{ V} = 4.7 \text{ V}$

$V_{B(Q2)} \cong V_{CEQ} - 0.7 \text{ V} = 3.3 \text{ V}$

34. $V_{CEQ} = \dfrac{V_{CC}}{2} = 5 \text{ V}, \quad V_{B(Q1)} \cong V_{CEQ} + 0.7 \text{ V} = 5.7 \text{ V}$

$V_{B(Q2)} \cong V_{CEQ} - 0.7 \text{ V} = 4.3 \text{ V}$

35. $I_1 = \dfrac{V_{CC} - 1.4 \text{ V}}{R_1 + R_2} = \dfrac{6.6 \text{ V}}{440 \, \Omega} = 15 \text{ mA}$

$$I_{C1(\text{ave})} = \frac{V_{CC}}{2\pi R_L} = \frac{8 \text{ V}}{75.4 \, \Omega} = 106 \text{ mA}$$

$I_{CC} = I_{C1(\text{ave})} + I_1 = 106 \text{ mA} + 15 \text{ mA} = 121 \text{ mA}$

$P_S = V_{CC}I_{CC} = (8 \text{ V})(121 \text{ mA}) = 968 \text{ mW}$

$$P_{L(\text{max})} = \frac{\text{PP}^2}{8R_L} \cong \frac{V_{CC}^2}{8R_L} = \frac{(8 \text{ V})^2}{96 \, \Omega} = 667 \text{ mW}$$

$$\eta = \frac{P_{L(\text{max})}}{P_S} \times 100 = \frac{667 \text{ mW}}{968 \text{ mW}} \times 100 = 68.9 \text{ \%}$$

36. $I_1 = \dfrac{V_{CC} - 1.4 \text{ V}}{R_1 + R_2} = \dfrac{8.6 \text{ V}}{2 \text{ k}\Omega} = 4.3 \text{ mA}$

$$I_{C1(\text{ave})} = \frac{V_{CC}}{2\pi R_L} = \frac{10 \text{ V}}{50.3 \, \Omega} \cong 199 \text{ mA}$$

$I_{CC} = I_{C1(\text{ave})} + I_1 = 199 \text{ mA} + 4.3 \text{ mA} \cong 203 \text{ mA}$

$P_S = V_{CC}I_{CC} = (10 \text{ V})(203 \text{ mA}) = 2.03 \text{ W}$

$$P_{L(\text{max})} = \frac{\text{PP}^2}{8R_L} \cong \frac{V_{CC}^2}{8R_L} = \frac{(10 \text{ V})^2}{64 \, \Omega} = 1.56 \text{ W}$$

$$\eta = \frac{P_{L(\text{max})}}{P_S} \times 100 = \frac{1.56 \text{ W}}{2.03 \text{ W}} \times 100 = 76.8 \text{ \%}$$

37. $I_1 = \dfrac{V_{CC} - 1.4 \text{ V}}{R_1 + R_2} = \dfrac{18.6 \text{ V}}{30 \text{ k}\Omega} = 620 \text{ }\mu\text{A}$

$$I_{C1(\text{ave})} = \frac{V_{CC}}{2\pi R_L} = \frac{20 \text{ V}}{201 \, \Omega} = 99.5 \text{ mA}$$

$I_{CC} = I_{C1(\text{ave})} + I_1 = 99.5 \text{ mA} + 620 \text{ }\mu\text{A} \cong 100 \text{ mA}$

$P_S = V_{CC}I_{CC} = (20 \text{ V})(100 \text{ mA}) = 2 \text{ W}$

$$P_{L(\text{max})} = \frac{\text{PP}^2}{8R_L} \cong \frac{V_{CC}^2}{8R_L} = \frac{(20 \text{ V})^2}{256 \, \Omega} = 1.56 \text{ W}$$

$$\eta = \frac{P_{L(\text{max})}}{P_S} \times 100 = \frac{1.56 \text{ W}}{2 \text{ W}} \times 100 = 78 \text{ \%}$$

38. $I_1 = \dfrac{V_{CC} - 1.4 \text{ V}}{R_1 + R_2} = \dfrac{4.6 \text{ V}}{6.6 \text{ k}\Omega} = 697 \text{ }\mu\text{A}$

$$I_{C1(\text{ave})} = \frac{V_{CC}}{2\pi R_L} = \frac{6 \text{ V}}{101 \, \Omega} = 59.4 \text{ mA}$$

$I_{CC} = I_{C1(\text{ave})} + I_1 = 59.4 \text{ mA} + 697 \text{ }\mu\text{A} = 60.1 \text{ mA}$

$P_S = V_{CC}I_{CC} = (6 \text{ V})(60.1 \text{ mA}) \cong 361 \text{ mW}$

$$P_{L(\text{max})} = \frac{\text{PP}^2}{8R_L} \cong \frac{V_{CC}^2}{8R_L} = \frac{(6 \text{ V})^2}{128 \, \Omega} = 281 \text{ mW}$$

$$\eta = \frac{P_{L(\text{max})}}{P_S} \times 100 = \frac{281 \text{ mW}}{361 \text{ mW}} \times 100 = 77.8 \text{ \%}$$

39. From Problem 3: $V_{CEQ} = 3.4$ V and $I_{CQ} = 10$ mA.
$P_D = V_{CEQ}I_{CQ} = (3.4 \text{ V})(10 \text{ mA}) = 34 \text{ mW}$

40. From Problem 4: $V_{CEQ} = 1.78$ V and $I_{CQ} = 2.77$ mA.
$P_D = V_{CEQ}I_{CQ} = (1.78 \text{ V})(2.77 \text{ mA}) = 4.93 \text{ mW}$

41. From Problem 17: $V_{CEQ} = 20$ V , $I_{CQ} = 24.1$ mA.
$P_D = V_{CEQ}I_{CQ} = (20 \text{ V})(24.1 \text{ mA}) = 482 \text{ mW}$

42. There is 3.8 V across R_1 and 6.5 V across R_2. These component voltages (which are equal under normal circumstances) indicate that one (or both) of the diodes is open.

43. The equal base and emitter voltages indicate that the base-emitter junction of Q_1 is shorted.

44. From Problem 35: $P_{L(\text{max})} = 667$ mW. To determine the value of $P_{\text{in(max)}}$, we have to solve for the amplifier power gain, as follows:

$$r'_e = \frac{h_{ic}}{h_{fc}} = \frac{4.8 \text{ k}\Omega}{240} = 20 \, \Omega$$

$$A_v = \frac{R_L}{r'_e + R_L} = \frac{12 \, \Omega}{32 \, \Omega} = 0.375$$

$Z_{\text{base}} = h_{fc}(r'_e + R_L) = (240)(32 \, \Omega) = 7.68 \text{ k}\Omega$

$Z_{\text{in}} = R_1 \parallel R_2 \parallel Z_{\text{base}}$
$\quad = (200 \, \Omega) \parallel (220 \, \Omega) \parallel (7.68 \text{ k}\Omega) = 108 \, \Omega$

$$A_i = h_{fc}\frac{Z_{\text{in}}}{Z_{\text{base}}} = (240)\frac{108 \, \Omega}{7.68 \text{ k}\Omega} = 3.38, \text{ and}$$

$A_p = A_i A_v = (3.38)(0.375) = 1.27$

Finally,

$$P_{\text{in(max)}} = \frac{P_{L(\text{max})}}{A_p} = \frac{667 \text{ mW}}{1.27} \cong 525 \text{ mW}.$$

45. $h_{ic} = h_{ie}$ and $h_{fc} \cong h_{fe}$, so each transistor has a value of $r'_e = \dfrac{h_{ie}}{h_{fe}} = \dfrac{1.2 \text{ k}\Omega}{220} = 5.45 \, \Omega$. For the second stage: $A_{v2} = \dfrac{R_L}{r'_e + R_L} = \dfrac{10\,\Omega}{15.5\,\Omega} = 0.6452$,

$Z_{base} = h_{fe}(r'_e + R_L) = (220)(15.5\,\Omega) = 3.41\,k\Omega$,

$Z_{in2} = R_5 \| R_6 \| Z_{base} = (1.8\,k\Omega)\|(1.8\,k\Omega)\|(3.41\,k\Omega) =$

$712\,\Omega$, and $A_{i2} = h_{fe}\dfrac{Z_{in}}{Z_{base}} = (220)\dfrac{712\,\Omega}{3.41\,k\Omega} \cong 46$.

For the first stage: $r_C = R_3 \| Z_{in2} = (1.2\,k\Omega)\|(712\,\Omega)$

$= 447\,\Omega$, $\quad A_{v1} = \dfrac{r_C}{r'_e} = \dfrac{447\,\Omega}{5.45\,\Omega} = 82$

$Z_{base} = h_{ie} = 1.2\,k\Omega$, $\;Z_{in1} = R_1 \| R_2 \| Z_{base} =$
$(43\,k\Omega)\|(6.8k\Omega)\|(1.2\,k\Omega) = 996\,\Omega$ Assuming
$R_L = Z_{in2}$:

$A_{i1} = h_{fe}\dfrac{Z_{in}r_C}{Z_{base}R_L} = (220)\dfrac{(996\,\Omega)(447\,\Omega)}{(1.2\,k\Omega)(712\,\Omega)} = 115$

$A_{vT} = A_{v1}A_{v2} = (82)(0.6452) = 52.9$,
$A_{iT} = A_{i1}A_{i2} = (115)(46) = 5.29 \times 10^3$,
$A_{pT} = A_{iT}A_{vT} = (5.29 \times 10^3)(52.9) = 2.8 \times 10^5$

46. From Problem 45: $r_{C1} = 447\,\Omega$ and $A_{v1} = 82$. For
Stage 2: PP $\cong V_{CC} = 30$ V. For Stage 1,

$V_{TH} = V_{CC}\dfrac{R_2}{R_1 + R_2} = (30\,V)\dfrac{6.8k\Omega}{49.8k\Omega} = 4.1$ V

$R_{TH} = R_1 \| R_2 = 43\,k\Omega \| 6.8\,k\Omega = 5.87\,k\Omega$

$I_{CQ} = \dfrac{V_{TH} - V_{BE}}{\dfrac{R_{TH}}{h_{FC}} + R_E} = \dfrac{4.1\,V - 0.7\,V}{\dfrac{5.87k\Omega}{200} + 300\,\Omega} = 10.3\,mA$

$V_{CEQ} = V_{CC} - I_{CQ}(R_3 + R_4)$
$\quad = 30\,V - (10.3\,mA)(1.5\,k\Omega) = 14.6$ V

$2V_{CEQ} = 29.2$ V, $\;2I_{CQ}r_C = 9.21$ V. Therefore, PP
$= 9.21$ V for the first stage. The overall compliance
equals the lowest stage value, so the overall PP is
also 9.21 V. Using this value, the maximum
allowable peak-to-peak input is found as: $v_{in(max)} =$

$\dfrac{PP}{A_v} = \dfrac{9.21\,V}{82} = 112\,mV_{pp}$. With a 20 mV_{pp} input,

the circuit is *not* driven to compliance. Since PP $=$
$2I_{CQ}r_C$, the circuit would most likely experience
cutoff clipping.

47. From Problems 45 and 46: $A_{v2} = 0.6542$ and
PP $= 9.21$ V. Using these values, the max Stage 2
output is found as $V_{pp} = A_{v2}PP = (0.6542)(9.21\,V) =$
6.03 V. Using this value, P_D for each transistor is

found as $P_D = \dfrac{V_{PP}^2}{40R_L} = \dfrac{(6.03\,V_{pp})^2}{(40)(10\,\Omega)} = 90.9$ mW.

This value is much lower than the 625 mW P_D
rating for the 2N3904, so the component can be
used.

48. According to its spec sheet, the 2N4124 has a value
of $V_{CEO} = 25$ V. Since this value is less than the
value of V_{CC} for the circuit (32 V), the transistor
cannot be used. (The transistor *must* be able to

withstand a value of $V_{CE} = V_{CC}$ in case the transistor
goes into cutoff.)
49. The 2N2222 has a maximum power dissipation
rating of 625 mW (at 25°C). With a value of $I_{CQ} =$
100 mA, the component can handle a value of

$V_{CEQ} = \dfrac{P_D}{I_{CQ}} = \dfrac{625\,mW}{100\,mA} = 6.25$ V

Providing a 20% safety margin,
$V_{CEQ} = (0.8)(6.25\,V) = 5$ V (maximum)

CHAPTER 12

Note: The following FET Drain Current equation is
used to solve many of the problems in this chapter:

$$I_D = I_{DSS}\left(1 - \dfrac{V_{GS}}{V_{GS(off)}}\right)^2 \qquad (12.1)$$

In order to simplify I_D calculations, the values relating
to this equation are usually presented in table format.
The values of V_{GS} used in the tables are chosen at
random (except when specified in the problem) and may
not match those chosen by your students.

EXAMPLE PRACTICE PROBLEMS   (CH 12)

12-1. $\quad I_D = I_{DSS}\left(1 - \dfrac{V_{GS}}{V_{GS(off)}}\right)^2 =$

$(12\,mA)\left(1 - \dfrac{-3\,V}{-6\,V}\right)^2 = (12\,mA)(0.25) = 3$ mA

12-2.

I_{DSS} (mA)	V_{GS} (V)	$V_{GS(off)}$ (V)	I_D (mA)
12	0	−20	12
12	−5	−20	6.75
12	−10	−20	3
12	−15	−20	0.75
12	−20	−20	0

Using the combinations of V_{GS} and I_D given in the
table, the curve is plotted as shown in Figure 12.79.

12-3.

I_{DSS} (mA)	V_{GS} (V)	$V_{GS(off)}$ (V)	I_D (mA)
(max) 20	0	−6	20
20	−2	−6	8.89
20	−4	−6	2.22
20	−6	−6	0
(min) 8	0	−2	8
8	−0.5	−2	4.5
8	−1.5	−2	0.5
8	−2	−2	0

Using the combinations of V_{GS} and I_D given in the table, the curves are plotted as shown in Figure 12.80.

12-4. $V_{GS} = V_{GG} = -5$ V, $\quad I_D = I_{DSS}\left(1 - \dfrac{V_{GS}}{V_{GS(off)}}\right)^2 =$

$(12\text{ mA})\left(1 - \dfrac{-5\text{ V}}{-10\text{ V}}\right)^2 = (12\text{ mA})(0.25) = 3\text{ mA},$

$V_{DS} = V_{DD} - I_D R_D = 10\text{ V} - (3\text{ mA})(2.2\text{ k}\Omega) = 3.4\text{ V}$

12-5. [This example has no practice problem.]

12-6.

I_{DSS} (mA)	V_{GS} (V)	$V_{GS(off)}$ (V)	I_D (mA)
(max) 10	0	–10	10
10	–4	–10	3.6
10	–8	–10	0.4
10	–10	–10	0
(min) 5	0	–5	5
5	–2	–5	1.8
5	–4	–5	0.2
5	–5	–5	0

Using the combinations of V_{GS} and I_D given in the table, the curves are plotted as shown in Figure 12.81.

The bias line position was determined using:

$V_{GS} = -8$ V and $\quad I_D = \dfrac{-V_{GS}}{R_S} = \dfrac{8\text{ V}}{2\text{ k}\Omega} = 4\text{ mA}$

The bias line extends from the origin through the point that corresponds to (–8 V, 4 mA).

12-7. Using the Q_{min} and Q_{max} points plotted in Practice Problem 12-6, the JFET is estimated to have a range of $I_D \cong 1.25$ mA to 2.5 mA. Using these values:

$V_{DS} = V_{DD} - I_D(R_D + R_S)$
$\quad = 9\text{ V} - (1.25\text{ mA})(3\text{ k}\Omega) = 5.25\text{ V (maximum)}$
and
$V_{DS} = V_{DD} - I_D(R_D + R_S)$
$\quad = 9\text{ V} - (2.5\text{ mA})(3\text{ k}\Omega) = 1.5\text{ V (minimum)}.$

12-8. The curves (shown in Figure 12.80) were plotted in Problem 12-3. The bias line (shown in Figure 12.82) is plotted using

$V_G = V_{DD}\dfrac{R_2}{R_1 + R_2} = (36\text{ V})\dfrac{3.3\text{ M}\Omega}{13.3\text{ M}\Omega} = 8.93\text{ V}$

$I_D = \dfrac{V_G}{R_S} = \dfrac{8.93\text{ V}}{3\text{ k}\Omega} = 2.98\text{ mA}$

12-9. The Q-point values are *estimated* using the curves in Figure 12.82. Q_{max} is $I_D = 4$ mA at V_{GS} = –3.5 V, and Q_{min} is $I_D = 3.25$ mA at $V_{GS} = -800$ mV. These combinations are verified as follows:

$Q_{max}: I_D = \dfrac{V_G - V_{GS}}{R_S} = \dfrac{8.93\text{ V} - (-3.5\text{ V})}{3\text{ k}\Omega} = 4.14\text{ mA}$

$Q_{min}: I_D = \dfrac{V_G - V_{GS}}{R_S} = \dfrac{8.93\text{ V} - (-800\text{ mV})}{3\text{ k}\Omega} = 3.24\text{ mA}$

12-10. From Problem 12-9: $I_D = 3.24$ mA to 4.14 mA.
$V_{DS} = V_{DD} - I_D(R_D + R_S)$
$\quad = 36\text{ V} - (3.24\text{ mA})(4.8\text{ k}\Omega) = 20.4\text{ V (max)}$
$V_{DS} = V_{DD} - I_D(R_D + R_S)$
$\quad = 36\text{ V} - (4.14\text{ mA})(4.8\text{ k}\Omega) = 16.1\text{ V (min)}$

12-11. $g_m = g_{m0}\left(1 - \dfrac{V_{GS}}{V_{GS(off)}}\right)$

$\quad = (8000\text{ }\mu S)\left(1 - \dfrac{-2\text{ V}}{-6\text{ V}}\right) = 5333\text{ }\mu S$

$g_m = g_{m0}\left(1 - \dfrac{V_{GS}}{V_{GS(off)}}\right)$

$\quad = (8000\text{ }\mu S)\left(1 - \dfrac{-4\text{ V}}{-6\text{ V}}\right) = 2667\text{ }\mu S$

12-12. The g_m values are found as:

$g_m = g_{m0}\left(1 - \dfrac{V_{GS}}{V_{GS(off)}}\right)$

$\quad = (4000\text{ }\mu S)\left(1 - \dfrac{-0.75\text{ V}}{-2\text{ V}}\right) = 2500\text{ }\mu S\text{ (min)}$

$g_m = g_{m0}\left(1 - \dfrac{V_{GS}}{V_{GS(off)}}\right)$

$\quad = (8000\text{ }\mu S)\left(1 - \dfrac{-3.2\text{ V}}{-8\text{ V}}\right) = 4800\text{ }\mu S\text{ (max)}$

The value of r_D is found as
$r_D = R_D \| R_L = (1.8\text{ k}\Omega) \| (4.7\text{ k}\Omega) = 1.3\text{ k}\Omega$ and
$A_v = g_m r_D = (2500\text{ }\mu S)(1.3\text{ k}\Omega) = 3.25\text{ (min)}$
$A_v = g_m r_D = (4800\text{ }\mu S)(1.3\text{ k}\Omega) = 6.24\text{ (max)}$

12-13. Using the minimum value of g_m :

$A_v = \dfrac{r_D}{r_S + (1/g_m)} = \dfrac{6.6\text{ k}\Omega}{1.5\text{ k}\Omega + 500\text{ }\Omega} = 3.30\text{ (min)}$

Using the maximum value of g_m :

$A_v = \dfrac{r_D}{r_S + (1/g_m)} = \dfrac{6.6\text{ k}\Omega}{1.5\text{ k}\Omega + 250\text{ }\Omega} = 3.77\text{ (max)}$

12-14. [This example has no practice problem.]

12-15. [This example has no practice problem.]

12-16. The minimum and maximum curves for the 2N5486 were plotted in Problem 12-3. The dc bias line is plotted using :

$V_G = V_{DD}\dfrac{R_2}{R_1 + R_2} = (20\text{ V})\dfrac{1\text{ M}\Omega}{2\text{ M}\Omega} = 10\text{ V}$ and

$I_D = \dfrac{V_G}{R_S} = \dfrac{10\text{ V}}{5\text{ k}\Omega} = 2\text{ mA}$ The curves and bias line shown indicate that the circuit has a range of $V_{GS} \cong -1$ V to -3.75 V.

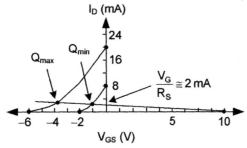

These values are used with the corresponding values of $V_{GS\,(\text{off})}$ and g_{m0} to obtain the values of g_m shown in the table below.

g_{m0} (μS)	V_{GS} (V)	$V_{GS\,(\text{off})}$ (V)	g_m (μS)
4000	-1	-2	2000
8000	-3.75	-6	3000

Now, $r_S = R_S \parallel R_L = (5\text{ k}\Omega) \parallel (20\text{ k}\Omega) = 4\text{ k}\Omega$. Using the minimum value of g_m :

$$A_v = \frac{r_S}{r_S + (1/g_m)} = \frac{4\text{ k}\Omega}{4\text{ k}\Omega + 500\,\Omega} = 0.889\ (\text{min})$$

Using the maximum value of g_m :

$$A_v = \frac{r_S}{r_S + (1/g_m)} = \frac{4\text{ k}\Omega}{4\text{ k}\Omega + 333\,\Omega} = 0.923\ (\text{max})$$

The minimum and maximum values of Z_{out} are found as:

I_{DSS} (mA)	V_{GS} (V)	$V_{GS\,(\text{off})}$ (V)	I_D (mA)
(min) 4	0	-0.5	4
4	-0.2	-0.5	1.4
4	-0.4	-0.5	0.16
4	-0.5	-0.5	0.0
(max) 10	0	-4.0	10
10	-1.0	-4.0	5.6
10	-3.0	-4.0	0.625
10	-4.0	-4.0	0.0

$$Z_{\text{out}} = R_S \parallel \frac{1}{g_m} = (5\text{ k}\Omega) \parallel \left(\frac{1}{3000\mu\text{S}}\right) \cong 312\,\Omega\ (\text{min})$$

$$Z_{\text{out}} = R_S \parallel \frac{1}{g_m} = (5\text{ k}\Omega) \parallel \left(\frac{1}{2000\mu\text{S}}\right) \cong 455\,\Omega\ (\text{max})$$

PRACTICE PROBLEMS (CH 12)

1. $I_D = I_{DSS}\left(1 - \dfrac{V_{GS}}{V_{GS\,(\text{off})}}\right)^2 = (8\text{ mA})\left(1 - \dfrac{-6\text{ V}}{-12\text{ V}}\right)^2$

$\quad = (8\text{ mA})(0.25) = 2\text{ mA}$

2. $I_D = I_{DSS}\left(1 - \dfrac{V_{GS}}{V_{GS\,(\text{off})}}\right)^2 = (16\text{ mA})\left(1 - \dfrac{-4\text{ V}}{-5\text{ V}}\right)^2$

$\quad = (16\text{ mA})(0.04) = 640\,\mu\text{A}$

3. Since $V_{GS} = 0$ V, $\quad I_D = I_{DSS} = 14\text{ mA}$

4. $I_D = I_{DSS}\left(1 - \dfrac{V_{GS}}{V_{GS\,(\text{off})}}\right)^2 = (10\text{ mA})\left(1 - \dfrac{-5\text{ V}}{-8\text{ V}}\right)^2$

$\quad = (10\text{ mA})(0.141) = 1.41\text{ mA}$

5. $I_D = I_{DSS}\left(1 - \dfrac{V_{GS}}{V_{GS\,(\text{off})}}\right)^2 = (12\text{ mA})\left(1 - \dfrac{-4\text{ V}}{-10\text{ V}}\right)^2$

$\quad = (12\text{ mA})(0.36) = 4.32\text{ mA}$

6. The magnitude of V_{GS} is greater than that of $V_{GS\,(\text{off})}$, so $I_D = 0$ mA.

7.

I_{DSS} (mA)	V_{GS} (V)	$V_{GS\,(\text{off})}$ (V)	I_D (mA)
(min) 1.0	0	-0.3	1.0
1.0	-0.1	-0.3	0.44
1.0	-0.2	-0.3	0.11
1.0	-0.3	-0.3	0.0
(max) 5.0	0	-3	5.0
5.0	-1	-3	2.2
5.0	-2	-3	0.56
5.0	-3	-3	0.0

Using the combinations of V_{GS} and I_D given in the table, the curves are plotted as shown.

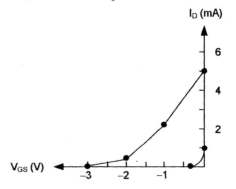

8.

I_{DSS} (mA)	V_{GS} (V)	$V_{GS\,(\text{off})}$ (V)	I_D (mA)
(min) 4	0	-0.5	4
4	-0.2	-0.5	1.4
4	-0.4	-0.5	0.16
4	-0.5	-0.5	0.0
(max) 10	0	-4.0	10
10	-1.0	-4.0	5.6
10	-3.0	-4.0	0.625
10	-4.0	-4.0	0.0

Using the combinations of V_{GS} and I_D given in the table, the curves are plotted as shown.

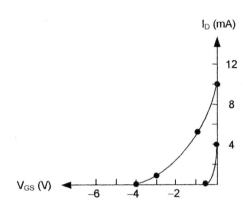

9.

I_{DSS} (mA)	V_{GS} (V)	$V_{GS(off)}$ (V)	I_D (mA)
(min) 1.0	−0.1	−0.5	0.64
1.0	−0.3	−0.5	0.16
(max) 5.0	−2	−6.0	2.2
5.0	−4	−6.0	0.56

Using the values in the table, and the points representing $V_{GS(off)}$ and I_{DSS}, the curves are plotted as shown.

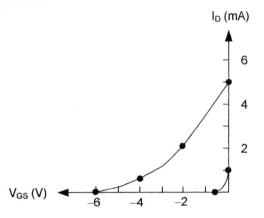

10.

I_{DSS} (mA)	V_{GS} (V)	$V_{GS(off)}$ (V)	I_D (mA)
(min) 2.0	−0.2	−1.0	1.28
2.0	−0.8	−1.0	0.08
(max) 9.0	−2.0	−7.0	4.59
9.0	−5.0	−7.0	0.74

Using the values in the table, and the points representing $V_{GS(off)}$ and I_{DSS}, the curves are plotted as shown on the following page.

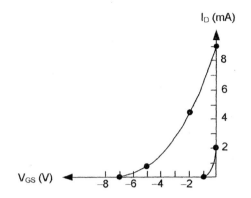

11.

I_{DSS} (mA)	V_{GS} (V)	$V_{GS(off)}$ (V)	I_D (mA)
4.0	−2.0	−5.0	1.44
4.0	−4.0	−5.0	0.16

Using the values in the table, and the points representing $V_{GS(off)}$ and I_{DSS}, the curve is plotted as shown.

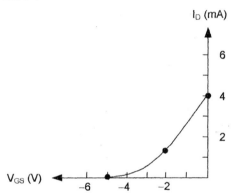

12.

I_{DSS} (mA)	V_{GS} (V)	$V_{GS(off)}$ (V)	I_D (µA)
1	−0.5	−2.5	640
1	−1	−2.5	360

Using the values in the table, and the points representing $V_{GS(off)}$ and I_{DSS}, the curve is plotted as shown.

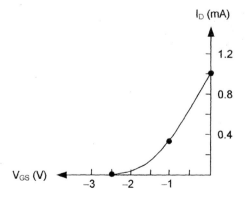

13. $I_D = I_{DSS}\left(1 - \dfrac{V_{GS}}{V_{GS(off)}}\right)^2 = (6 \text{ mA})\left(1 - \dfrac{-1 \text{ V}}{-2 \text{ V}}\right)^2$

$= (6 \text{ mA})(0.25) = 1.5 \text{ mA}$

$V_{DS} = V_{DD} - I_D R_D = 10 \text{ V} - (1.5 \text{ mA})(3 \text{ k}\Omega) = 5.5 \text{ V}$

14. $I_D = I_{DSS}\left(1 - \dfrac{V_{GS}}{V_{GS(off)}}\right)^2 = (6 \text{ mA})\left(1 - \dfrac{-3 \text{ V}}{-4 \text{ V}}\right)^2$

$= (6 \text{ mA})(0.0625) = 375 \text{ }\mu\text{A}$

$V_{DS} = V_{DD} - I_D R_D = 8 \text{ V} - (375 \text{ }\mu\text{A})(1 \text{ k}\Omega) = 7.63 \text{ V}$

15. The curves that follow were originally plotted as shown in the solution to problem 12-3. The bias line is a vertical line at $V_{GS} = V_{GG} = -1$ V. The Q-points (shown in the figure) indicate a range of $I_D \cong 2$ mA to 14 mA. However, the circuit limits the drain current to $I_D = \dfrac{V_{DD}}{R_D} = \dfrac{10 \text{ V}}{3 \text{ k}\Omega} = 3.3 \text{ mA}$.

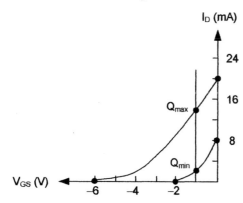

Therefore, the circuit has a range of $I_D = 2$ mA to 3.3 mA.

Alternate Solution: Since gate bias provides a fixed value of V_{GS}, we can find the minimum and maximum values of I_D using equation (12-1) as follows:

I_{DSS} (mA)	V_{GS} (V)	$V_{GS(off)}$ (V)	I_D (mA)
20	−1	−6	13.9
8	−1	−2	2

Then the limit of $I_D = \dfrac{V_{DD}}{R_D} = \dfrac{10 \text{ V}}{3 \text{ k}\Omega} = 3.3 \text{ mA}$ is

calculated. This gives a range of $I_D = 2$ to 3.3 mA.

16. Since gate bias provides a fixed value of V_{GS}, we can determine the range of I_D as follows:

$I_D = I_{DSS}\left(1 - \dfrac{V_{GS}}{V_{GS(off)}}\right)^2 = (4 \text{ mA})\left(1 - \dfrac{-3 \text{ V}}{-5 \text{ V}}\right)^2$

$= 640 \text{ }\mu\text{A}$

$I_D = I_{DSS}\left(1 - \dfrac{V_{GS}}{V_{GS(off)}}\right)^2 = (8 \text{ mA})\left(1 - \dfrac{-3 \text{ V}}{-10 \text{ V}}\right)^2$

$= 3.92 \text{ mA}$

17. Using the maximum values given in Problem 11, the *maximum* value of I_D is found as

$I_D = I_{DSS}\left(1 - \dfrac{V_{GS}}{V_{GS(off)}}\right)^2 = (4 \text{ mA})\left(1 - \dfrac{-3 \text{ V}}{-5 \text{ V}}\right)^2$

$= 640 \text{ }\mu\text{A}$

Since there is no minimum curve, the minimum value of I_D for the circuit is assumed to be 0 A.

18. Using the maximum values given in Problem 12, the *maximum* value of I_D is found as

$I_D = I_{DSS}\left(1 - \dfrac{V_{GS}}{V_{GS(off)}}\right)^2 = (1 \text{ mA})\left(1 - \dfrac{-1 \text{ V}}{-2.5 \text{ V}}\right)^2$

$= 360 \text{ }\mu\text{A}$

Since there is not minimum curve, the minimum value of I_D for the circuit is assumed to be 0 A.

19. The curves are plotted as shown in Problem 7.

Assuming $V_{GS} = -2$ V: $I_D = \dfrac{-V_{GS}}{R_S} = \dfrac{2 \text{ V}}{1 \text{ k}\Omega} = 2 \text{ mA}$

The bias line is then drawn from the origin to the (−2 V, 2 mA) point. Using the Q-points, the following ranges are approximated: $V_{GS} = -167$ mV to − 1.4 V and $I_D = 250$ μA to 1.5 mA. Using these values of I_D,

$V_{DS} = V_{DD} - I_D(R_D + R_S) = 12 \text{ V} - (250 \text{ }\mu\text{A})(4.3 \text{ k}\Omega)$
$= 10.9 \text{ V (maximum)}$ and

$V_{DS} = V_{DD} - I_D(R_D + R_S) = 12 \text{ V} - (1.5 \text{ mA})(4.3 \text{ k}\Omega)$
$= 5.55 \text{ V (minimum)}$

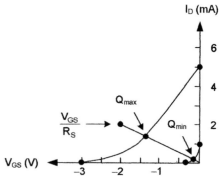

20. The curves are plotted as shown in Problem 8. Assuming $V_{GS} = -4$ V:

$I_D = \dfrac{-V_{GS}}{R_S} = \dfrac{4 \text{ V}}{800 \text{ }\Omega} = 5 \text{ mA}$

The bias line is then drawn from the origin to the (−4 V, 5 mA) point. Using the Q-points, the following ranges are approximated: $V_{GS} = -250$ mV to −2 V and $I_D = 500$ μA to 2.5 mA. Using these values of I_D,

$V_{DS} = V_{DD} - I_D(R_D + R_S) = 15 \text{ V} - (500 \text{ }\mu\text{A})(2.8 \text{ k}\Omega)$
$= 13.6 \text{ V (maximum)}$ and

$V_{DS} = V_{DD} - I_D(R_D + R_S) = 15 \text{ V} - (2 \text{ mA})(2.8 \text{ k}\Omega)$
$= 9.4 \text{ V (minimum)}$

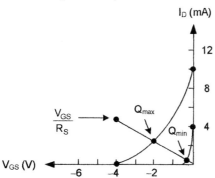

21. The curves are plotted as shown in Problem 10.

Assuming $V_{GS} = -4$ V: $I_D = \dfrac{-V_{GS}}{R_S} = \dfrac{4 \text{ V}}{1 \text{ k}\Omega} = 4$ mA

The bias line is then drawn from the origin to the $(-4 \text{ V}, 4 \text{ mA})$ point. Using the Q-points, the following ranges are approximated: $V_{GS} = -500$ mV to -3 V and $I_D = 500 \text{ μA}$ to 2.9 mA. Using these values of I_D,
$V_{DS} = V_{DD} - I_D(R_D + R_S) = 16 \text{ V} - (500 \text{ μA})(3 \text{ k}\Omega)$
$= 14.5 \text{ V (maximum) and}$
$V_{DS} = V_{DD} - I_D(R_D + R_S) = 16 \text{ V} - (2.9 \text{ mA})(3 \text{ k}\Omega)$
$= 7.3 \text{ V (minimum)}$

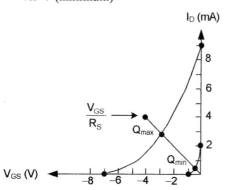

22. The curve is plotted as shown in Problem 11.
Assuming $V_{GS} = -3$ V:

$I_D = \dfrac{-V_{GS}}{R_S} = \dfrac{3 \text{ V}}{1.5 \text{ k}\Omega} = 2$ mA

The bias line is then drawn from the origin to the $(-3 \text{ V}, 2 \text{ mA})$ point (as shown at the top of the following page). Using the Q-points, the following ranges are approximated: $V_{GS} = 0$ V to -2 V and $I_D = 0$ mA to 1.4 mA. Using these values of I_D,
$V_{DS} = V_{DD} - I_D(R_D + R_S)$
$= 6 \text{ V} - (0 \text{ mA})(3 \text{ k}\Omega) = 6 \text{ V (maximum) and}$
$V_{DS} = V_{DD} - I_D(R_D + R_S)$
$= 6 \text{ V} - (1.4 \text{ mA})(3 \text{ k}\Omega) = 1.8 \text{ V (minimum)}$

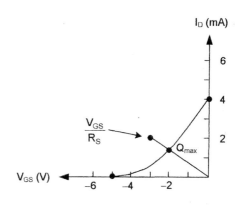

23.

I_{DSS} (mA)	V_{GS} (V)	$V_{GS(off)}$ (V)	I_D (mA)
(min) 2	−0.5	−2	1.13
2	−1	−2	0.50
(max) 10	−2	−8	5.63
10	−6	−8	0.63

Using the combinations of V_{GS} and I_D given in the table, the curves are plotted as shown. Using the values in the table, and the points representing $V_{GS(off)}$ and I_{DSS}, the curves are plotted as shown. The bias line is plotted using the following values:

$$V_G = V_{CC}\left(\dfrac{R_2}{R_1 + R_2}\right) = (30 \text{ V})\left(\dfrac{1 \text{ M}\Omega}{3 \text{ M}\Omega}\right) = 10 \text{ V}$$

$$I_D = \dfrac{V_G}{R_S} = \dfrac{10 \text{ V}}{11 \text{ k}\Omega} \cong 910 \text{ μA}$$

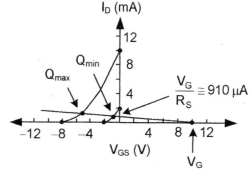

The Q-points are used to approximate a range of $I_D = 1$ mA to 1.5 mA. Using these values of I_D,
$V_{DS} = V_{DD} - I_D(R_D + R_S) = 30 \text{ V} - (1 \text{ mA})(21 \text{ k}\Omega)$
$= 9.0 \text{ V (maximum) and}$
$V_{DS} = V_{DD} - I_D(R_D + R_S) = 30 \text{ V} - (1.5 \text{ mA})(21 \text{ k}\Omega)$
$= -1.5 \text{ V (minimum)}$
Since this circuit cannot have a value of $V_{DS} = -1.5$ V, we assume that the circuit has a minimum value of $V_{DS} \cong 0$ V.

24.

I_{DSS} (mA)	V_{GS} (V)	$V_{GS(off)}$ (V)	I_D (mA)
(min) 5	−1	−4	2.81
5	−2	−4	1.25

(max) 10	−2	−8	5.63
10	−4	−8	2.50

Using the values in the table, and the points representing $V_{GS(off)}$ and I_{DSS}, the curves are plotted as shown.

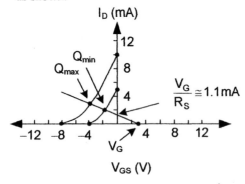

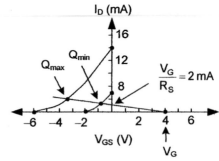

The Q-points are used to approximate a range of $I_D =$ 3 mA to 4 mA. Using these values of I_D,

$V_{DS} = V_{DD} - I_D(R_D + R_S) = 24\ V - (3\ mA)(4k\Omega)$
$\quad = 12\ V\ \text{(maximum)}$ and
$V_{DS} = V_{DD} - I_D(R_D + R_S) = 12\ V - (4\ mA)(4\ k\Omega)$
$\quad = 8\ V\ \text{(minimum)}.$

The bias line is plotted using :

$V_G = V_{CC}\left(\dfrac{R_2}{R_1 + R_2}\right) = (12\ V)\left(\dfrac{1\ M\Omega}{4\ M\Omega}\right) = 3\ V$

$I_D = \dfrac{V_G}{R_S} = \dfrac{3\ V}{2.7\ k\Omega} \cong 1.11\ mA$

The Q-points are used to approximate a range of $I_D =$ 2 mA to 3 mA. Using these values of I_D,

$V_{DS} = V_{DD} - I_D(R_D + R_S) = 12\ V - (2\ mA)(4.2\ k\Omega)$
$\quad = 3.6\ V\ \text{(maximum)}$ and
$V_{DS} = V_{DD} - I_D(R_D + R_S) = 12\ V - (3\ mA)(4.2\ k\Omega)$
$\quad = -0.6\ V\ \text{(minimum)}$

Since this circuit cannot have a value of $V_{DS} =$ −0.6 V, we assume that the circuit has a minimum value of $V_{DS} \cong 0\ V.$

25.

I_{DSS} (mA)	V_{GS} (V)	$V_{GS\,(off)}$ (V)	I_D (mA)
(min) 5	−0.5	−2	2.81
5	−1	−2	1.25
(max) 14	−2	−6	6.22
14	−4	−6	1.56

Using the values in the table, and the points representing $V_{GS(off)}$ and I_{DSS}, the curves are plotted as shown. The bias line is plotted using the following values:

$V_G = V_{CC}\left(\dfrac{R_2}{R_1 + R_2}\right) = (24\ V)\left(\dfrac{2\ M\Omega}{12\ M\Omega}\right) = 4\ V$

$I_D = \dfrac{V_G}{R_S} = \dfrac{4\ V}{2\ k\Omega} \cong 2\ mA$

26.

I_{DSS} (mA)	V_{GS} (V)	$V_{GS\,(off)}$ (V)	I_D (mA)
(min) 4	−1	−4	2.25
4	−2	−4	1.0
(max) 8	−2	−8	4.5
8	−4	−8	2.0

Using the values in the table, and the points representing $V_{GS(off)}$ and I_{DSS}, the curves are plotted as shown. The bias line is plotted using the following values:

$V_G = V_{CC}\left(\dfrac{R_2}{R_1 + R_2}\right) = (40\ V)\left(\dfrac{3\ M\Omega}{15\ M\Omega}\right) = 8\ V,$

$I_D = \dfrac{V_G}{R_S} = \dfrac{8\ V}{8\ k\Omega} = 1\ mA$

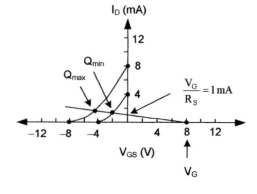

The Q-points are used to approximate a range of $I_D =$ 1.5 mA to 1.75 mA. Using these values of I_D,

$V_{DS} = V_{DD} - I_D(R_D + R_S) = 40\ V - (1.5\ mA)(20\ k\Omega)$
$\quad = 10\ V\ \text{(maximum)}$ and

$V_{DS} = V_{DD} - I_D(R_D + R_S) = 40\text{ V} - (1.75\text{ mA})(20\text{ k}\Omega)$
$= 5\text{ V (minimum)}.$

27. Using $g_m = g_{m0}\left(1 - \dfrac{V_{GS}}{V_{GS(\text{off})}}\right)$, substitute as follows:

$g_m = (3000\text{ μS})\left(1 - \dfrac{-0.2\text{ V}}{-0.3\text{ V}}\right) = 1000\text{ μS (min)}$

$g_m = (6000\text{ μS})\left(1 - \dfrac{-0.2\text{ V}}{-3.0\text{ V}}\right) = 5600\text{ μS (max)}$

28. Using $g_m = g_{m0}\left(1 - \dfrac{V_{GS}}{V_{GS(\text{off})}}\right)$, substitute as follows:

$g_m = (3500\text{ μS})\left(1 - \dfrac{-0.4\text{ V}}{-0.5\text{ V}}\right) = 700\text{ μS (min)}$

$g_m = (7000\text{ μS})\left(1 - \dfrac{-0.4\text{ V}}{-4.0\text{ V}}\right) = 6300\text{ μS (max)}$

29.

g_{m0} (μS)	V_{GS} (V)	$V_{GS(\text{off})}$ (V)	g_m (μS)
6000	−1	−5	4800
6000	−2.5	−5	3000
6000	−4	−5	1200

30.

g_{m0} (μS)	V_{GS} (V)	$V_{GS(\text{off})}$ (V)	g_m (μS)
4500	−1	−2.5	2700
4500	−1.5	−2.5	1800
4500	−2	−2.5	900

31. The curves and bias line for Figure 12.60 are shown in the solution to Problem 23. From the curves, the following range is *estimated*: $V_{GS} = 750\text{ mV to }5\text{ V}$

Using $g_m = g_{m0}\left(1 - \dfrac{V_{GS}}{V_{GS(\text{off})}}\right)$, substitute as follows:

$g_m = (2000\text{ μS})\left(1 - \dfrac{-0.75\text{ V}}{-2.0\text{ V}}\right) = 1250\text{ μS and}$

$g_m = (5000\text{ μS})\left(1 - \dfrac{-5\text{ V}}{-8\text{ V}}\right) = 1875\text{ μS}$

The value of r_D is found as
$r_D = R_D \| R_L = (10\text{ k}\Omega) \| (10\text{ k}\Omega) = 5\text{ k}\Omega$, and
$A_v = g_m r_D = (1250\text{ μS})(5\text{ k}\Omega) = 6.25\text{ (min)}$
$A_v = g_m r_D = (1875\text{ μS})(5\text{ k}\Omega) = 9.38\text{ (max)}$

32. The curves and bias line for Figure 12.61 are shown in the solution to Problem 24. From the curves, this range is *estimated*: $V_{GS} = 1.75\text{ V to }3.9\text{ V}.$

Using $g_m = g_{m0}\left(1 - \dfrac{V_{GS}}{V_{GS(\text{off})}}\right)$, substitute as follows:

$g_m = (3000\text{ μS})\left(1 - \dfrac{-1.75\text{ V}}{-4.0\text{ V}}\right) = 1688\text{ μS and}$

$g_m = (6000\text{ μS})\left(1 - \dfrac{-3.9\text{ V}}{-8.0\text{ V}}\right) = 3075\text{ μS}$

The value of r_D is found as
$r_D = R_D \| R_L = (1.5\text{ k}\Omega) \| (10\text{ k}\Omega) = 1.3\text{ k}\Omega$, and
$A_v = g_m r_D = (1688\text{ μS})(1.3\text{ k}\Omega) = 2.19\text{ (min)}$
$A_v = g_m r_D = (3075\text{ μS})(1.3\text{ k}\Omega) = 4\text{ (max)}$

33. The curves and bias line for Figure 12.62 are shown in the solution to Problem 25. From the curves, this range is *estimated*: $V_{GS} = 750\text{ mV to }3.5\text{V}$. Using

$g_m = g_{m0}\left(1 - \dfrac{V_{GS}}{V_{GS(\text{off})}}\right)$, substitute as follows:

$g_m = (1000\text{ μS})\left(1 - \dfrac{-0.75\text{ V}}{-2.0\text{ V}}\right) = 625\text{ μS and}$

$g_m = (2500\text{ μS})\left(1 - \dfrac{-3.5\text{ V}}{-6\text{ V}}\right) = 1042\text{ μS}$

The value of r_D is found as
$r_D = R_D \| R_L = (2\text{ k}\Omega) \| (20\text{ k}\Omega) = 1.82\text{ k}\Omega$, and
$A_v = g_m r_D = (625\text{ μS})(1.82\text{ k}\Omega) = 1.14\text{ (min)}$
$A_v = g_m r_D = (1042\text{ μS})(1.82\text{ k}\Omega) = 1.90\text{ (max)}$

34. The curves and bias line for Figure 12.63 are shown in the solution to Problem 26. From the curves, this range is *estimated*: $V_{GS} = 2.07\text{ V to }4.5\text{ V}.$

Using $g_m = g_{m0}\left(1 - \dfrac{V_{GS}}{V_{GS(\text{off})}}\right)$, substitute as follows:

$g_m = (2000\text{ μS})\left(1 - \dfrac{-2.0\text{ V}}{-4.0\text{ V}}\right) = 1000\text{ μS and}$

$g_m = (8000\text{ μS})\left(1 - \dfrac{-4.5\text{ V}}{-8.0\text{ V}}\right) = 3500\text{ μS}$

The value of r_D is found as
$r_D = R_D \| R_L = (12\text{ k}\Omega) \| (8\text{ k}\Omega) = 4.8\text{ k}\Omega$, and
$A_v = g_m r_D = (1000\text{ μS})(4.8\text{ k}\Omega) = 4.8\text{ (min)}$
$A_v = g_m r_D = (3500\text{ μS})(4.8\text{ k}\Omega) = 16.8\text{ (max)}$

35.

I_{DSS} (mA)	V_{GS} (V)	$V_{GS(\text{off})}$ (V)	I_D (mA)
(min) 5	−1	−5	3.2
5	−2	−5	1.8
(max) 10	−2	−10	6.4
10	−5	−10	2.5

Using the values in the table, and the points representing $V_{GS(\text{off})}$ and I_{DSS}, the curves are plotted as shown. The bias line is plotted using the following values:

$$V_G = V_{CC}\left(\frac{R_2}{R_1 + R_2}\right) = (18 \text{ V})\left(\frac{12 \text{ M}\Omega}{24 \text{ M}\Omega}\right) = 9 \text{ V}$$

$$I_D = \frac{V_G}{R_S + r_S} = \frac{9 \text{ V}}{3 \text{ k}\Omega} = 3 \text{ mA}$$

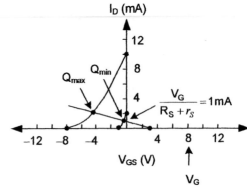

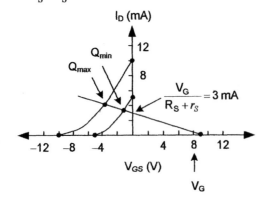

The Q-points are used to *approximate* a range of $V_{GS} = -1$ V to -3.75 V.

Using $g_m = g_{m0}\left(1 - \frac{V_{GS}}{V_{GS(\text{off})}}\right)$, substitute as follows:

$$g_m = (2000 \text{ } \mu\text{S})\left(1 - \frac{-1 \text{ V}}{-5 \text{ V}}\right) = 1600 \text{ } \mu\text{S} \quad \text{and}$$

$$g_m = (4000 \text{ } \mu\text{S})\left(1 - \frac{-3.75 \text{ V}}{-10 \text{ V}}\right) = 2500 \text{ } \mu\text{S}$$

The value of r_D is found as
$r_D = R_D \parallel R_L = (4.7 \text{ k}\Omega) \parallel (4.7 \text{ k}\Omega) = 2.35 \text{ k}\Omega$. Using the minimum value of g_m:

$$A_v = \frac{r_D}{r_S + (1/g_m)} = \frac{2.35 \text{ k}\Omega}{300 \text{ }\Omega + 625 \text{ }\Omega} = 2.54 \text{ (min)}$$

Using the maximum value of g_m:

$$A_v = \frac{r_D}{r_S + (1/g_m)} = \frac{2.35 \text{ k}\Omega}{300 \text{ }\Omega + 400 \text{ }\Omega} = 3.36 \text{ (max)}$$

36.

I_{DSS} (mA)	V_{GS} (V)	$V_{GS(\text{off})}$ (V)	I_D (mA)
(min) 2	−0.25	−1	1.13
2	−0.5	−1	0.5
(max) 10	−2	−8	5.63
10	−4	−8	2.5

Using the values in the table, and the points representing $V_{GS(\text{off})}$ and I_{DSS}, the curves are plotted as shown on the following page. The bias line is plotted using the following values:

$$V_G = V_{CC}\left(\frac{R_2}{R_1 + R_2}\right) = (12 \text{ V})\left(\frac{1 \text{ M}\Omega}{4 \text{ M}\Omega}\right) = 3 \text{ V}$$

$$I_D = \frac{V_G}{R_S + r_S} = \frac{3 \text{ V}}{3 \text{ k}\Omega} = 1 \text{ mA}$$

The Q-points are used to *approximate* a range of $V_{GS} = -250$ mV to -4.25 V.

Using $g_m = g_{m0}\left(1 - \frac{V_{GS}}{V_{GS(\text{off})}}\right)$, substitute as follows:

$$g_m = (2000 \text{ } \mu\text{S})\left(1 - \frac{-250 \text{ mV}}{-1 \text{ V}}\right) = 1500 \text{ } \mu\text{S} \quad \text{and}$$

$$g_m = (4000 \text{ } \mu\text{S})\left(1 - \frac{-4.25 \text{ V}}{-8 \text{ V}}\right) = 1875 \text{ } \mu\text{S}$$

The value of r_D is found as
$r_D = R_D \parallel R_L = (2.2 \text{ k}\Omega) \parallel (10 \text{ k}\Omega) = 1.8 \text{ k}\Omega$. Using the minimum value of g_m:

$$A_v = \frac{r_D}{r_S + (1/g_m)} = \frac{1.8 \text{ k}\Omega}{300 \text{ }\Omega + 667 \text{ }\Omega} = 1.86 \text{ (min)}$$

Using the maximum value of g_m:

$$A_v = \frac{r_D}{r_S + (1/g_m)} = \frac{1.8 \text{ k}\Omega}{300 \text{ }\Omega + 533 \text{ }\Omega} = 2.16 \text{ (max)}$$

37. $Z_{in} = R_1 \parallel R_2 = (2 \text{ M}\Omega) \parallel (1 \text{ M}\Omega) = 667 \text{ k}\Omega$

38. $Z_{in} = R_1 \parallel R_2 = (3 \text{ M}\Omega) \parallel (1 \text{ M}\Omega) = 750 \text{ k}\Omega$

39. $r_S = R_S \parallel R_L = (1 \text{ k}\Omega) \parallel (1 \text{ k}\Omega) = 500 \text{ }\Omega$

$$A_v = \frac{r_S}{r_S + (1/g_m)} = \frac{500 \text{ }\Omega}{500 \text{ }\Omega + 1 \text{ k}\Omega} = 0.333$$

$Z_{in} = R_1 \parallel R_2 = (5.1 \text{ M}\Omega) \parallel (5.1 \text{ M}\Omega) = 2.55 \text{ M}\Omega$

$$Z_{out} = R_S \parallel \frac{1}{g_m} = (1 \text{ k}\Omega) \parallel (1 \text{ k}\Omega) = 500 \text{ }\Omega$$

40. $r_S = R_S \parallel R_L = (910 \text{ }\Omega) \parallel (10 \text{ k}\Omega) = 834 \text{ }\Omega$

$$A_v = \frac{r_S}{r_S + (1/g_m)} = \frac{834 \text{ }\Omega}{834 \text{ }\Omega + 200 \text{ }\Omega} = 0.807$$

$Z_{in} = R_1 \parallel R_2 = (10 \text{ M}\Omega) \parallel (10 \text{ M}\Omega) = 5 \text{ M}\Omega$

$$Z_{out} = R_S \parallel \frac{1}{g_m} = (910 \text{ }\Omega) \parallel (200 \text{ }\Omega) = 164 \text{ }\Omega$$

41. $r_S = R_S \parallel R_L = (470 \text{ }\Omega) \parallel (15 \text{ k}\Omega) = 456 \text{ }\Omega$

$$A_v = \frac{r_S}{r_S + (1/g_m)} = \frac{456 \text{ }\Omega}{456 \text{ }\Omega + 400 \text{ }\Omega} = 0.533$$

$Z_{in} = R_1 \parallel R_2 = (9.1 \text{ M}\Omega) \parallel (4.7 \text{ M}\Omega) = 3.1 \text{ M}\Omega$

$$Z_{out} = R_S \parallel \frac{1}{g_m} = (470 \text{ }\Omega) \parallel (400 \text{ }\Omega) = 216 \text{ }\Omega$$

42. $r_S = R_S \parallel R_L = (1\text{ k}\Omega) \parallel (10\text{ k}\Omega) = 909\ \Omega$

$A_v = \dfrac{r_S}{r_S + (1/g_m)} = \dfrac{909\ \Omega}{909\ \Omega + 333\ \Omega} = 0.732$

$Z_{\text{in}} = R_1 \parallel R_2 = (10\text{ M}\Omega) \parallel (8.2\text{ M}\Omega) = 4.51\text{ M}\Omega$

$Z_{\text{out}} = R_S \parallel \dfrac{1}{g_m} = (1\text{ k}\Omega) \parallel (333\ \Omega) = 250\ \Omega$

43. $r_D = R_D \parallel R_L = (1\text{ k}\Omega) \parallel (10\text{ k}\Omega) = 909\ \Omega$

$A_v = g_m r_D = (4200\ \mu\text{S})(909\ \Omega) = 3.82$

$Z_{\text{in}} = R_S \parallel \dfrac{1}{g_m} = (1\text{ k}\Omega) \parallel (238\ \Omega) = 192\ \Omega$

$r_d = \dfrac{1}{y_{os}} = 2.5\text{ k}\Omega$

$Z_{\text{out}} = R_D \parallel r_d = (1\text{ k}\Omega) \parallel (2.5\text{ k}\Omega) = 714\ \Omega$

44. $r_D = R_D \parallel R_L = (3.3\text{ k}\Omega) \parallel (12\text{ k}\Omega) = 2.59\text{ k}\Omega$

$A_v = g_m r_D = (5000\ \mu\text{S})(2.59\text{ k}\Omega) = 12.95$

$Z_{\text{in}} = R_S \parallel \dfrac{1}{g_m} = (3.3\text{ k}\Omega) \parallel (200\ \Omega) = 189\ \Omega$

$r_d = \dfrac{1}{y_{os}} = 2\text{ k}\Omega$

$Z_{\text{out}} = R_D \parallel r_d = (1\text{ k}\Omega) \parallel (2\text{ k}\Omega) = 667\ \Omega$

45. There is a signal at the JFET gate, but not at either the drain or source terminals. The dc voltages at the source and drain indicate that the JFET is conducting, so the problem is most likely an open JFET gate.

46. The resistor between the gate and V_{DD} (which we normally identify as R_1) is open. When this resistor opens, the remaining components form a self-bias circuit.

47. The source and load dc voltages are equal. This indicates that the output coupling capacitor is shorted.

48. Assuming that the value of V_{DD} is normal, the problem must be an open drain resistor (R_D).

49. The JFET source is connected to the BJT collector, which means that $I_D = I_C$. Assuming the BJT is an ideal component, $I_C = I_E = I_D$ and $I_D = \dfrac{V_E}{R_E}$. Since the base of the BJT is tied to ground, $V_E \cong -0.7\text{ V}$.

Therefore $I_{DQ} \cong I_E = \left|\dfrac{V_{RE}}{R_E}\right| = \left|\dfrac{-17.3\text{ V}}{4.7\text{ k}\Omega}\right| = 3.68\text{ mA}$, and

$V_D = V_{DD} - (I_D R_D) = 18\text{ V} - (3.68\text{ mA})(2.4\text{ k}\Omega)$
$\quad = 9.17\text{ V}$

50. Using the values shown in the 2N5486 spec sheet (Section 12.6.2), the curves are plotted as shown on the following page. The bias line is plotted using the following values:

$V_G = V_{CC}\left(\dfrac{R_2}{R_1 + R_2}\right) = (80\text{ V})\left(\dfrac{10\text{ M}\Omega}{20\text{ M}\Omega}\right) = 40\text{ V}$

$I_D = \dfrac{V_G}{R_S} = \dfrac{40\text{ V}}{2.7\text{ k}\Omega} = 14.8\text{ mA}$

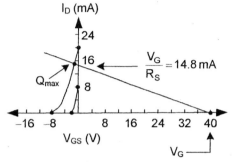

The *maximum ratings* chart on the spec sheet lists maximum values of $I_D = 30$ mA and $V_{DG} = 25$ V_{dc}. The curve shows a maximum drain current of approximately 15 mA. At this value,

$V_D = V_{DD} - I_D R_D = 80\text{ V} - (15\text{ mA})(330\ \Omega)$
$\quad = 72.5\text{ V (minimum)}$

With a fixed value of $V_G = 40$ V, V_{DG} has a minimum value of $V_{DG} = V_D - V_G = 72.5\text{ V} - 40\text{ V} = 32.5\text{ V}$. Since this value exceeds the maximum component rating of 25 V, the device *cannot* be used in the circuit.

51. The spec sheet for the 2N5486 lists the following ranges: $V_{GS(\text{off})} = -2$ to -8 V and $I_{DSS} = 8$ to 20 mA. For the circuit shown, the bias line is plotted using the following values:

$V_G = V_{CC}\left(\dfrac{R_2}{R_1 + R_2}\right) = (40\text{ V})\left(\dfrac{10\text{ M}\Omega}{20\text{ M}\Omega}\right) = 20\text{ V}$

$I_D = \dfrac{V_G}{R_S} = \dfrac{20\text{ V}}{470\ \Omega} = 42.6\text{ mA}$

This value clearly exceeds the maximum rated value of I_{DSS} (as well as the maximum allowable I_D rating of 30 mA), so the component *cannot* be used in the circuit.

52. According to the component spec sheet, the 2N5462 is a p-channel JFET. Therefore, it *cannot* be used in the circuit.

CHAPTER 13

Note: The following FET Drain Current equation is used to solve many of the problems in this chapter:

$$I_D = I_{DSS}\left(1 - \dfrac{V_{GS}}{V_{GS(\text{off})}}\right)^2 \qquad (12.1)$$

In order to simplify I_D calculations, the values relating to this equation are presented in table format. The values of V_{GS} used in the tables are chosen at random (except when specified in the problem) and may not match those chosen by your students.

EXAMPLE PRACTICE PROBLEMS   (CH 13)

13-1.

I_{DSS} (mA)	V_{GS} (V)	$V_{GS\,(off)}$ (V)	I_D (mA)
(min) 8	−4	−4	0
8	−2	−4	2
8	0	−4	8
8	2	−4	18
8	4	−4	32
(max) 12	−4	−6	1.3
12	−2	−6	5.3
12	−0	−6	12
12	2	−6	21.3
12	4	−6	33.3

Using the combinations of V_{GS} and I_D given in the table, the curves are plotted as shown in text Figure 13.43 (at the end of the chapter).

13-2. $k = \dfrac{I_{D(on)}}{\left(V_{GS} - V_{GS(th)}\right)^2} = \dfrac{14\ \text{mA}}{(12\ \text{V} - 2\ \text{V})^2}$

$= 1.4 \times 10^{-4}\ \text{A/V}^2$.   For $V_{GS} = 16$ V,

$I_D = k\,(V_{GS} - V_{GS(th)})^2$

$= (1.4 \times 10^{-4}\ \text{A/V}^2)(16\ \text{V} - 2\ \text{V})^2 = 27.4$ mA

13-3. From Practice Problem 13-2: $I_{D(on)} = 14$ mA
when $V_{GS} = V_{DS} = 12$ V.

$I_D = I_{D(on)} = 14$ mA

$V_{DS} = V_{DD} - R_D I_{D(on)} = 14\ \text{V} - (510\ \Omega)(14\ \text{mA})$

$= 6.86$ V

PRACTICE PROBLEMS   (CH 13)

1.

I_{DSS} (mA)	V_{GS} (V)	$V_{GS\,(off)}$ (V)	I_D (mA)
8	−4	−4	0
8	−2	−4	2
8	0	−4	8
8	2	−4	18
8	4	−4	32

The points listed in the table are used to plot the curve in Figure 13.43.

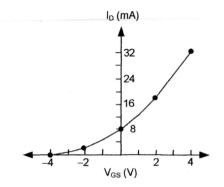

2.

I_{DSS} (mA)	V_{GS} (V)	$V_{GS\,(off)}$ (V)	I_D (mA)
(min) 12	−8	−8	0
12	−4	−8	3
12	0	−8	12
12	2	−8	18.8
12	4	−8	27

The points listed in the table are used to plot the curve.

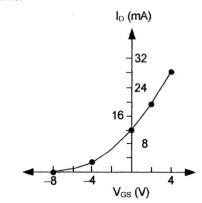

3.

I_{DSS} (mA)	V_{GS} (V)	$V_{GS\,(off)}$ (V)	I_D (mA)
(min) 6	−2	−4	1.5
6	2	−4	13.5
6	4	−4	24
(max) 9	−3	−6	2.25
9	3	−6	20.3
9	6	−6	36

The points listed in the table are used to plot the curve that follows.

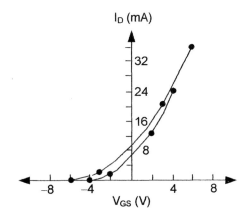

At $V_{GS} = 0$ V, $g_m = g_{m0} = 3000$ μS. At $V_{GS} = 5$ V,

$$g_m = g_{m0}\left(1 - \frac{V_{GS}}{V_{GS(\text{off})}}\right) = (3000 \text{ μS})\left(1 - \frac{5 \text{ V}}{-8 \text{ V}}\right)$$

$$= 4875 \text{ μS}$$

7. $k = \dfrac{I_{D(\text{on})}}{\left(V_{GS} - V_{GS(\text{th})}\right)^2} = \dfrac{12 \text{ mA}}{(8 \text{ V} - 4 \text{ V})^2}$

$$= 7.5 \times 10^{-4} \text{ A/V}^2$$

$I_D = k\,(V_{GS} - V_{GS(\text{th})})^2 = (7.5 \times 10^{-4})(6 \text{ V} - 4 \text{ V})^2$

$$= 3 \text{ mA}$$

8. $k = \dfrac{I_{D(\text{on})}}{\left(V_{GS} - V_{GS(\text{th})}\right)^2} = \dfrac{10 \text{ mA}}{(8 \text{ V} - 2 \text{ V})^2}$

$$= 2.78 \times 10^{-4} \text{ A/V}^2$$

$I_D = k\,(V_{GS} - V_{GS(\text{th})})^2 = (2.78 \times 10^{-4})(12 \text{ V} - 2 \text{ V})^2$

$$= 27.8 \text{ mA}$$

9. $k = \dfrac{I_{D(\text{on})}}{\left(V_{GS} - V_{GS(\text{th})}\right)^2} = \dfrac{8 \text{ mA}}{(4 \text{ V} - 1 \text{ V})^2}$

$$= 8.89 \times 10^{-4} \text{ A/V}^2.$$

At $V_{GS} = 1$ V, $I_D = k\,(V_{GS} - V_{GS(\text{th})})^2$

$= (8.89 \times 10^{-4})(1 \text{ V} - 1 \text{ V})^2 = 0$ mA

At $V_{GS} = 4$ V, $I_D = I_{D(\text{on})} = 8$ mA

At $V_{GS} = 1$ V, $I_D = k\,(V_{GS} - V_{GS(\text{th})})^2$

$= (8.89 \times 10^{-4})(5 \text{ V} - 1 \text{ V})^2 = 14.2$ mA

10. $k = \dfrac{I_{D(\text{on})}}{\left(V_{GS} - V_{GS(\text{th})}\right)^2} = \dfrac{2 \text{ mA}}{(5 \text{ V} - 3 \text{ V})^2}$

$$= 5 \times 10^{-4} \text{ A/V}^2$$

At $V_{GS} = 3$ V, $I_D = k\,(V_{GS} - V_{GS(\text{th})})^2$

$= (5 \times 10^{-4})(3 \text{ V} - 3 \text{ V})^2 = 0$ mA

At $V_{GS} = 5$ V, $I_D = I_{D(\text{on})} = 2$ mA

At $V_{GS} = 8$ V, $I_D = k\,(V_{GS} - V_{GS(\text{th})})^2$

$= (5 \times 10^{-4})(8 \text{ V} - 3 \text{ V})^2 = 12.5$ mA

11. $I_D = I_{D(\text{on})} = 8$ mA

$V_{DS} = V_{DD} - I_D R_D = 32 \text{ V} - (8 \text{ mA})(2 \text{ k}\Omega) = 16$ V

12. $I_D = I_{D(\text{on})} = 12$ mA

$V_{DS} = V_{DD} - I_D R_D = 24 \text{ V} - (12 \text{ mA})(1 \text{ k}\Omega) = 12$ V

13. $I_D = I_{D(\text{on})} = 10$ mA

$V_{DS} = V_{DD} - I_D R_D = 14 \text{ V} - (10 \text{ mA})(680 \text{ }\Omega) = 7.2$ V

14. $I_D = I_{D(\text{on})} = 4$ mA

$V_{DS} = V_{DD} - I_D R_D = 8 \text{ V} - (4 \text{ mA})(1 \text{ k}\Omega) = 4$ V

15. $I_D = I_{D(\text{on})} = 20$ mA

$V_{DS} = V_{DD} - I_D R_D = 10 \text{ V} - (20 \text{ mA})(200 \text{ }\Omega) = 6$ V

16. $I_D = I_{D(\text{on})} = 18$ mA

$V_{DS} = V_{DD} - I_D R_D = 15 \text{ V} - (18 \text{ mA})(390 \text{ }\Omega) = 7.98$ V

17. The output waveform is in phase with the input signal and has a $+24$ V_{dc} reference. These characteristics indicate that the drain signal is a result of V_{in} passing through the 10 MΩ feedback resistor. Q_1 is open.

18. The circuit has a value of $V_{GS} = 0$ V. With this input, the circuit *should* have values of

---

4.

I_{DSS} (mA)	V_{GS} (V)	$V_{GS(\text{off})}$ (V)	I_D (mA)
(min) 5	−2	−5	1.8
5	2	−5	9.8
5	5	−5	20
(max) 10	−5	−10	2.5
10	5	−10	22.5
10	10	−10	40

The points listed in the table are used to plot the curve.

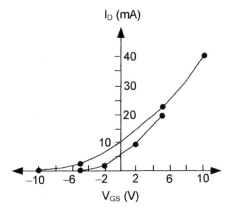

5. From Problem 1: $V_{GS(\text{off})} = -4$ V. At $V_{GS} = -2$ V,

$$g_m = g_{m0}\left(1 - \frac{V_{GS}}{V_{GS(\text{off})}}\right) = (2000 \text{ μS})\left(1 - \frac{-2 \text{ V}}{-4 \text{ V}}\right)$$

$$= 1000 \text{ μS}$$

At $V_{GS} = 0$ V, $g_m = g_{m0} = 2000$ μS. At $V_{GS} = 2$ V,

$$g_m = g_{m0}\left(1 - \frac{V_{GS}}{V_{GS(\text{off})}}\right) = (2000 \text{ μS})\left(1 - \frac{2 \text{ V}}{-4 \text{ V}}\right)$$

$$= 3000 \text{ μS}$$

6. From Problem 2: $V_{GS(\text{off})} = -8$ V. At $V_{GS} = -5$ V,

$$g_m = g_{m0}\left(1 - \frac{V_{GS}}{V_{GS(\text{off})}}\right) = (3000 \text{ μS})\left(1 - \frac{-5 \text{ V}}{-8 \text{ V}}\right)$$

$$= 1125 \text{ μS}$$

49

$I_D = I_{DSS} = 8$ mA and $V_D = V_{DD} - I_D R_D = 8$ V. The value of $V_D = 0$ V could be caused by an open drain resistor (R_D) or a MOSFET that is shorted from drain to source.

19. For the *zero bias* circuit shown, $g_m = g_{m0} = 2600$ μS to 3200 μS. There is no load connected to the amplifier, so $A_v = g_m R_D = (2600$ μS$)(1$ kΩ$) = 2.6$ (min) and $A_v = g_m R_D = (3200$ μS$)(1$ kΩ$) = 3.2$ (max).

20. The analysis begins with plotting the devices curves and bias line. Since the circuit is self-biased, we are interested only in the depletion mode operation of the MOSFET.

Curve	I_{DSS} (mA)	V_{GS} (V)	$V_{GS(off)}$ (V)	I_D (mA)
Minimum	4	−4	−8	1.0
	4	−2	−8	2.3
Maximum	8	−6	−12	2.0
	8	−3	−12	4.5

Using the values in the table, and the points representing $V_{GS(off)}$ and I_{DSS}, the curve is plotted as shown.

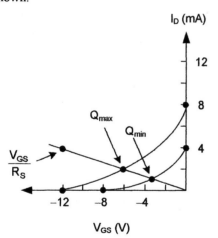

Assuming $V_{GS} = -12$ V, $I_D = \dfrac{-V_{GS}}{R_S} = \dfrac{12\text{ V}}{3\text{ k}\Omega} = 4$ mA.

The bias line is then drawn from the origin to the $(-12$ V, 4 mA) point. Using the Q-points, we estimate a range of $V_{GS} = -3.5$ V to -6 V. Using these values,

$$g_m = g_{m0}\left(1 - \frac{V_{GS}}{V_{GS(off)}}\right) = (2000\text{ μS})\left(1 - \frac{-3.5\text{ V}}{-8\text{ V}}\right) =$$

1125 μS (minimum), and $g_m = g_{m0}\left(1 - \dfrac{V_{GS}}{V_{GS(off)}}\right) =$

$(3800\text{ μS})\left(1 - \dfrac{-6\text{ V}}{-12\text{ V}}\right) = 1900$ μS (maximum). The

circuit does not have a load and the source resistor is

not bypassed, so the (min) and (max) values of A_v are found as:

$$A_v = \frac{R_D}{R_S + (1/g_m)} = \frac{2\text{ k}\Omega}{3\text{ k}\Omega + 889\ \Omega} = 0.514 \text{ (min)}$$

$$A_v = \frac{R_D}{R_S + (1/g_m)} = \frac{2\text{ k}\Omega}{3\text{ k}\Omega + 526\ \Omega} = 0.567 \text{ (max)}$$

21. The analysis begins with plotting the MOSFET transconductance curve and the circuit bias line. The curve is plotted using the values in the table that follow.

I_{DSS} (mA)	V_{GS} (V)	$V_{GS(off)}$ (V)	I_D (mA)
5	−3	−5	0.8
5	−2	−5	1.8
5	2	−5	9.8

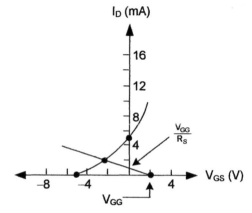

From the curve, the maximum value of I_D is approximated as $I_D = 2$ mA. It would seem that minimum drain current would be assumed to be $I_D = 1$ mA, as determined by the intersection of the bias line and the y-axis of the graph. However, a D-MOSFET is capable of enhancement-mode (positive V_{GS}) operation. Thus, in the absence of a minimum transconductance curve, the minimum value of I_D must be assumed to correspond to the point where the bias line intersects the x-axis in the enhancement region of operation. Therefore, the assumed range of I_D is 0 mA to 2 mA.

22. When $V_A = 0$ V, Q_2 is biased *on* and Q_1 is biased *off*. When $V_A = +5$ V, Q_2 is biased *off* and Q_1 is biased *on*. When $V_B = 0$ V, Q_3 is biased *on* and Q_4 is biased *off*. When $V_B = +5$ V, Q_3 is biased *off* and Q_4 is biased *on*. Based on these statements, any +5 V input will

- Open Q_2 and/or Q_3, isolating the output from $+V_{SS}$.
- Short the output to ground via Q_1 and/or Q_4.

When $V_A = V_B = 0$ V:

- Q_2 and Q_3 conduct, shorting the output to $+V_{SS}$.
- Q_1 and Q_4 are both biased *off*, isolating the output from ground.
-

Thus, a +5 V output only occurs when *both* inputs are at 0 V.

23. $Z_{in(G)} = \dfrac{V_{GS}}{I_G} = \dfrac{32\text{ V}}{800\text{ pA}} = 40\text{ G}\Omega$ and

$Z_{in} = R_1 \parallel R_2 \parallel Z_{in(G)} = (5.1\text{ M}\Omega) \parallel (5.1\text{ M}\Omega) \parallel (40\text{ G}\Omega)$
$\quad = 2.5498\text{ M}\Omega$

Assuming $Z_{in(G)}$ is infinite,

$Z_{in} = R_1 \parallel R_2 = (5.1\text{ M}\Omega) \parallel (5.1\text{ M}\Omega) = 2.55\text{ M}\Omega$.
The difference between the two values is approximately 200 Ω.

24. According to its spec sheet, the BS107 MOSFET has values of $V_{GS(th)} = 1.0$ to 3.0 V and $I_{DSS} = 30$ nA (maximum).

CHAPTER 14

EXAMPLE PRACTICE PROBLEMS (CH 14)

14-1. $\text{BW} = f_{C2} - f_{C1} = 1.5\text{ MHz} - 400\text{ Hz} = 1.4996\text{ MHz}$

14-2. $f_0 = \sqrt{f_{C1} f_{C2}} = \sqrt{(400\text{ Hz})(1.5\text{ MHz})} = 24.5\text{ kHz}$

14-3. $\dfrac{f_0}{f_{C1}} = \dfrac{24.5\text{ kHz}}{400\text{ Hz}} = 61.3,$

$\dfrac{f_{C2}}{f_0} = \dfrac{1.5\text{ MHz}}{24.5\text{ kHz}} = 61.2$

(The 0.1 difference is due to rounding.)

14-4. $f_{C1} = \dfrac{f_0^2}{f_{C2}} = \dfrac{(30\text{ kHz})^2}{300\text{ kHz}} = 3\text{ kHz}$

$\text{BW} = f_{C2} - f_{C1} = 300\text{ kHz} - 3\text{ kHz} = 297\text{ kHz}$

14-5. $f_{C2} = \dfrac{f_0^2}{f_{C1}} = \dfrac{(25\text{ kHz})^2}{5\text{ kHz}} = 125\text{ kHz}$

$\text{BW} = f_{C2} - f_{C1} = 125\text{ kHz} - 5\text{ kHz} = 120\text{ kHz}$

14-6. $A_{p(dB)} = 10 \log \dfrac{P_{out}}{P_{in}} = 10 \log \dfrac{6\text{ W}}{420\text{ μW}} = 41.5\text{ dB}$

14-7. $A_{p1} = 10 \log (100) = 20\text{ dB}, A_{p2} = 10 \log (86) = 19.3\text{ dB}, A_{p3} = 10 \log (45) = 16.5\text{ dB}$
$A_{p(T)} = 20\text{ dB} + 19.3\text{ dB} + 16.5\text{ dB} = 55.8\text{ dB}$
$A_{p(T)} = A_{p1} A_{p2} A_{p3} = (100)(86)(45) = 3.87 \times 10^5$
$A_{p(T)} = 10 \log (3.87 \times 10^5) = 55.9\text{ dB}$
(The 0.1 difference is due to rounding.)

14-8. $R_{in} = R_1 \parallel R_2 \parallel h_{ie} = (56\text{ k}\Omega) \parallel (5.6\text{ k}\Omega) \parallel (5\text{ k}\Omega)$
$\quad = 2.52\text{ k}\Omega$

$f_{1B} = \dfrac{1}{2\pi (R_S + R_{in}) C_{C1}}$

$\quad = \dfrac{1}{2\pi (3.52\text{ k}\Omega)(1\,\mu\text{F})} = 45.2\text{ Hz}$

14-9. $f_{1C} = \dfrac{1}{2\pi (R_C + R_L) C_{C2}} =$

$\dfrac{1}{2\pi (5.1\text{ k}\Omega)(2.2\,\mu\text{F})} = 14.2\text{ Hz}$

14-10. $r'_e = \dfrac{h_{ie}}{h_{fe}} = \dfrac{5\text{ k}\Omega}{200} = 25\ \Omega,$

$R_{th} = R_S \parallel R_1 \parallel R_2 = (1\text{ k}\Omega) \parallel (56\text{ k}\Omega) \parallel (5.6\text{ k}\Omega) = 836\ \Omega$

$R_{out} = r'_e + \dfrac{R_{th}}{h_{fc}} = 25\ \Omega + \dfrac{836\ \Omega}{201} = 29.2\ \Omega,$

$f_{1E} = \dfrac{1}{2\pi R_{out} C_B} = \dfrac{1}{2\pi (29.2\ \Omega)(100\,\mu\text{F})} = 54.5\text{ Hz}$

14-11. $\Delta A_{v(dB)} = 20 \log \dfrac{1}{\sqrt{1 + \left(\dfrac{f_{C1}}{f}\right)^2}}$

$\quad = 20 \log \dfrac{1}{\sqrt{1 + \left(\dfrac{8\text{ kHz}}{4\text{ kHz}}\right)^2}} = -6.99\text{ dB}$

$A_{v(dB)} = A_{v(mid)} + \Delta A_{v(dB)} = 23\text{ dB} - 6.99\text{ dB} = 16\text{ dB}$

14-12. $r'_e = \dfrac{h_{ie}}{h_{fe}} = \dfrac{650\ \Omega}{250} = 2.6\ \Omega$

$C_{be} = \dfrac{1}{2\pi f_T r'_e} = \dfrac{1}{2\pi (200\text{ MHz})(2.6\ \Omega)} \cong 306\text{ pF}$

14-13. $C_{in(M)} \cong A_v C_{bc} = (240)(4\text{ pF}) = 960\text{ pF}$
$C_{out(M)} \cong C_{bc} = 4\text{ pF}$

14-14. $r_C = R_C \parallel R_L = (3.6\text{ k}\Omega) \parallel (1.5\text{ k}\Omega) = 1.06\text{ k}\Omega$

$A_v = \dfrac{h_{fe} r_C}{h_{ie}} = \dfrac{(200)(1.06\text{ k}\Omega)}{5\text{ k}\Omega} = 42.4$

$C_{in(M)} \cong A_v C_{bc} = (42.4)(4\text{ pF}) = 170\text{ pF}$
$R_{th} = R_1 \parallel R_2 \parallel R_S = (56\text{ k}\Omega) \parallel (5.6\text{ k}\Omega) \parallel (1\text{ k}\Omega) = 836\ \Omega$

$r'_e = \dfrac{h_{ie}}{h_{fe}} = \dfrac{5\text{ k}\Omega}{200} = 25\ \Omega$

$C_{be} = \dfrac{1}{2\pi f_T r'_e} = \dfrac{1}{2\pi (300\text{ MHz})(25\ \Omega)} = 21.2\text{ pF}$

$f_{2B} = \dfrac{1}{2\pi (R_{th} \parallel h_{ie})(C_{be} + C_{in(M)})} =$

$\dfrac{1}{2\pi (836\ \Omega \parallel 5\text{ k}\Omega)(21.2\text{ pF} + 170\text{ pF})} = 1.16\text{ MHz}$

14-15. From Problem 14-14: $r_C = 1.06\text{ k}\Omega$ and $C_{out(M)} = 4\text{ pF}$. With a purely resistive load, $C_L = 0\text{ F}$.

$$f_{2C} = \frac{1}{2\pi r_C (C_{out(M)} + C_L)} = \frac{1}{2\pi (1.06\text{ k}\Omega)(4\text{ pF})}$$
$$= 37.5\text{ MHz}$$

14-16. [This example has no practice problem.]

14-17. $R_{in} = R_1 \parallel R_2 = (10\text{ M}\Omega) \parallel (10\text{ M}\Omega) = 5\text{ M}\Omega$

$$f_{1G} = \frac{1}{2\pi (R_S + R_{in})C_{C1}} =$$
$$\frac{1}{2\pi (5\text{ M}\Omega)(3.3\text{ }\mu\text{F})} \cong 0.01\text{ Hz}$$

14-18. $R_{in} = R_1 \parallel R_2 = (10\text{ M}\Omega) \parallel (1\text{ M}\Omega) = 909\text{ k}\Omega$

$$f_{1G} = \frac{1}{2\pi (R_S + R_{in})C_{C1}}$$
$$= \frac{1}{2\pi (909\text{ k}\Omega)(0.01\text{ }\mu\text{F})} = 17.5\text{ Hz}$$

$$f_{1D} = \frac{1}{2\pi (R_D + R_L)C_{C2}} = \frac{1}{2\pi (6.1\text{ k}\Omega)(0.1\text{ }\mu\text{F})}$$
$$= 261\text{ Hz}$$

The value of f_{C1} for the circuit is the higher of the terminal cutoff frequencies, 261 Hz.

14-19. $C_{in(M)} = C_{gd}(g_m r_D + 1)$
$= (3\text{ pF}) [(3200\text{ }\mu\text{S}) (1.8\text{ k}\Omega) + 1]$
$= 20.3\text{ pF}$

14-20. $R_{th} = R_S \parallel R_{in} = (820\text{ }\Omega) \parallel (909\text{ k}\Omega) = 819\text{ }\Omega$,
$r_D = R_D \parallel R_L = (1.1\text{ k}\Omega) \parallel (5\text{ k}\Omega) = 902\text{ }\Omega$,
$A_v = g_m r_D = (2200\text{ }\mu\text{S})(902\text{ }\Omega) = 1.98$
$C_{in(M)} = C_{gd}(g_m r_D + 1) = (4\text{ pF})(2.98) = 11.9\text{ pF}$
$C_G = C_{gs} + C_{in(M)} = 5\text{ pF} + 11.9\text{ pF} = 16.9\text{ pF}$

$$f_{2G} = \frac{1}{2\pi R_{th} C_G} = \frac{1}{2\pi (819\text{ }\Omega)(16.9\text{ pF})}$$
$$= 11.5\text{ MHz}$$

$$C_{out(M)} = C_{gd}\frac{g_m r_D + 1}{g_m r_D} = (4\text{ pF})\frac{2.98}{1.98} = 6.02\text{ pF}$$

$C_D = C_{out(M)} + C_{ds} + C_L = 6.02\text{ pF} + 2\text{ pF} + 0\text{ pF}$
$= 8.02\text{ pF}$

$$f_{2D} = \frac{1}{2\pi r_D C_D} = \frac{1}{2\pi (902\text{ }\Omega)(8.02\text{ pF})} = 22\text{ MHz}$$

14-21. $C_{gd} = C_{rss} = 3\text{ pF}$
$C_{ds} = C_{oss} - C_{rss} = 4\text{ pF} - 3\text{ pF} = 1\text{ pF}$
$C_{gs} = C_{iss} - C_{rss} = 12\text{ pF} - 3\text{ pF} = 9\text{ pF}$

14-22. $f_{C2(T)} = f_{C2} \sqrt{2^{1/n} - 1} = (800\text{ kHz}) \sqrt{2^{1/4} - 1}$
$= (800\text{ kHz})(0.435) = 348\text{ kHz}$

14-23. $f_{C1(T)} = \dfrac{f_{C1}}{\sqrt{2^{1/n} - 1}} = \dfrac{800\text{ Hz}}{\sqrt{2^{1/3} - 1}} = \dfrac{800\text{ Hz}}{0.5098}$
$= 1.57\text{ kHz}$

PRACTICE PROBLEMS (CH 14)

1. $BW = f_{C2} - f_{C1} = 640\text{ kHz} - 1.2\text{ kHz} = 638.8\text{ kHz}$
$f_0 = \sqrt{f_{C1} f_{C2}} = \sqrt{(1.2\text{ kHz})(640\text{ kHz})} = 27.7\text{ kHz}$

2. $BW = f_{C2} - f_{C1} = 748\text{ kHz} - 3.4\text{ kHz} = 744.6\text{ kHz}$
$f_0 = \sqrt{f_{C1} f_{C2}} = \sqrt{(3.4\text{ kHz})(748\text{ kHz})} = 50.4\text{ kHz}$

3. $BW = f_{C2} - f_{C1} = 489.6\text{ kHz} - 5.2\text{ kHz} = 484.4\text{ kHz}$
$f_0 = \sqrt{f_{C1} f_{C2}} = \sqrt{(5.2\text{ kHz})(489.6\text{ kHz})} = 50.5\text{ kHz}$

4. $BW = f_{C2} - f_{C1} = 822.7\text{ kHz} - 1.4\text{ kHz} = 821.3\text{ kHz}$
$f_0 = \sqrt{f_{C1} f_{C2}} = \sqrt{(1.4\text{ kHz})(822.7\text{ kHz})} = 33.9\text{ kHz}$

5. $f_0 = \sqrt{f_{C1} f_{C2}} = \sqrt{(2.6\text{ kHz})(483.6\text{ kHz})} = 35.5\text{ kHz}$

$\dfrac{f_0}{f_{C1}} = \dfrac{35.5\text{ kHz}}{2.6\text{ kHz}} = 13.7$, $\dfrac{f_{C2}}{f_0} = \dfrac{483.6\text{ kHz}}{35.5\text{ kHz}} = 13.6$

(The difference is due to rounding.)

6. $f_0 = \sqrt{f_{C1} f_{C2}} = \sqrt{(1\text{ kHz})(345\text{ kHz})} = 18.6\text{ kHz}$

$\dfrac{f_0}{f_{C1}} = \dfrac{18.6\text{ kHz}}{1\text{ kHz}} \cong 18.6$, $\dfrac{f_{C2}}{f_0} = \dfrac{345\text{ kHz}}{18.6\text{ kHz}} \cong 18.6$

7. $f_{C1} = \dfrac{f_0^2}{f_{C2}} = \dfrac{(72\text{ kHz})^2}{548\text{ kHz}} = 9.46\text{ kHz}$

$BW = f_{C2} - f_{C1} = 548\text{ kHz} - 9.46\text{ kHz} = 538.5\text{ kHz}$

8. $f_{C1} = \dfrac{f_0^2}{f_{C2}} = \dfrac{(22.8\text{ kHz})^2}{321\text{ kHz}} = 1.62\text{ kHz}$

$BW = f_{C2} - f_{C1} = 321\text{ kHz} - 1.62\text{ kHz} = 319.38\text{ kHz}$

9. $f_{C2} = \dfrac{f_0^2}{f_{C1}} = \dfrac{(48\text{ kHz})^2}{2\text{ kHz}} = 1.152\text{ MHz}$

$BW = f_{C2} - f_{C1} = 1.152\text{ MHz} - 2\text{ kHz} = 1.15\text{ MHz}$

10. $f_{C2} = \dfrac{f_0^2}{f_{C1}} = \dfrac{(36\text{ kHz})^2}{4.3\text{ kHz}} = 301.4\text{ kHz}$

$BW = f_{C2} - f_{C1} = 301.4\text{ kHz} - 4.3\text{ kHz} = 297.1\text{ kHz}$

11. $R_{in} = R_1 \parallel R_2 \parallel h_{ie} = (91\text{ k}\Omega) \parallel (16\text{ k}\Omega) \parallel (3\text{ k}\Omega)$
$= 2.46\text{ k}\Omega$

$$f_{1B} = \frac{1}{2\pi (R_S + R_{in})C_{C1}} = \frac{1}{2\pi (3.06\text{ k}\Omega)(0.1\text{ }\mu\text{F})}$$
$$= 520\text{ Hz}$$

12. $R_{in} = R_1 \parallel R_2 \parallel h_{ie} = (14\text{ k}\Omega) \parallel (2.4\text{ k}\Omega) \parallel (4\text{ k}\Omega)$
$= 1.35\text{ k}\Omega$

$$f_{1B} = \frac{1}{2\pi (R_S + R_{in})C_{C1}} = \frac{1}{2\pi (1.85\text{ k}\Omega)(1\text{ }\mu\text{F})}$$
$$= 86\text{ Hz}$$

13. $f_{1C} = \dfrac{1}{2\pi (R_C + R_L)C_{C2}}$

$$= \frac{1}{2\pi (9.4\text{ k}\Omega)(0.1\text{ }\mu\text{F})} = 169\text{ Hz}$$

52

14. $f_{1C} = \dfrac{1}{2\pi(R_C + R_L)C_{C2}}$

$= \dfrac{1}{2\pi(5.8\,\text{k}\Omega)(0.047\,\mu\text{F})} = 584\,\text{Hz}$

15. $R_{th} = R_1 \parallel R_2 \parallel R_S = (91\,\text{k}\Omega)\parallel(16\,\text{k}\Omega)\parallel(600\,\Omega)$

$= 575\,\Omega, \qquad r'_e = \dfrac{h_{ie}}{h_{fe}} = \dfrac{3\,\text{k}\Omega}{150} = 20\,\Omega,$

$R_{\text{out}} = r'_e + \dfrac{R_{th}}{h_{fc}} = 20\,\Omega + \dfrac{575\,\Omega}{151} = 23.8\,\Omega$

$f_{1E} = \dfrac{1}{2\pi R_{\text{out}}C_B} = \dfrac{1}{2\pi(23.8\,\Omega)(33\,\mu\text{F})} = 203\,\text{Hz}$

16. $R_{th} = R_1 \parallel R_2 \parallel R_S = (14\,\text{k}\Omega)\parallel(2.4\,\text{k}\Omega)\parallel(500\,\Omega)$

$= 402\,\Omega, \qquad r'_e = \dfrac{h_{ie}}{h_{fe}} = \dfrac{4\,\text{k}\Omega}{100} = 40\,\Omega,$

$R_{\text{out}} = r'_e + \dfrac{R_{th}}{h_{fc}} = 40\,\Omega + \dfrac{402\,\Omega}{101} = 44\,\Omega$

$f_{1E} = \dfrac{1}{2\pi R_{\text{out}}C_B} = \dfrac{1}{2\pi(44\,\Omega)(33\,\mu\text{F})} = 110\,\text{Hz}$

17. At $f = 7\,\text{kHz}$,

$\Delta A_v = 20\log\dfrac{1}{\sqrt{1+(8\,\text{kHz}/7\,\text{kHz})^2}} = -3.63\,\text{dB}$

$A_v = A_{v(\text{mid})} + \Delta A_{v(\text{dB})} = 32\,\text{dB} - 3.63\,\text{dB} \cong 28.4\,\text{dB}$
At $f = 5\,\text{kHz}$,

$\Delta A_v = 20\log\dfrac{1}{\sqrt{1+(8\,\text{kHz}/5\,\text{kHz})^2}} = -5.51\,\text{dB}$

$A_v = A_{v(\text{mid})} + \Delta A_{v(\text{dB})} = 32\,\text{dB} - 5.51\,\text{dB} \cong 26.5\,\text{dB}$
At $f = 4\,\text{kHz}$,

$\Delta A_v = 20\log\dfrac{1}{\sqrt{1+(8\,\text{kHz}/4\,\text{kHz})^2}} = -6.99\,\text{dB}$

$A_v = A_{v(\text{mid})} + \Delta A_{v(\text{dB})} = 32\,\text{dB} - 6.99\,\text{dB} \cong 25\,\text{dB}$
At $f = 1\,\text{kHz}$,

$\Delta A_v = 20\log\dfrac{1}{\sqrt{1+(8\,\text{kHz}/1\,\text{kHz})^2}} = -18.1\,\text{dB}$

$A_v = A_{v(\text{mid})} + \Delta A_{v(\text{dB})} = 32\,\text{dB} - 18.1\,\text{dB} = 13.9\,\text{dB}$

18. At $f = 18\,\text{kHz}$,

$\Delta A_v = 20\log\dfrac{1}{\sqrt{1+(12\,\text{kHz}/18\,\text{kHz})^2}} = -1.6\,\text{dB}$

$A_v = A_{v(\text{mid})} + \Delta A_{v(\text{dB})} = 16\,\text{dB} - 1.6\,\text{dB} = 14.4\,\text{dB}$
At $f = 12\,\text{kHz}$,

$\Delta A_v = 20\log\dfrac{1}{\sqrt{1+(12\,\text{kHz}/12\,\text{kHz})^2}} = -3\,\text{dB}$

$A_v = A_{v(\text{mid})} + \Delta A_{v(\text{dB})} = 16\,\text{dB} - 3\,\text{dB} = 13\,\text{dB}$
At $f = 10\,\text{kHz}$,

$\Delta A_v = 20\log\dfrac{1}{\sqrt{1+(12\,\text{kHz}/10\,\text{kHz})^2}} = -3.87\,\text{dB}$

$A_v = A_{v(\text{mid})} + \Delta A_{v(\text{dB})} = 16\,\text{dB} - 3.87\,\text{dB} = 12.13\,\text{dB}$
At $f = 2\,\text{kHz}$,

$\Delta A_v = 20\log\dfrac{1}{\sqrt{1+(12\,\text{kHz}/2\,\text{kHz})^2}} = -15.7\,\text{dB}$

$A_v = A_{v(\text{mid})} + \Delta A_{v(\text{dB})} = 16\,\text{dB} - 15.7\,\text{dB} = 0.3\,\text{dB}$

19. From Problems 11, 13, and 15, $f_{1B} = 520\,\text{Hz}$, $f_{1C} = 169\,\text{Hz}$, $f_{1E} = 203\,\text{Hz}$. f_{C1} equals the highest of these values, 520 Hz.

20. From Problems 12, 14, and 16, $f_{1B} = 86\,\text{Hz}$, $f_{1C} = 584\,\text{Hz}$, $f_{1E} = 110\,\text{Hz}$. f_{C1} equals the highest of these values, 584 Hz.

21. $r'_e \cong \dfrac{25\,\text{mV}}{10\,\text{mA}} = 2.5\,\Omega$

$C_{be} = \dfrac{1}{2\pi f_T r'_e} = \dfrac{1}{2\pi(200\,\text{MHz})(2.5\,\Omega)} = 318\,\text{pF}$

22. $r'_e \cong \dfrac{25\,\text{mV}}{1\,\text{mA}} = 25\,\Omega$

$C_{be} = \dfrac{1}{2\pi f_T r'_e} = \dfrac{1}{2\pi(400\,\text{MHz})(25\,\Omega)} = 15.9\,\text{pF}$

23. $C_{\text{in(M)}} \cong A_v C_{bc} = (100)(7\,\text{pF}) = 700\,\text{pF}$,
$C_{\text{out(M)}} \cong C_{bc} = 7\,\text{pF}$

24. $C_{\text{in(M)}} = (A_v + 1)C_{bc} = (5)(3\,\text{pF}) = 15\,\text{pF}$

$C_{\text{out(M)}} = C_{bc}\dfrac{A_v + 1}{A_v} = (3\,\text{pF})\dfrac{5}{4} = 3.75\,\text{pF}$

25. $r_C = R_C \parallel R_L = (7.2\,\text{k}\Omega)\parallel(2.2\,\text{k}\Omega) = 1.69\,\text{k}\Omega$

$A_v = \dfrac{h_{fe}r_C}{h_{ie}} = \dfrac{(150)(1.69\,\text{k}\Omega)}{3\,\text{k}\Omega} = 84.5$

$C_{\text{in(M)}} \cong A_v C_{bc} = (84.5)(7\,\text{pF}) = 592\,\text{pF}$

$r'_e = \dfrac{h_{ie}}{h_{fe}} = \dfrac{3\,\text{k}\Omega}{150} = 20\,\Omega$

$C_{be} = \dfrac{1}{2\pi f_T r'_e} = \dfrac{1}{2\pi(300\,\text{MHz})(20\,\Omega)} = 26.5\,\text{pF}$

$R_{th} = R_1 \parallel R_2 \parallel R_S = (91\,\text{k}\Omega)\parallel(16\,\text{k}\Omega)\parallel(600\,\Omega) = 575\,\Omega$

$f_{2B} = \dfrac{1}{2\pi(R_{th}\parallel h_{ie})(C_{be} + C_{\text{in(M)}})}$

$= \dfrac{1}{2\pi(575\,\Omega\parallel 3\,\text{k}\Omega)(26.5\,\text{pF} + 592\,\text{pF})} \cong 533\,\text{kHz}$

26. $r_C = R_C \parallel R_L = (1.1\,\text{k}\Omega)\parallel(4.7\,\text{k}\Omega) = 891\,\Omega$

$A_v = \dfrac{h_{fe}r_C}{h_{ie}} = \dfrac{(100)(891\,\Omega)}{4\,\text{k}\Omega} = 22.3$

$C_{\text{in(M)}} \cong A_v C_{bc} = (22.3)(9\,\text{pF}) = 201\,\text{pF}$

$r'_e = \dfrac{h_{ie}}{h_{fe}} = \dfrac{4\,\text{k}\Omega}{100} = 40\,\Omega$

$$C_{be} = \frac{1}{2\pi f_T r'_e} = \frac{1}{2\pi(400\,\text{MHz})(40\,\Omega)} = 9.95\,\text{pF}$$

$$R_{th} = R_1 \| R_2 \| R_S = (14\,\text{k}\Omega)\|(2.4\,\text{k}\Omega)\|(500\,\Omega) = 402\,\Omega$$

$$f_{2B} = \frac{1}{2\pi(R'_{\text{in}} \| h_{ie})(C_{be} + C_{\text{in(M)}})}$$

$$= \frac{1}{2\pi(402\,\Omega\,\|\,4\,\text{k}\Omega)(9.95\,\text{pF} + 201\,\text{pF})} = 2.07\,\text{MHz}$$

27. $C_{\text{out(M)}} \cong C_{bc} = 7\,\text{pF}$

$r_C = R_C \| R_L = (7.2\,\text{k}\Omega)\|(2.2\,\text{k}\Omega) = 1.69\,\text{k}\Omega$

For a purely resistive load, $C_L = 0\,\text{F}$, and

$$f_{2C} = \frac{1}{2\pi r_C(C_{\text{out(M)}} + C_L)} = \frac{1}{2\pi(1.69\,\text{k}\Omega)(7\,\text{pF})}$$

$$= 13.5\,\text{MHz}$$

28. $C_{\text{out(M)}} \cong C_{bc} = 9\,\text{pF}$

$r_C = R_C \| R_L = (1.1\,\text{k}\Omega)\|(4.7\,\text{k}\Omega) = 891\,\Omega$

For a purely resistive load, $C_L = 0\,\text{F}$, and

$$f_{2C} = \frac{1}{2\pi r_C(C_{\text{out(M)}} + C_L)} = \frac{1}{2\pi(891\,\Omega)(9\,\text{pF})}$$

$$= 19.8\,\text{MHz}$$

29. $R_{\text{in}} = R_1 \| R_2 \| h_{ie} = (12\,\text{k}\Omega)\|(2.2\,\text{k}\Omega)\|(3.4\,\text{k}\Omega)$

$\qquad = 1.2\,\text{k}\Omega$

$$f_{1B} = \frac{1}{2\pi(R_S + R_{\text{in}})C_{C1}} = \frac{1}{2\pi(2\,\text{k}\Omega)(3.3\,\mu\text{F})}$$

$$= 24.1\,\text{Hz}$$

$$f_{1C} = \frac{1}{2\pi(R_C + R_L)C_{C2}} = \frac{1}{2\pi(26.2\,\text{k}\Omega)(0.1\,\mu\text{F})}$$

$$= 60.7\,\text{Hz}, \quad r'_e = \frac{h_{ie}}{h_{fe}} = \frac{3.4\,\text{k}\Omega}{200} = 17\,\Omega,$$

$R_{th} = R_1 \| R_2 \| R_S = (12\,\text{k}\Omega)\|(2.2\,\text{k}\Omega)\|(800\,\Omega)$

$\qquad = 559\,\Omega$

$$R_{\text{out}} = r'_e + \frac{R'_{\text{in}}}{h_{fe}} = 17\,\Omega + \frac{559\,\Omega}{200} = 19.8\,\Omega$$

$$f_{1E} = \frac{1}{2\pi R_{\text{out}}C_B} = \frac{1}{2\pi(19.8\,\Omega)(100\,\mu\text{F})} = 80.4\,\text{Hz},$$

$r_C = R_C \| R_L = 6.2\,\text{k}\Omega\|(20\,\text{k}\Omega) = 4.73\,\text{k}\Omega,$

$$A_v = \frac{h_{fe}r_C}{h_{ie}} = \frac{(200)(4.73\,\text{k}\Omega)}{3.4\,\text{k}\Omega} = 278$$

$C_{\text{in(M)}} = A_v C_{bc} = (278)(2\,\text{pF}) = 556\,\text{pF}$

$$C_{be} = \frac{1}{2\pi f_T r'_e} = \frac{1}{2\pi(800\,\text{MHz})(17\,\Omega)} = 11.7\,\text{pF}$$

$$f_{2B} = \frac{1}{2\pi(R'_{\text{in}} \| h_{ie})(C_{be} + C_{\text{in(M)}})}$$

$$= \frac{1}{2\pi(559\,\Omega\,\|\,3.4\,\text{k}\Omega)(11.7\,\text{pF} + 556\,\text{pF})} = 584\,\text{kHz}$$

$C_{\text{out(M)}} \cong C_{bc} = 2\,\text{pF}$. The load is resistive, so $C_L = 0\,\text{F}$

and $f_{2C} = \dfrac{1}{2\pi r_C(C_{\text{out(M)}} + C_L)} = \dfrac{1}{2\pi(4.73\,\text{k}\Omega)(2\,\text{pF})}$

$= 16.8\,\text{MHz}$. This circuit has values of $f_{C1} =$ 80.4 Hz and $f_{C2} = 584\,\text{kHz}$.

30. $R_{\text{in}} = R_1 \| R_2 \| h_{ie} = (7.5\,\text{k}\Omega)\|(1.2\,\text{k}\Omega)\|(3\,\text{k}\Omega) = 769\,\Omega,$

$$f_{1B} = \frac{1}{2\pi(R_S + R_{\text{in}})C_{C1}} = \frac{1}{2\pi(1.169\,\text{k}\Omega)(4.7\,\mu\text{F})}$$

$\qquad \cong 29\,\text{Hz},$

$$f_{1C} = \frac{1}{2\pi(R_C + R_L)C_{C2}} = \frac{1}{2\pi(18.3\,\text{k}\Omega)(0.47\,\mu\text{F})}$$

$$= 18.5\,\text{Hz}, \qquad r'_e = \frac{h_{ie}}{h_{fe}} = \frac{3\,\text{k}\Omega}{180} = 16.7\,\Omega,$$

$R_{th} = R_1 \| R_2 \| R_S = (7.5\,\text{k}\Omega)\|(1.2\,\text{k}\Omega)\|(400\,\Omega)$

$\qquad = 288\,\Omega$

$$R_{\text{out}} = r'_e + \frac{R_{th}}{h_{fe}} = 16.7\,\Omega + \frac{288\,\Omega}{180} = 18.3\,\Omega$$

$$f_{1E} = \frac{1}{2\pi R_{\text{out}}C_B} = \frac{1}{2\pi(18.3\,\Omega)(100\,\mu\text{F})} \cong 87\,\text{Hz}$$

$r_C = R_C \| R_L = (3.3\,\text{k}\Omega)\|(15\,\text{k}\Omega) = 2.7\,\text{k}\Omega$

$$A_v = \frac{h_{fe}r_C}{h_{ie}} = \frac{(180)(2.7\,\text{k}\Omega)}{3\,\text{k}\Omega} = 162$$

$C_{\text{in(M)}} = A_v C_{bc} = (162)(4\,\text{pF}) = 648\,\text{pF}$

$$C_{be} = \frac{1}{2\pi f_T r'_e} = \frac{1}{2\pi(500\,\text{MHz})(16.7\,\Omega)} = 19.1\,\text{pF}$$

$$f_{2B} = \frac{1}{2\pi(R'_{\text{in}} \| h_{ie})(C_{be} + C_{\text{in(M)}})}$$

$$= \frac{1}{2\pi(288\,\Omega\,\|\,3\,\text{k}\Omega)(19.1\,\text{pF} + 648\,\text{pF})} = 908\,\text{kHz}$$

$C_{\text{out(M)}} \cong C_{bc} = 4\,\text{pF}. \quad C_L = 0\,\text{F}$ and

$$f_{2C} = \frac{1}{2\pi r_C(C_{\text{out(M)}} + C_L)} = \frac{1}{2\pi(2.7\,\text{k}\Omega)(4\,\text{pF})}$$

$= 14.7\,\text{MHz}$. This circuit has values of $f_{C1} = 87\,\text{Hz}$ and $f_{C2} = 908\,\text{kHz}$.

31. $R_{\text{in}} = R_1 \| R_2 = (2\,\text{M}\Omega)\|(1\,\text{M}\Omega) = 667\,\text{k}\Omega$

$$f_{1G} = \frac{1}{2\pi(R_S + R_{\text{in}})C_{C1}}$$

$$= \frac{1}{2\pi(669\,\text{k}\Omega)(0.033\,\mu\text{F})} = 7.21\,\text{Hz}$$

32. $R_{\text{in}} = R_1 \| R_2 = (3\,\text{M}\Omega)\|(1\,\text{M}\Omega) = 750\,\text{k}\Omega$

$$f_{1G} = \frac{1}{2\pi(R_S + R_{\text{in}})C_{C1}}$$

$$= \frac{1}{2\pi(751\,\text{k}\Omega)(0.01\,\mu\text{F})} = 21.2\,\text{Hz}$$

33. $f_{1D} = \dfrac{1}{2\pi(R_D + R_L)C_{C2}} = \dfrac{1}{2\pi(20\,\text{k}\Omega)(0.33\,\mu\text{F})}$

$\qquad = 24.1\,\text{Hz}$

34. $f_{1D} = \dfrac{1}{2\pi(R_D + R_L)C_{C2}} = \dfrac{1}{2\pi(11.5\,\text{k}\Omega)(0.01\,\mu\text{F})}$
$= 1.38\,\text{kHz}$

35. $R_{th} = R_1 \| R_2 \| R_S = (2\,\text{M}\Omega)\|(1\,\text{M}\Omega)\|(2\,\text{k}\Omega) \cong 1.99\,\text{k}\Omega$
$r_D = R_D \| R_L = (10\,\text{k}\Omega)\|(10\,\text{k}\Omega) = 5\,\text{k}\Omega$
$A_v = g_m r_D = (2400\,\mu\text{S})(5\,\text{k}\Omega) = 12$
$C_{\text{in(M)}} = C_{gd}(g_m r_D + 1) = (3\,\text{pF})(13) = 39\,\text{pF}$
$C_G = C_{gs} + C_{\text{in(M)}} = 2\,\text{pF} + 39\,\text{pF} = 41\,\text{pF}$
$f_{2G} = \dfrac{1}{2\pi R_{th}C_G} = \dfrac{1}{2\pi(1.99\,\text{k}\Omega)(39\,\text{pF})} = 2.05\,\text{MHz}$

$C_{\text{out(M)}} \cong C_{gd} = 3\,\text{pF}$
$C_D = C_{\text{out(M)}} + C_{ds} + C_L = 3\,\text{pF} + 1\,\text{pF} + 0\,\text{pF} = 4\,\text{pF}$
$f_{2D} = \dfrac{1}{2\pi r_D C_D} = \dfrac{1}{2\pi(5\,\text{k}\Omega)(4\,\text{pF})} = 7.96\,\text{MHz}$

36. $R_{th} = R_1 \| R_2 \| R_S = (3\,\text{M}\Omega)\|(1\,\text{M}\Omega)\|(1\,\text{k}\Omega) \cong 999\,\Omega$
$r_D = R_D \| R_L = (1.5\,\text{k}\Omega)\|(10\,\text{k}\Omega) = 1.3\,\text{k}\Omega$
$A_v = g_m r_D = (5000\,\mu\text{S})(1.3\,\text{k}\Omega) = 6.5$
$C_{\text{in(M)}} = C_{gd}(g_m r_D + 1) = (4\,\text{pF})(7.5) = 30\,\text{pF}$
$C_G = C_{gs} + C_{\text{in(M)}} = 7\,\text{pF} + 30\,\text{pF} = 37\,\text{pF}$
$f_{2G} = \dfrac{1}{2\pi R_{th}C_G} = \dfrac{1}{2\pi(999\,\Omega)(37\,\text{pF})} = 4.31\,\text{MHz}$

$C_{\text{out(M)}} = C_{gd}\left(\dfrac{g_m r_D + 1}{g_m r_D}\right) = 4\,\text{pF} + \dfrac{7.5}{6.5} = 4.62\,\text{pF}$
$C_D = C_{\text{out(M)}} + C_{ds} + C_L = 4.62\,\text{pF} + 3\,\text{pF} + 0\,\text{pF}$
$= 7.62\,\text{pF}$
$f_{2D} = \dfrac{1}{2\pi r_D C_D} = \dfrac{1}{2\pi(1.3\,\text{k}\Omega)(7.62\,\text{pF})} = 16.1\,\text{MHz}$

37. $C_{gd} = C_{rss} = 9\,\text{pF}$, $C_{gs} = C_{iss} - C_{rss} = 14\,\text{pF} - 9\,\text{pF} = 5\,\text{pF}$, $C_{ds} = C_{oss} - C_{rss} = 10\,\text{pF} - 9\,\text{pF} = 1\,\text{pF}$

38. $C_{gd} = C_{rss} = 9\,\text{pF}$, $C_{gs} = C_{iss} - C_{rss} = 12\,\text{pF} - 9\,\text{pF} = 3\,\text{pF}$, $C_{ds} = C_{oss} - C_{rss} = 16\,\text{pF} - 9\,\text{pF} = 7\,\text{pF}$

39. $R_{\text{in}} = R_1 \| R_2 = (12\,\text{M}\Omega) \| (3\,\text{M}\Omega) = 2.4\,\text{M}\Omega$

$f_{1G} = \dfrac{1}{2\pi(R_S + R_{\text{in}})C_{C1}}$
$= \dfrac{1}{2\pi(2.404\,\text{M}\Omega)(1.1\,\text{nF})} = 60.2\,\text{Hz}$

$f_{1D} = \dfrac{1}{2\pi(R_D + R_L)C_{C2}}$
$= \dfrac{1}{2\pi(20\,\text{k}\Omega)(0.01\,\mu\text{F})} \cong 796\,\text{Hz}$

$R_{th} = R_1 \| R_2 \| R_S = (12\,\text{M}\Omega)\|(3\,\text{M}\Omega)\|(4\,\text{k}\Omega) \cong 3.99\,\text{k}\Omega$
$r_D = R_D \| R_L = (12\,\text{k}\Omega)\|(8\,\text{k}\Omega) = 4.8\,\text{k}\Omega$
$A_v = g_m r_D = (2500\,\mu\text{S})(4.8\,\text{k}\Omega) = 12$
$C_{\text{in(M)}} = C_{gd}(g_m r_D + 1) = (2\,\text{pF})(13) = 26\,\text{pF}$
$C_G = C_{gs} + C_{\text{in(M)}} = 6\,\text{pF} + 26\,\text{pF} = 32\,\text{pF}$
$f_{2G} = \dfrac{1}{2\pi R_{th}C_G} = \dfrac{1}{2\pi(3.99\,\text{k}\Omega)(32\,\text{pF})} = 1.25\,\text{MHz}$

$C_{\text{out(M)}} = C_{gd}\left(\dfrac{g_m r_D + 1}{g_m r_D}\right) = 2\,\text{pF}\left(\dfrac{13}{12}\right) = 2.17\,\text{pF}$
$C_D = C_{\text{out(M)}} + C_{ds} + C_L = 2.17\,\text{pF} + 1\,\text{pF} + 0\,\text{pF}$
$= 3.17\,\text{pF}$,
$f_{2D} = \dfrac{1}{2\pi r_D C_D} = \dfrac{1}{2\pi(4.8\,\text{k}\Omega)(3.17\,\text{pF})} = 10.5\,\text{MHz}$

The cutoff frequencies for the circuit are
$f_{C1} = 796\,\text{Hz}$ and $f_{C2} = 1.25\,\text{MHz}$.

40. $R_{\text{in}} = R_1 \| R_2 = (10\,\text{M}\Omega) \| (2\,\text{M}\Omega) = 1.67\,\text{M}\Omega$

$f_{1G} = \dfrac{1}{2\pi(R_S + R_{\text{in}})C_{C1}}$
$= \dfrac{1}{2\pi(1.67\,\text{M}\Omega)(0.003\,\mu\text{F})} = 31.8\,\text{Hz}$

$f_{1D} = \dfrac{1}{2\pi(R_D + R_L)C_{C2}}$
$= \dfrac{1}{2\pi(22\,\text{k}\Omega)(0.01\,\mu\text{F})} \cong 723\,\text{Hz}$

$R_{th} = R_1 \| R_2 \| R_S = (10\,\text{M}\Omega)\|(2\,\text{M}\Omega)\|(3\,\text{k}\Omega) = 2.99\,\text{k}\Omega$
$r_D = R_D \| R_L = (2\,\text{k}\Omega)\|(20\,\text{k}\Omega) = 1.82\,\text{k}\Omega$
$A_v = g_m r_D = (6500\,\mu\text{S})(1.82\,\text{k}\Omega) = 11.8$
$C_{\text{in(M)}} = C_{gd}(g_m r_D + 1) = (3\,\text{pF})(12.8) = 38.4\,\text{pF}$
$C_G = C_{gs} + C_{\text{in(M)}} = 4\,\text{pF} + 38.4\,\text{pF} = 42.4\,\text{pF}$
$f_{2G} = \dfrac{1}{2\pi R_{th}C_G} = \dfrac{1}{2\pi(2.99\,\text{k}\Omega)(42.4\,\text{pF})} = 1.26\,\text{MHz}$

$C_{\text{out(M)}} = C_{gd}\left(\dfrac{g_m r_D + 1}{g_m r_D}\right) = 3\,\text{pF}\left(\dfrac{12.8}{11.8}\right) = 3.25\,\text{pF}$
$C_D = C_{\text{out(M)}} + C_{ds} + C_L = 3.25\,\text{pF} + 2\,\text{pF} + 0\,\text{pF}$
$= 5.25\,\text{pF}$

$f_{2D} = \dfrac{1}{2\pi r_D C_D} = \dfrac{1}{2\pi(1.82\,\text{k}\Omega)(5.25\,\text{pF})} = 16.7\,\text{MHz}$

The cutoff frequencies for the circuit are
$f_{C1} = 723\,\text{Hz}$ and $f_{C2} = 1.26\,\text{MHz}$.

41. $f_{C2(T)} = f_{C2}\sqrt{2^{1/n} - 1} = (120\,\text{kHz})\sqrt{2^{1/2} - 1}$
$= (120\,\text{kHz})(0.6436) = 77.2\,\text{kHz}$

42. $f_{C1(T)} = \dfrac{f_{C1}}{\sqrt{2^{1/n} - 1}} = \dfrac{3\,\text{kHz}}{\sqrt{2^{1/2} - 1}} = \dfrac{3\,\text{kHz}}{0.6436} = 4.66\,\text{kHz}$

43. $f_{C1(T)} = \dfrac{f_{C1}}{\sqrt{2^{1/n} - 1}} = \dfrac{2\,\text{kHz}}{\sqrt{2^{1/2} - 1}} = \dfrac{2\,\text{kHz}}{0.6436} = 3.11\,\text{kHz}$

$f_{C2(T)} = f_{C2}\sqrt{2^{1/n} - 1} = (840\,\text{kHz})\sqrt{2^{1/2} - 1}$
$= (840\,\text{kHz})(0.6436) = 541\,\text{kHz}$
$\text{BW} = f_{C2} - f_{C1} = 541\,\text{kHz} - 3.11\,\text{kHz} \cong 538\,\text{kHz}$

44. $f_{C1(T)} = \dfrac{f_{C1}}{\sqrt{2^{1/n} - 1}} = \dfrac{1.5\,\text{kHz}}{\sqrt{2^{1/4} - 1}} = \dfrac{1.5\,\text{kHz}}{0.435} = 3.45\,\text{kHz}$

$f_{C2(T)} = f_{C2}\sqrt{2^{1/n} - 1} = (620\,\text{kHz})\sqrt{2^{1/4} - 1}$
$= (620\,\text{kHz})(0.435) \cong 270\,\text{kHz}$
$\text{BW} = f_{C2} - f_{C1} = 270\,\text{kHz} - 3.45\,\text{kHz} \cong 267\,\text{kHz}$

The table below is developed using the given cutoff frequencies for Circuit 1 ($f_{1E} = 32$ kHz, $f_{1C} = 16$ kHz, $f_{1B} = 2$ kHz). The values of ΔA_v listed are calculated using $\Delta A_v = 20\log\dfrac{1}{\sqrt{1+(f_{C1}/f)^2}}$.

f (kHz)	ΔA_v at f (dB)			
	Emitter	Collector	Base	Total
32	−3.01	−0.97	−0.02	−4.00
16	−6.99	−3.01	−0.07	−10.1
8	−12.3	−6.99	−0.26	−19.6
4	−18.1	−12.3	−0.97	−31.4
2	−24.1	−18.1	−3.01	−45.2

The following table is developed using the cutoff frequencies for Circuit 2 ($f_{1C} = 12$ kHz, $f_{1B} = 8$ kHz, $f_{1E} = 4$ kHz).

f (kHz)	ΔA_v at f (dB)			
	Collector	Base	Emitter	Total
32	−0.57	−0.26	−0.07	−0.90
16	−1.94	−0.97	−0.26	−3.17
8	−5.12	−3.01	−0.97	−9.11
4	−10.0	−6.99	−3.01	−20.0
2	−15.7	−12.3	−6.99	−35

The Bode plot and frequency response curve for Circuit 1 are drawn as shown.

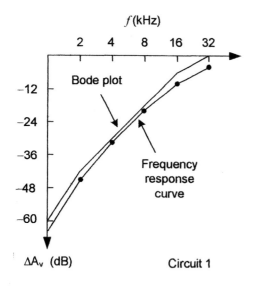

Circuit 1

The Bode plot and frequency response curve for Circuit 2 are drawn as shown.

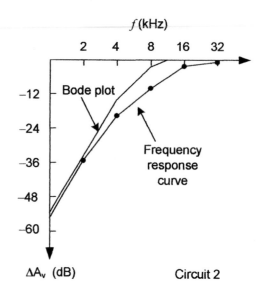

Circuit 2

45. The solution begins with performing a complete frequency analysis of the circuit, as follows:

$R_{in} = R_1 \| R_2 \| h_{ie} = (40\text{ k}\Omega)\|(10\text{ k}\Omega)\|(3\text{ k}\Omega)$
$\quad = 2.18\text{ k}\Omega$,

$f_{1B} = \dfrac{1}{2\pi(R_S + R_{in})C_{C1}} = \dfrac{1}{2\pi(2.58\text{ k}\Omega)(10\,\mu\text{F})}$
$\quad = 6.17\text{ Hz}$

$f_{1C} = \dfrac{1}{2\pi(R_C + R_L)C_{C2}} = \dfrac{1}{2\pi(5.9\text{ k}\Omega)(1\,\mu\text{F})}$

$\quad \cong 27\text{ Hz}, \qquad r'_e = \dfrac{h_{ie}}{h_{fe}} = \dfrac{3\text{ k}\Omega}{200} = 15\,\Omega$

$R_{th} = R_1 \| R_2 \| R_S = (40\text{ k}\Omega)\|(10\text{ k}\Omega)\|(400\,\Omega)$
$\quad = 381\,\Omega$

$R_{out} = r'_e + \dfrac{R_{th}}{h_{fe}} = 15\,\Omega + \dfrac{381\,\Omega}{200} = 16.9\,\Omega$

$f_{1E} = \dfrac{1}{2\pi R_{out}C_B} = \dfrac{1}{2\pi(16.9\,\Omega)(33\,\mu\text{F})} = 285\text{ Hz}$

$r_C = R_C \| R_L = (3.9\text{ k}\Omega)\|(2\text{ k}\Omega) = 1.32\text{ k}\Omega$

$A_v = \dfrac{h_{fe}r_C}{h_{ie}} = \dfrac{(200)(1.32\text{ k}\Omega)}{3\text{ k}\Omega} = 88$

$C_{in(M)} = A_v C_{bc} = (88)(6\text{ pF}) = 528\text{ pF}$

$C_{be} = \dfrac{1}{2\pi f_T r'_e} = \dfrac{1}{2\pi(400\text{ MHz})(15\,\Omega)} = 26.5\text{ pF}$

$f_{2B} = \dfrac{1}{2\pi(R'_{in}\|h_{ie})(C_{be} + C_{in(M)})}$

$\quad = \dfrac{1}{2\pi(381\,\Omega\|3\text{ k}\Omega)(26.5\text{ pF} + 528\text{ pF})} = 849\text{ kHz}$

$C_{out(M)} \cong C_{bc} = 6\text{ pF}$

56

$$f_{2C} = \frac{1}{2\pi r_C \left(C_{out(M)} + C_L\right)}$$

$$= \frac{1}{2\pi \left(1.32 \text{ k}\Omega\right)\left(6 \text{ pF} + 0 \text{ pF}\right)} = 20.1 \text{ MHz}$$

The normal cutoff frequencies for the circuit are $f_{C1} = 285$ Hz and $f_{C2} = 849$ kHz, and the geometric center frequency is

$$f_0 = \sqrt{f_{C1} f_{C2}} = \sqrt{(285 \text{ Hz})(849 \text{ kHz})} = 15.6 \text{ kHz}.$$

If the load opens: $r_C = R_C = 3.9$ kΩ

$$A_v = \frac{h_{fe} r_C}{h_{ie}} = \frac{(200)(3.9 \text{ k}\Omega)}{3 \text{ k}\Omega} = 260$$

$$C_{in(M)} = A_v C_{bc} = (260)(6 \text{ pF}) = 1.56 \text{ nF}$$

$$f_{2B} = \frac{1}{2\pi(R'_{in} \| h_{ie})(C_{be} + C_{in(M)})}$$

$$= \frac{1}{2\pi(381 \ \Omega \| 3 \text{ k}\Omega)(26.5 \text{ pF} + 1.56 \text{ nF})} = 297 \text{ kHz}$$

$$f_{2C} = \frac{1}{2\pi r_C \left(C_{out(M)} + C_L\right)}$$

$$= \frac{1}{2\pi \left(3.9 \text{ k}\Omega\right)\left(6 \text{ pF} + 0 \text{ pF}\right)} = 6.8 \text{ MHz}.$$

The open-load cutoff frequencies for the circuit are $f_{C1} = 285.2$ Hz and $f_{C2} = 297$ kHz, and the geometric center frequency is

$$f_0 = \sqrt{f_{C1} f_{C2}} = \sqrt{(285 \text{ Hz})(297 \text{ kHz})} = 9.2 \text{ kHz}.$$

The change in geometric center frequency is $\Delta f_0 = 15.6$ kHz – 9.2 kHz = 6.4 kHz.

CHAPTER 15

EXAMPLE PRACTICE PROBLEMS   (CH 15)

15-1. For Figure 15.8c: $V_{diff} = V_2 - V_1 = -1$ V $- (-3$ V$) = 2$ V. The positive result indicates that V_{out} is *positive*. For Figure 15.8d: $V_{diff} = V_2 - V_1 = -3$ V $- 0$ V $= -3$ V. The negative result indicates that V_{out} is *negative*.

15-2. $V_{out} = A_v V_{in} = (140)(40 \text{ mV}_{pp}) = 5.6 \text{ V}_{pp}$

15-3. Since $R_L > 10$ kΩ, the limits on the op-amp output are $V_{pk(+)} = +V - 1$ V $= 11$ V and $V_{pk(-)} = -V + 1$ V $= -11$ V. The maximum peak-to-peak output equals the difference between these two values, 22 V$_{PP}$. The maximum peak-to-peak input is found as $\quad V_{in} = \dfrac{V_{out}}{A_v} = \dfrac{22 \text{ V}_{PP}}{140} = 157 \text{ mV}_{PP}$

15-4. Using the curve in Figure 15.10, the maximum output voltage swing is estimated at 24 V$_{PP}$, or $\pm$ 12 V$_{pk}$. Since this value is greater than the maximum possible output from the circuit, we use

the general guideline for circuits with $R_L < 10$ kΩ. Thus, $V_{pk(-)} = (-V) + 2$ V $= -10$ V, and $V_{pk(+)} = (+V) - 2$ V $= +10$ V The maximum peak-to-peak output equals the difference between these two values, 20 V$_{PP}$. Finally, the maximum peak-to-peak input is found as $\quad V_{in} = \dfrac{V_{out}}{A_v} = \dfrac{20 \text{ V}_{PP}}{140} = 143 \text{ mV}_{PP}$

15-5. $f_{max} = \dfrac{\text{slew rate}}{2\pi V_{pk}} = \dfrac{0.4 \text{ V}/\mu\text{s}}{2\pi (10 \text{ V})} = 6.37 \text{ kHz}$

15-6. $f_{max} = \dfrac{\text{slew rate}}{2\pi V_{pk}} = \dfrac{0.4 \text{ V}/\mu\text{s}}{2\pi (2 \text{ V})} = 31.8 \text{ kHz}$

15-7. $A_{CL} = \dfrac{R_f}{R_{in}} = \dfrac{250 \text{ k}\Omega}{1 \text{ k}\Omega} = 250, \quad Z_{in} \cong R_{in} = 1 \text{ k}\Omega,$

Z_{out} is lower than the output impedance of the op-amp, 50 Ω (maximum),

$$\text{CMRR} = \frac{A_{CL}}{A_{CM}} = \frac{250}{0.02} = 12{,}500$$

$$v_{out} = A_{CL} v_{in} = (250)(50 \text{ mV}_{PP}) = 12.5 \text{ V}_{PP}$$

$$f_{max} = \frac{\text{slew rate}}{2\pi V_{pk}} = \frac{0.75 \text{ V}/\mu\text{s}}{2\pi (6.25 \text{ V}_{pk})} = 19.1 \text{ kHz}$$

15-8. $A_{CL} = \dfrac{R_f}{R_{in}} + 1 = \dfrac{250 \text{ k}\Omega}{1 \text{ k}\Omega} + 1 = 251,$

$Z_{in} \geq 1.5$ MΩ (the rated input impedance of the op-amp), $Z_{out} < 50$ Ω (the rated output impedance of the op-amp), $\quad \text{CMRR} = \dfrac{A_{CL}}{A_{CM}} = \dfrac{251}{0.02} = 12{,}550$

$$v_{out} = A_{CL} v_{in} = (251)(50 \text{ mV}_{PP}) = 12.6 \text{ V}_{PP}$$

$$f_{max} = \frac{\text{slew rate}}{2\pi V_{pk}} = \frac{0.75 \text{ V}/\mu\text{s}}{2\pi (6.3 \text{ V}_{pk})} = 18.9 \text{ kHz}$$

15-9. $A_{CL} = 1$, $Z_{in} = 1.5$ MΩ (the rated value for the op-amp), $Z_{out} = 50$ Ω maximum (the rated value for the op-amp), $\quad \text{CMRR} = \dfrac{1}{A_{CM}} = \dfrac{1}{0.02} = 50,$

$$v_{out} = v_{in} = 12 \text{ V}_{PP}$$

$$f_{max} = \frac{\text{slew rate}}{2\pi V_{pk}} = \frac{0.75 \text{ V}/\mu\text{s}}{2\pi (6 \text{ V}_{pk})} = \frac{750 \text{ kHz}}{37.7} \, 19.9 \text{ kHz}$$

15-10. $f_C = \dfrac{f_{unity}}{A_{CL}} = \dfrac{25 \text{ MHz}}{200} = 125 \text{ kHz}$

BW $= f_C = 125$ kHz

15-11. $A_{CL} = \log^{-1} \dfrac{52 \text{ dB}}{20} = 398$

$A_{CL} f_C = (398)(10 \text{ kHz}) = 3.98$ MHz. Since $A_{CL} f_C$ is lower than the f_{unity} rating of the op-amp (5 MHz), it may be used in the application.

15-12. $A_{CL} = \dfrac{A_{OL}}{1 + \alpha_v A_{OL}} = \dfrac{200{,}000}{1 + (0.01)(200{,}000)} \cong 100$

15-13. $A_{CL} = \dfrac{R_f}{R_{in}} = \dfrac{220\,k\Omega}{2\,k\Omega} = 110$

$\alpha_v = \dfrac{1}{A_{CL}} = \dfrac{1}{110} = 0.0091$

$(1 + \alpha_v A_{OL}) = 1 + (0.0091)(180{,}000) = 1639$

15-14. $A_{CL} = \dfrac{R_f}{R_{in}} + 1 = \dfrac{220\,k\Omega}{1\,k\Omega} + 1 = 221$

$\alpha_v = \dfrac{1}{A_{CL}} = \dfrac{1}{221} = 0.0045$

$1 + \alpha_v A_{OL} = 1 + (0.0045)(200{,}000) = 901$

$Z_{in(f)} = Z_{in}(1 + \alpha_v A_{OL}) = (2\,M\Omega)(901) = 1.8\,G\Omega$

15-15. From Problem 15-14: $1 + \alpha_v A_{OL} = 901$

$Z_{out(f)} = \dfrac{Z_{out}}{1 + \alpha_v A_{OL}} = \dfrac{75\,\Omega}{901} = 83.2\,m\Omega$

PRACTICE PROBLEMS CH. 15

1. (a) $V_{diff} = V_2 - V_1 = 2.5\,V - 2\,V = 0.5\,V$. The positive result indicates that V_{out} is *positive*.
   (b) $V_{diff} = V_2 - V_1 = -2\,V - (-1\,V) = -1\,V$. The negative result indicates that V_{out} is *negative*.
   (c) $V_{diff} = V_2 - V_1 = -1\,V - (-2\,V) = 1\,V$. The positive result indicates that V_{out} is *positive*.

2. (a) $V_{diff} = V_2 - V_1 = 2.8\,V - 3\,V = -0.2\,V$. The negative result indicates that V_{out} is *negative*.
   (b) $V_{diff} = V_2 - V_1 = 2.2\,V - 1.8\,V = 0.4\,V$. The positive result indicates that V_{out} is *positive*.
   (c) $V_{diff} = V_2 - V_1 = 0\,V - (-3\,V) = 3\,V$. The positive result indicates that V_{out} is *positive*.

3. Since $R_L < 10\,k\Omega$, the limits on the op-amp output are $V_{pk(+)} = +V - 2\,V = 8\,V$ and $V_{pk(-)} = -V + 2\,V = -8\,V$. The maximum peak-to-peak output equals the difference between these two values, $16\,V_{PP}$.

4. Since $R_L > 10\,k\Omega$, the limits on the op-amp output are $V_{pk(+)} = +V - 1\,V = 14\,V$ and $V_{pk(-)} = -V + 1\,V = -14\,V$. The maximum peak-to-peak output equals the difference between these two values, $28\,V_{PP}$.

5. From Problem 3: $V_{out} = 16\,V_{PP}$ (max)

   $V_{in} = \dfrac{V_{out}}{A_v} = \dfrac{16\,V_{PP}}{120} = 133\,mV_{PP}$

6. From Problem 4: $V_{out} = 28\,V_{PP}$ (max)

   $V_{in} = \dfrac{V_{out}}{A_v} = \dfrac{28\,V_{PP}}{220} = 127\,mV_{PP}$

7. Since $R_L > 10\,k\Omega$, the limits on the op-amp output are $V_{pk(+)} = +V - 1\,V = 15\,V$ and $V_{pk(-)} = -V + 1\,V = -15\,V$. The maximum peak-to-peak output equals the difference between these two values, $30\,V_{PP}$.

Finally, the maximum peak-to-peak input is found as $V_{in} = \dfrac{V_{out}}{A_v} = \dfrac{30\,V_{PP}}{200} = 150\,mV_{PP}$.

8. Since $R_L < 10\,k\Omega$, the limits on the op-amp output are $V_{pk(+)} = +V - 2\,V = 12\,V$ and $V_{pk(-)} = -V + 2\,V = -12\,V$. The maximum peak-to-peak output equals the difference between these two values, $24\,V_{PP}$. Finally, the maximum peak-to-peak input is found as $V_{in} = \dfrac{V_{out}}{A_v} = \dfrac{24\,V_{PP}}{120} = 200\,mV_{PP}$.

9. $V_{io} = \dfrac{V_{out(offset)}}{A_v} = \dfrac{2.4\,V}{200} = 12\,mV$

10. $V_{io} = \dfrac{V_{out(offset)}}{A_v} = \dfrac{960\,mV}{120} = 8\,mV$

11. $v_{out} = A_v v_{in} = (200)(10\,mV_{PP}) = 2\,V_{PP}$

    $f_{max} = \dfrac{\text{slew rate}}{2\pi V_{pk}} = \dfrac{0.9\,V/\mu s}{2\pi(1\,V)} = 143\,kHz$

12. $v_{out} = A_v v_{in} = (120)(40\,mV_{PP}) = 4.8\,V_{PP}$

    $f_{max} = \dfrac{\text{slew rate}}{2\pi V_{pk}} = \dfrac{0.3\,V/\mu s}{2\pi(2.4\,V_{pk})} = 19.9\,kHz$

13. $v_{out} = A_v v_{in} = (300)(24\,mV_{PP}) = 7.2\,V_{PP}$

    $f_{max} = \dfrac{\text{slew rate}}{2\pi V_{pk}} = \dfrac{0.8\,V/\mu s}{2\pi(3.6\,V_{pk})} = 35.4\,kHz$

14. $v_{out} = A_v v_{in} = (100)(100\,mV_{PP}) = 10\,V_{PP}$

    $f_{max} = \dfrac{\text{slew rate}}{2\pi V_{pk}} = \dfrac{0.5\,V/\mu s}{2\pi(5\,V_{pk})} = 15.9\,kHz$

15. $A_{CL} = \dfrac{R_f}{R_{in}} = \dfrac{120\,k\Omega}{1\,k\Omega} = 120$

    $Z_{in} \cong R_{in} = 1\,k\Omega$, Z_{out} is lower than the rated output impedance of the op-amp, $50\,\Omega$ (maximum).

    $CMRR = \dfrac{A_{CL}}{A_{CM}} = \dfrac{120}{0.02} = 6000$

    $v_{out} = A_{CL} v_{in} = (120)(100\,mV_{PP}) = 12\,V_{PP}$

    $f_{max} = \dfrac{\text{slew rate}}{2\pi V_{pk}} = \dfrac{3\,V/\mu s}{2\pi(6\,V_{pk})} = 79.6\,kHz$

16. $A_{CL} = \dfrac{R_f}{R_{in}} = \dfrac{300\,k\Omega}{2\,k\Omega} = 150$

    $Z_{in} \cong R_{in} = 2\,k\Omega$, Z_{out} is lower than the rated output impedance of the op-amp, $100\,\Omega$ (maximum).

    $CMRR = \dfrac{A_{CL}}{A_{CM}} = \dfrac{150}{0.015} = 10{,}000$

    $v_{out} = A_{CL} v_{in} = (150)(40\,mV_{PP}) = 6\,V_{PP}$

    $f_{max} = \dfrac{\text{slew rate}}{2\pi V_{pk}} = \dfrac{12\,V/\mu s}{2\pi(3\,V_{pk})} = 637\,kHz$

17. $A_{CL} = \dfrac{R_f}{R_{in}} = \dfrac{100\,\text{k}\Omega}{100\,\text{k}\Omega} = 1$

$Z_{in} \cong R_{in} = 100\,\text{k}\Omega$, Z_{out} is lower than the rated output impedance of the op-amp, 75 Ω (maximum).

$\text{CMRR} = \dfrac{A_{CL}}{A_{CM}} = \dfrac{1}{0.005} = 200$

$v_{out} = A_{CL}v_{in} = (1)(16\,\text{V}_{PP}) = 16\,\text{V}_{PP}$

$f_{max} = \dfrac{\text{slew rate}}{2\pi V_{pk}} = \dfrac{8\,\text{V}/\mu\text{s}}{2\pi\,(8\,\text{V}_{pk})} = 159\,\text{kHz}$

18. $A_{CL} = \dfrac{R_f}{R_{in}} = \dfrac{110\,\text{k}\Omega}{1.1\,\text{k}\Omega} = 100$

$Z_{in} \cong R_{in} = 1.1\,\text{k}\Omega$, Z_{out} is lower than the rated output impedance of the op-amp, 50 Ω (maximum).

$\text{CMRR} = \dfrac{A_{CL}}{A_{CM}} = \dfrac{100}{0.012} = 8333$

$v_{out} = A_{CL}v_{in} = (100)(180\,\text{mV}_{PP}) = 18\,\text{V}_{PP}$

$f_{max} = \dfrac{\text{slew rate}}{2\pi V_{pk}} = \dfrac{2\,\text{V}/\mu\text{s}}{2\pi\,(9\,\text{V}_{pk})} = 35.4\,\text{kHz}$

19. $A_{CL} = \dfrac{R_f}{R_{in}} + 1 = \dfrac{200\,\text{k}\Omega}{2\,\text{k}\Omega} + 1 = 101$, $Z_{in} \geq 1\,\text{M}\Omega$

$Z_{out} < 40\,\Omega$, $\text{CMRR} = \dfrac{A_{CL}}{A_{CM}} = \dfrac{101}{0.002} = 50{,}500$

$v_{out} = A_{CL}v_{in} = (101)(120\,\text{mV}_{PP}) = 12.12\,\text{V}_{PP}$

$f_{max} = \dfrac{\text{slew rate}}{2\pi V_{pk}} = \dfrac{3\,\text{V}/\mu\text{s}}{2\pi\,(6.06\,\text{V}_{pk})} = 78.8\,\text{kHz}$

20. $A_{CL} = \dfrac{R_f}{R_{in}} + 1 = \dfrac{300\,\text{k}\Omega}{150\,\text{k}\Omega} + 1 = 3$, $Z_{in} \geq 2.5\,\text{M}\Omega$

$Z_{out} < 80\,\Omega$, $\text{CMRR} = \dfrac{A_{CL}}{A_{CM}} = \dfrac{3}{0.04} = 75$

$v_{out} = A_{CL}v_{in} = (3)(8\,\text{V}_{PP}) = 24\,\text{V}_{PP}$

$f_{max} = \dfrac{\text{slew rate}}{2\pi V_{pk}} = \dfrac{12\,\text{V}/\mu\text{s}}{2\pi\,(12\,\text{V}_{pk})} = 159\,\text{kHz}$

21. $A_{CL} = \dfrac{R_f}{R_{in}} + 1 = \dfrac{120\,\text{k}\Omega}{3\,\text{k}\Omega} + 1 = 41$, $Z_{in} \geq 2\,\text{M}\Omega$

$Z_{out} < 100\,\Omega$, $\text{CMRR} = \dfrac{A_{CL}}{A_{CM}} = \dfrac{41}{0.033} = 1242$

$v_{out} = A_{CL}v_{in} = (41)(400\,\text{mV}_{pp}) = 16.4\,\text{V}_{PP}$

$f_{max} = \dfrac{\text{slew rate}}{2\pi V_{pk}} = \dfrac{15\,\text{V}/\mu s}{2\pi(8.2\,\text{V}_{pk})} = 291\,\text{kHz}$

22. $A_{CL} = \dfrac{R_f}{R_{in}} + 1 = \dfrac{100\,\text{k}\Omega}{20\,\text{k}\Omega} + 1 = 6$, $Z_{in} \geq 1.8\,\text{M}\Omega$

$Z_{out} < 110\,\Omega$, $\text{CMRR} = \dfrac{A_{CL}}{A_{CM}} = \dfrac{6}{0.014} = 429$

23. $v_{out} = A_{CL}v_{in} = (6)(2\,\text{V}_{PP}) = 12\,\text{V}_{PP}$

$f_{max} = \dfrac{\text{slew rate}}{2\pi V_{pk}} = \dfrac{20\,\text{V}/\mu\text{s}}{2\pi\,(6\,\text{V}_{pk})} = 531\,\text{kHz}$

23. $A_{CL} = 1$

$Z_{in} = 5\,\text{M}\Omega$ and Z_{out} equals the rated output impedance of the op-amp, 40 Ω (maximum).

$\text{CMRR} = \dfrac{1}{A_{CM}} = \dfrac{1}{0.001} = 1000$, $v_{out} = v_{in} = 10\,\text{V}_{PP}$

$f_{max} = \dfrac{\text{slew rate}}{2\pi V_{pk}} = \dfrac{10\,\text{V}/\mu\text{s}}{2\pi\,(5\,\text{V}_{pk})} = 318\,\text{kHz}$

24. $A_{CL} = 1$

$Z_{in} = 3.5\,\text{M}\Omega$ and Z_{out} equals the rated output impedance of the op-amp, 60 Ω (maximum).

$\text{CMRR} = \dfrac{1}{A_{CM}} = \dfrac{1}{0.005} = 200$, $v_{out} = v_{in} = 20\,\text{V}_{PP}$

$f_{max} = \dfrac{\text{slew rate}}{2\pi V_{pk}} = \dfrac{8\,\text{V}/\mu\text{s}}{2\pi\,(10\,\text{V}_{pk})} = 127\,\text{kHz}$

25. $\text{BW} = \dfrac{f_{unity}}{A_{CL}} = \dfrac{12\,\text{MHz}}{400} = 30\,\text{kHz}$

26. $\text{BW} = \dfrac{f_{unity}}{A_{CL}} = \dfrac{14\,\text{MHz}}{320} = 43.8\,\text{kHz}$

27. $A_{CL} = \log^{-1}\dfrac{42\,\text{dB}}{20} = 126$

$\text{BW} = \dfrac{f_{unity}}{A_{CL}} = \dfrac{25\,\text{MHz}}{126} = 198\,\text{kHz}$

28. $A_{CL} = \log^{-1}\dfrac{20\,\text{dB}}{20} = 10$

$\text{BW} = \dfrac{f_{unity}}{A_{CL}} = \dfrac{1\,\text{MHz}}{10} = 100\,\text{kHz}$

29. $A_{CL}f_C = (200)(120\,\text{kHz}) = 24\,\text{MHz}$.
$A_{CL}f_C < f_{unity}$, so the component can be used.

30. $A_{CL} = \log^{-1}\dfrac{A_{v(dB)}}{20} = \log^{-1}\dfrac{24\,\text{dB}}{20} = 15.8$

$A_{CL}f_C = (15.8)(40\,\text{kHz}) = 632\,\text{kHz}$.
$A_{CL}f_C < f_{unity}$, so the component can be used.

31. $f_{unity} = A_{CL}f_C = (120)(100\,\text{kHz}) = 12\,\text{MHz}$

32. $f_{unity} = A_{CL}f_C = (300)(88\,\text{kHz}) = 26.4\,\text{MHz}$

33. $A_{CL} = \dfrac{R_f}{R_{in}} = \dfrac{100\,\text{k}\Omega}{1\,\text{k}\Omega} = 100$,

$f_{unity} = A_{CL}f_C = (100)(250\,\text{kHz}) = 25\,\text{MHz}$

34. $A_{CL} = \dfrac{R_f}{R_{in}} = \dfrac{360\,\text{k}\Omega}{1.2\,\text{k}\Omega} = 300$,

$f_{unity} = A_{CL}f_C = (300)(100\,\text{kHz}) = 30\,\text{MHz}$

35. $A_{CL} = \dfrac{A_{OL}}{1 + \alpha_v A_{OL}} = \dfrac{1000}{1 + (0.22)(1000)} = 4.52$

36. $A_{CL} = \dfrac{A_{OL}}{1 + \alpha_v A_{OL}} = \dfrac{588}{1 + (0.092)(588)} = 10.7$

37. $A_{CL} = \dfrac{A_{OL}}{1 + \alpha_v A_{OL}} = \dfrac{150{,}000}{1 + (0.008)(150{,}000)} \cong 125$

38. $A_{CL} = \dfrac{A_{OL}}{1 + \alpha_v A_{OL}} = \dfrac{200{,}000}{1 + (0.015)(200{,}000)} \cong 664$

39. From Problem 35: $A_{OL} = 1000$.

$1 + \alpha_v A_{OL} = 1 + (0.22)(1000) = 221$

$Z_{in(f)} \cong R_{in} = 48 \text{ k}\Omega$

$Z_{out(f)} = \dfrac{Z_{out}}{1 + \alpha_v A_{OL}} = \dfrac{220 \ \Omega}{221} = 0.995 \ \Omega$

40. $1 + \alpha_v A_{OL} = 1 + (0.008)(150{,}000) = 1201$

$Z_{in(f)} \cong R_{in} = 1.2 \text{ k}\Omega$

$Z_{out(f)} = \dfrac{Z_{out}}{1 + \alpha_v A_{OL}} = \dfrac{80 \ \Omega}{1201} = 66.6 \text{ m}\Omega$

41. $A_{CL} = \dfrac{R_f}{R_{in}} = \dfrac{100 \text{ k}\Omega}{1 \text{ k}\Omega} = 100$

$\alpha_v = \dfrac{1}{A_{CL}} = \dfrac{1}{100} = 0.01, \quad Z_{in(f)} \cong R_{in} = 1 \text{ k}\Omega$

$Z_{out(f)} = \dfrac{Z_{out}}{1 + \alpha_v A_{OL}} = \dfrac{100 \ \Omega}{1 + (0.01)(200{,}000)} = 50 \text{ m}\Omega$

42. $A_{CL} = \dfrac{R_f}{R_{in}} = \dfrac{360 \text{ k}\Omega}{1.2 \text{ k}\Omega} = 300$

$\alpha_v = \dfrac{1}{A_{CL}} = \dfrac{1}{300} = 0.0033, \quad Z_{in(f)} \cong R_{in} = 1.2 \text{ k}\Omega,$

$Z_{out(f)} = \dfrac{Z_{out}}{1 + \alpha_v A_{OL}} = \dfrac{75 \ \Omega}{1 + (0.0033)(180{,}000)} = 126 \text{m}\Omega$

43. The gain of the circuit should be $A_{CL} = \dfrac{R_f}{R_{in}} + 1 = 11$

and the output from the circuit should be 11 mV$_{PP}$. As shown, the output is being driven to compliance. The most likely cause of this problem is an open feedback resistor (R_f).

44. The input signal is dropped across the input resistor, with the remainder of the circuit acting as a low-amplitude oscillator. The cause of this problem is an open input resistor (R_{in}).

45. The readings at TP-1, TP-2, and TP-3 indicate that there is 10 μA through the series combination of the input resistor (R_{in1}) and the feedback resistor (R_{f1} Since the first op-amp is not responding to the input, the most likely problem is an open inverting input.). The 120 mV at TP-3 is most likely just a dc offset from the first op-amp.

46. The output from the first stage is 10 times what it should be. This indicates that a 100 kΩ resistor has been mistakenly installed for R_{f1}.

47. The output from the first op-amp should be at -400 mV but it is at –4 V. This indicates that R_{f1} is open.

48. There are several plausible causes for this combination of readings. The input to the first op-amp could be shorted, as could its output. There could also be a fault in the power supply that powers the circuit. The operation of the power supply can be checked at the $+V$ and $-V$ inputs to the circuit.

49. Circuit (a) has a common-mode input of 10 V and an output of 20 mV, and $A_{CM} = \dfrac{V_{out}}{V_{in}} = \dfrac{20 \text{ mV}}{10 \text{ V}} = 0.002$. Circuit (b) shows that the op-amp has a value of $A_{OL} = \dfrac{V_{out}}{V_{in}} = \dfrac{8 \text{ V}}{8 \text{ mV}} = 1000$. Using these two values, CMRR $= \dfrac{A_{OL}}{A_{CM}} = \dfrac{1000}{0.002} = 500{,}000$.

50. The required value of A_{CL} is found as $A_{CL} = \dfrac{v_{out}}{v_{in}} = \dfrac{12.5 \text{ V}_{pk}}{100 \text{ mV}_{pk}} = 125$ (where 12.5 V$_{pk}$ = 25 V$_{pp}$).

Since $A_{CL} = \dfrac{R_f}{R_{in}} + 1$, $\dfrac{R_f}{R_{in}} = A_{CL} - 1 = 124$. Any combination of resistors that fulfills $R_f = 124R_{in}$ will work, as shown below.

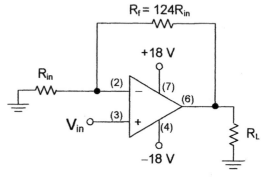

51. From Figure 22.71, $R_{in} = R_1 = 2 \text{ k}\Omega$, $R_f = R_2 = 200 \text{ k}\Omega$ and $R_L = R_3 = 3 \text{ k}\Omega$. Since the input is applied to the inverting input via R_1 and the noninverting input is tied to ground, the circuit is an *inverting amplifier*. Therefore,

$A_{CL} = \dfrac{R_f}{R_{in}} = \dfrac{200 \, k\Omega}{2 \, k\Omega} = 100$

$v_{out} = A_{CL}v_{in} = (100)(160 \text{ mV}_{PP}) = 16 \text{ V}_{PP}$

$f_{max} = \dfrac{\text{slew rate}}{2\pi V_{pk}} = \dfrac{0.7 \text{ V/μs}}{2\pi (8 \text{ V})} = 13.9 \text{ kHz}.$

52. According to the LM301 spec sheet, the component has a CMRR of 90 dB (typical).

53. The LM833 is a dual op-amp. Assuming that the output is being taken from pin 1, the op-amp is wired as follows: Pin 2 (inverting input), pin 3 (noninverting input), pin 8 ($+V$), and pin 4 ($-V$).

CHAPTER 16

EXAMPLE PRACTICE PROBLEMS   (CH 16)

16-1. $V_{diff} = V_{in} - V_{ref} = 2.001\ V - 2\ V = 1\ mV$, $V_{out} = A_{OL}V_{diff} = (70,000)(1\ mV) = 70\ V$. This is beyond the circuit limits, so $V_{out} \cong +V - 1\ V = 11\ V$. $V_{diff} = V_{in} - V_{ref} = 1.999\ V - 2\ V = -1\ mV$, $V_{out} = A_{OL}V_{diff} = (70,000)(-1\ mV) = -70\ V$. This is beyond the circuit limits, so $V_{out} \cong -V + 1\ V = -11\ V$.

16-2. $V_{ref} = +V\dfrac{R_2}{R_1 + R_2} = (8\ V)\dfrac{1.8\ k\Omega}{4.8\ k\Omega} = +3\ V$

16-3. $V_{ref} = -V\dfrac{R_2}{R_1 + R_2} = (-10V)\dfrac{120\ k\Omega}{150\ k\Omega} = -8\ V$.

The circuit triggers when $V_{in} = -V$, indicating that R_1 is shorted or R_2 is open.

16-4. $V_{out} = -R_f\left(\dfrac{V_1}{R_1} + \dfrac{V_2}{R_2} + \dfrac{V_3}{R_3}\right)$

$= (-2\ k\Omega)\left(\dfrac{1\ V}{1\ k\Omega} + \dfrac{500\ mV}{1\ k\Omega} + \dfrac{1.5\ V}{1\ k\Omega}\right) = -6\ V$

16-5. $V_{out} = -R_f\left(\dfrac{V_1}{R_1} + \dfrac{V_2}{R_2} + \dfrac{V_3}{R_3}\right)$

$= (-1\ k\Omega)\left(\dfrac{2\ V}{3\ k\Omega} + \dfrac{1\ V}{3\ k\Omega} + \dfrac{6\ V}{3\ k\Omega}\right) = -3\ V$

16-6. $-V_{out} = \dfrac{R_f}{R_1}V_1 + \dfrac{R_f}{R_2}V_2 + \dfrac{R_f}{R_3}V_3$

$= \dfrac{2\ k\Omega}{200\ \Omega}V_1 + \dfrac{2\ k\Omega}{400\ \Omega}V_2 + \dfrac{2\ k\Omega}{2\ k\Omega}V_3$

$= 10V_1 + 5V_2 + V_3$.

For the voltages given,
$-V_{out} = (10)(1\ V) + (5)(1\ V) + 1\ V = 16\ V$ and $V_{out} = -16\ V$.

PRACTICE PROBLEMS   (CH 16)

1. V_{ref} is the potential at the inverting input, 0 V.

2. $V_{ref} = +V\dfrac{R_2}{R_1 + R_2} = (5\ V)\dfrac{33\ k\Omega}{43\ k\Omega} = 3.84\ V$

3. $V_{ref} = [+V - (-V)]\dfrac{R_2}{R_1 + R_2} + (-V)$

$= (24\ V)\dfrac{10\ k\Omega}{15\ k\Omega} - 12\ V = 4\ V$

4. $V_{ref} = [+V - (-V)]\dfrac{R_2}{R_1 + R_2} + (-V)$

$= (16\ V)\dfrac{12\ k\Omega}{112\ k\Omega} - 8\ V = -6.29\ V$

5. $A_{CL} = \dfrac{R_f}{R_1} = \dfrac{100\ k\Omega}{2\ k\Omega} = 50$ (maximum)

6. $A_{CL} = \dfrac{R_f}{R_1} = \dfrac{100\ k\Omega}{10\ k\Omega} = 10$ (maximum)

7. $-V_{out} = \dfrac{R_f}{R_1}V_1 + \dfrac{R_f}{R_2}V_2 + \dfrac{R_f}{R_3}V_3$

$= \dfrac{10\ k\Omega}{10\ k\Omega}V_1 + \dfrac{10\ k\Omega}{10\ k\Omega}V_2 + \dfrac{10\ k\Omega}{10\ k\Omega}V_3$

$= V_1 + V_2 + V_3 = 2\ V + (-3\ V) + 6\ V = 5\ V$
and $V_{out} = -5\ V$

8. $-V_{out} = \dfrac{R_f}{R_1}V_1 + \dfrac{R_f}{R_2}V_2 + \dfrac{R_f}{R_3}V_3$

$= \dfrac{10\ k\Omega}{10\ k\Omega}V_1 + \dfrac{10\ k\Omega}{20\ k\Omega}V_2 + \dfrac{10\ k\Omega}{50\ k\Omega}V_3$

$= V_1 + 0.5V_2 + 0.2V_3$
$= 3\ V + (0.5)(2\ V) + (0.2)(-1\ V) = 3.8\ V$
and $V_{out} = -3.8\ V$

9. $-V_{out} = \dfrac{R_f}{R_1}V_1 + \dfrac{R_f}{R_2}V_2 + \dfrac{R_f}{R_3}V_3$

$= \dfrac{30\ k\Omega}{20\ k\Omega}V_1 + \dfrac{30\ k\Omega}{10\ k\Omega}V_2 + \dfrac{30\ k\Omega}{20\ k\Omega}V_3$

$= 1.5V_1 + 3V_2 + 1.5V_3$
$= (1.5)(1\ V) + (3)(400\ mV) + (1.5)(1.1\ V)$
$= 4.35\ V$ and $V_{out} = -4.35\ V$

10. $-V_{out} = \dfrac{R_f}{R_1}V_1 + \dfrac{R_f}{R_2}V_2 + \dfrac{R_f}{R_3}V_3$

$= \dfrac{24\ k\Omega}{20\ k\Omega}V_1 + \dfrac{24\ k\Omega}{10\ k\Omega}V_2 + \dfrac{24\ k\Omega}{20\ k\Omega}V_3$

$= 1.2V_1 + 2.4V_2 + 1.2V_3$
$= (1.2)(1\ V) + (2.4)(400\ mV) + (1.2)(1.1\ V)$
$= 3.48\ V$ and $V_{out} = -3.48\ V$

11.   With five inputs, $R_f = \dfrac{15\ k\Omega}{5} = 3\ k\Omega$.

12.   With four inputs, $R_f = \dfrac{20\ k\Omega}{4} = 5\ k\Omega$.

13.   The circuit is a *difference amplifier*. For the inputs given, $V_{out} = V_2 - V_1 = 6\ V - 4\ V = 2\ V$.

14.   With R_3 and R_4 changed to 150 kΩ,

$$V_{out} = \frac{R_3}{R_1}(V_2 - V_1) = \frac{150\,\text{k}\Omega}{100\,\text{k}\Omega}(3\,\text{V} - 1\,\text{V}) = 3\,\text{V}$$

15. The negative output indicates that the potential at the inverting input to the op-amp is more positive than the potential at the noninverting input. That is, the potential at the inverting input is always more positive than v_{in}. The problem could be R_1 *shorted* or R_2 *open*.

16. The circuit is acting as an inverting amplifier with $A_{CL} = 2$. C_f is open.

17. The circuit equation is

$$-V_{out} = \frac{10\,\text{k}\Omega}{2\,\text{k}\Omega}V_1 + \frac{10\,\text{k}\Omega}{1\,\text{k}\Omega}V_2 + \frac{10\,\text{k}\Omega}{10\,\text{k}\Omega}V_3$$

$$= -V_{out} = 5V_1 + 10V_2 + V_3$$

For the inputs listed, the circuit should have a value of

$$-V_{out} = (5)(-1\,\text{V}) + (10)(1\,\text{V}) + 2\,\text{V} = 7\,\text{V}$$

If V_1 is isolated from the circuit,

$$-V_{out} = (5)(0\,\text{V}) + (10)(1\,\text{V}) + 2\,\text{V} = 12\,\text{V and } V_{out} = -12\,\text{V}$$. Thus, the readings indicate that R_1 is open.

18. The KA741 has a rating of $Z_{in} = 2\,\text{M}\Omega$ (typical). For the first stage, $r_C = R_C \| Z_{in} \cong R_C = 620\,\Omega$ and

$$A_v = \frac{h_{fe}r_C}{h_{ie}} = \frac{(200)(620\,\Omega)}{2\,\text{k}\Omega} = 62.$$ For the inverting

amplifier, $A_{CL} = \dfrac{R_{f1}}{R_{f2}} = \dfrac{2\,\text{k}\Omega}{1\,\text{k}\Omega} = 2.$

Finally, $A_{v(T)} = A_v A_{CL} = (62)(2) = 124.$

19. $V_{R2} = V_Z$ (as described in Section 16.5.2). The Q_1 emitter current is found as

$$I_E = \frac{V_Z}{R_2} = \frac{6.8\,\text{V}}{6.2\,\text{k}\Omega} = 1.1\,\text{mA}$$

For $R_L = 1\,\text{k}\Omega$,
$$V_{CE} \cong V_{CC} - I_E(R_2 + R_L)$$
$$= 12\,\text{V} - (1.1\,\text{mA})(7.2\,\text{k}\Omega) = 4.08\,\text{V}$$
For $R_L = 3\,\text{k}\Omega$,
$$V_{CE} \cong V_{CC} - I_E(R_2 + R_L)$$
$$= 12\,\text{V} - (1.1\,\text{mA})(9.2\,\text{k}\Omega) = 1.88\,\text{V}$$

20. Here is one of many possible solutions: An inverting amplifier with $A_{CL} = 1$ is used to convert V_2 to $-V_2$. The circuit equation can be rewritten as

$$-V_{out} = \frac{1}{2}V_1 + \frac{1}{2}(-V_2) + \frac{1}{3}V_3 .$$ This equation is

implemented using the resistor relationships shown in the circuit.

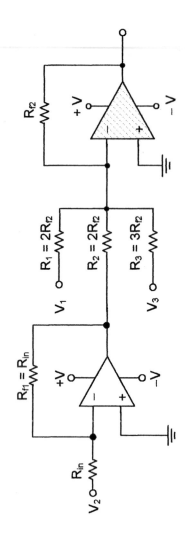

21. The circuit is drawn below.

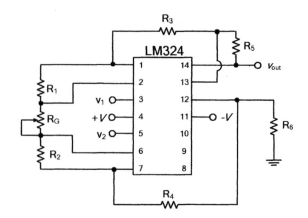

CHAPTER 17

EXAMPLE PRACTICE PROBLEMS   CH. 17

17-1. $Q = \dfrac{f_0}{\text{BW}} = \dfrac{1200 \text{ kHz}}{20 \text{ kHz}} = 60$

17-2. $\text{BW} = \dfrac{f_0}{Q} = \dfrac{1400 \text{ kHz}}{25} = 56 \text{ kHz}$

17-3. $f_0 = \sqrt{f_{C1}f_{C2}} = \sqrt{(980 \text{ kHz})(1080 \text{ kHz})}$
$= 1029 \text{ kHz}$

$f_{\text{ave}} = \dfrac{f_{C1}+f_{C2}}{2} = \dfrac{980 \text{ kHz}+1080 \text{ kHz}}{2}$
$= 1030 \text{ kHz}.$

$Q = \dfrac{f_0}{\text{BW}} = \dfrac{1029 \text{ Hz}}{(1080 \text{ kHz}-980 \text{ kHz})} = 10.3$

17-4. $f_C = \dfrac{1}{2\pi R_1 C_1} = \dfrac{1}{2\pi(47 \text{ k}\Omega)(0.033 \,\mu\text{F})} = 103 \text{ Hz}$

$A_{\text{CL}} = \dfrac{R_{f1}}{R_{f2}} + 1 = \dfrac{10 \text{ k}\Omega}{10 \text{ k}\Omega} + 1 = 2$

17-5. $f_C = \dfrac{1}{2\pi\sqrt{R_1 R_2 C_1 C_2}}$
$= \dfrac{1}{2\pi\sqrt{(12 \text{ k}\Omega)(12 \text{ k}\Omega)(10 \text{ nF})(22 \text{ nf})}} = 894 \text{ Hz}$

17-6. $f_{C2} = \dfrac{1}{2\pi\sqrt{R_1 R_2 C_1 C_2}}$
$= \dfrac{1}{2\pi\sqrt{(12 \text{ k}\Omega)(12 \text{ k}\Omega)(0.01 \,\mu\text{F})(0.02 \,\mu\text{F})}}$
$= 938 \text{ Hz}$

$f_{C1} = \dfrac{1}{2\pi\sqrt{R_3 R_4 C_3 C_4}}$
$= \dfrac{1}{2\pi\sqrt{(20 \text{ k}\Omega)(39 \text{ k}\Omega)(0.01 \,\mu\text{F})(0.01 \,\mu\text{F})}}$
$= 570 \text{ Hz}$

$\text{BW} = f_{C2} - f_{C1} = 938 \text{ Hz} - 570 \text{ Hz} = 368 \text{ Hz}$
$f_0 = \sqrt{f_{C1}f_{C2}} = \sqrt{(570 \text{ Hz})(938 \text{ Hz})} = 731 \text{ Hz}$
$Q = \dfrac{f_0}{\text{BW}} = \dfrac{731 \text{ Hz}}{368 \text{ Hz}} = 1.99$

17-7. $f_0 = \dfrac{1}{2\pi\sqrt{(R_1 \| R_2)R_f C_1 C_2}}$
$= \dfrac{1}{2\pi\sqrt{(30 \text{ k}\Omega\|30 \text{ k}\Omega)(68 \text{ k}\Omega)(0.22 \,\mu\text{F})(0.1 \,\mu\text{F})}}$
$= 33.6 \text{ Hz}$

17-8. $C = \sqrt{C_1 C_2} = \sqrt{(0.22 \,\mu\text{F})(0.1 \,\mu\text{F})} = 0.15 \,\mu\text{F}$
$Q = \pi f_0 R_f C = \pi(33.6 \text{ Hz})(68 \text{ k}\Omega)(0.15 \,\mu\text{F}) = 1.08$
$\text{BW} = \dfrac{f_0}{Q} = \dfrac{33.6 \text{ Hz}}{1.08} = 31.1 \text{ Hz}$

17-9. $Q = \dfrac{f_0}{\text{BW}} = \dfrac{20 \text{ kHz}}{5 \text{ kHz}} = 4.$ Approximations:

$f_{C1} \cong f_0 - \dfrac{\text{BW}}{2} = 20 \text{ kHz} - \dfrac{5 \text{ kHz}}{2} = 17.5 \text{ kHz}$

$f_{C2} \cong f_0 + \dfrac{\text{BW}}{2} = 20 \text{ kHz} + \dfrac{5 \text{ kHz}}{2} = 22.5 \text{ kHz}.$

More accurately:

$f_{C1} \cong f_0 \sqrt{1 + \left(\dfrac{1}{2Q}\right)^2} - \dfrac{\text{BW}}{2}$

$= (20 \text{ kHz})\sqrt{1 + \left(\dfrac{1}{8}\right)^2} - \dfrac{5 \text{ kHz}}{2} = 17.66 \text{ kHz}$

$f_{C2} \cong f_0 \sqrt{1 + \left(\dfrac{1}{2Q}\right)^2} + \dfrac{\text{BW}}{2}$

$= (20 \text{ kHz})\sqrt{1 + \left(\dfrac{1}{8}\right)^2} + \dfrac{5 \text{ kHz}}{2} = 22.66 \text{ kHz}.$

For f_{C1},
$\% \text{ of error} = \dfrac{|17.66 \text{ kHz} - 17.5 \text{ kHz}|}{17.66 \text{ kHz}} \times 100$
$= 0.91\%.$

For f_{C2},
$\% \text{ of error} = \dfrac{|22.66 \text{ kHz} - 22.5 \text{ kHz}|}{22.66 \text{ kHz}} \times 100 = 0.71\%$

17-10. [This example has no practice problem.]

17-11. $A_{\text{CL}} = \dfrac{R_f}{2R_1} = \dfrac{68 \text{ k}\Omega}{(2)(30 \text{ k}\Omega)} = 1.13$

17-12. $f_0 = \dfrac{1}{2\pi\sqrt{LC}} = \dfrac{1}{2\pi\sqrt{(33 \text{ mH})(0.1 \,\mu\text{F})}}$
$= 2.77 \text{ kHz}$

17-13. $X_L = 2\pi f L = 2\pi(2.77 \text{ kHz})(33 \text{ mH}) = 574 \,\Omega$
$Q = \dfrac{X_L}{R_W} = \dfrac{574 \,\Omega}{18 \,\Omega} = 31.9$

17-14. $R_P = Q^2 R_W = (31.9)^2 (18 \,\Omega) = 18.3 \text{ k}\Omega$
$r_C = R_P \| R_L = (18.3 \text{ k}\Omega)\|(10 \text{ k}\Omega) = 6.47 \text{ k}\Omega$
$Q_L = \dfrac{r_C}{X_L} = \dfrac{6.47 \text{ k}\Omega}{574 \,\Omega} = 11.3$

17-15. $\text{BW} = \dfrac{f_0}{Q_L} = \dfrac{2.77 \text{ kHz}}{11.3} = 245 \text{ Hz}$

63

PRACTICE PROBLEMS   (CH 17)

1. $Q = \dfrac{f_0}{BW} = \dfrac{14\,\text{kHz}}{2\,\text{kHz}} = 7$

2. $Q = \dfrac{f_0}{BW} = \dfrac{1200\,\text{kHz}}{300\,\text{kHz}} = 4$

3. $BW = \dfrac{f_0}{Q} = \dfrac{800\,\text{kHz}}{6.2} = 129\,\text{kHz}$

4. $BW = \dfrac{f_0}{Q} = \dfrac{1100\,\text{kHz}}{25} = 44\,\text{kHz}$

5. $BW = \dfrac{f_0}{Q} = \dfrac{740\,\text{kHz}}{2.4} = 308\,\text{kHz}$

   $Q = \dfrac{f_0}{BW} = \dfrac{388\,\text{kHz}}{40\,\text{kHz}} = 9.7$

   $BW = \dfrac{f_0}{Q} = \dfrac{1050\,\text{kHz}}{5.6} = 188\,\text{kHz}$

   $Q = \dfrac{f_0}{BW} = \dfrac{920\,\text{kHz}}{600\,\text{kHz}} = 1.53$

6. $f_0 = \sqrt{f_{C1}f_{C2}} = \sqrt{(1180\,\text{kHz})(1300\,\text{kHz})}$
   $= 1239\,\text{kHz}$

   $f_{ave} = \dfrac{f_{C1} + f_{C2}}{2} = \dfrac{1180\,\text{kHz} + 1300\,\text{kHz}}{2}$
   $= 1240\,\text{kHz}$

   $Q = \dfrac{f_0}{BW} = \dfrac{1239\,\text{kHz}}{1300\,\text{kHz} - 1180\,\text{kHz}} = 10.3$

7. $BW = f_C = \dfrac{1}{2\pi R_1 C_1} = \dfrac{1}{2\pi(100\,\text{k}\Omega)(0.01\,\mu\text{F})}$

   $= 159\,\text{Hz}, \quad A_{CL} = \dfrac{R_{f1}}{R_{f2}} + 1 = \dfrac{100\,\text{k}\Omega}{10\,\text{k}\Omega} + 1 = 11$

8. $BW = f_C = \dfrac{1}{2\pi R_1 C_1} = \dfrac{1}{2\pi(82\,\text{k}\Omega)(0.015\,\mu\text{F})}$

   $= 129\,\text{Hz}, \quad A_{CL} = \dfrac{R_{f1}}{R_{f2}} + 1 = \dfrac{159\,\text{k}\Omega}{20\,\text{k}\Omega} + 1 = 8.5$

9. $BW = f_C = \dfrac{1}{2\pi\sqrt{R_1 R_2 C_1 C_2}}$

   $= \dfrac{1}{2\pi\sqrt{(10\,\text{k}\Omega)(10\,\text{k}\Omega)(1\,\text{nF})(2.2\,\text{nf})}} = 10.7\,\text{kHz}$

   $A_{CL} = \dfrac{R_{f1}}{R_{f2}} + 1 = \dfrac{15\,\text{k}\Omega}{30\,\text{k}\Omega} + 1 = 1.5$

10. $BW = f_C = \dfrac{1}{2\pi\sqrt{R_1 R_2 C_1 C_2}}$

    $= \dfrac{1}{2\pi\sqrt{(33\,\text{k}\Omega)(33\,\text{k}\Omega)(100\,\text{pF})(200\,\text{pf})}} = 34.1\,\text{kHz}$

The unity gain filter has a value of $A_{CL} = 1$.

11. For Stage 1: $f_C = \dfrac{1}{2\pi\sqrt{R_1 R_2 C_1 C_2}}$

    $= \dfrac{1}{2\pi\sqrt{(33\,\text{k}\Omega)(33\,\text{k}\Omega)(10\,\text{nF})(22\,\text{nf})}} = 325\,\text{Hz}$

    For Stage 2: $f_C = \dfrac{1}{2\pi R_3 C_3} = \dfrac{1}{2\pi(33\,\text{k}\Omega)(15\,\text{nF})} \cong$

    322 Hz . The BW is assumed to be the lower of these values, 322 Hz.

    $A_{CL1} = \dfrac{R_{f1}}{R_{f2}} + 1 = \dfrac{27\,\text{k}\Omega}{47\,\text{k}\Omega} + 1 = 1.57$

    $A_{CL2} = \dfrac{R_{f3}}{R_{f4}} + 1 = \dfrac{5.1\,\text{k}\Omega}{20\,\text{k}\Omega} + 1 = 1.26$

    $A_{CL(T)} = A_{CL1}A_{CL2} = (1.57)(1.26) = 1.98$

12. For Stage 1: $f_C = \dfrac{1}{2\pi\sqrt{R_1 R_2 C_1 C_2}}$

    $= \dfrac{1}{2\pi\sqrt{(47\,\text{k}\Omega)(47\,\text{k}\Omega)(10\,\text{nF})(22\,\text{nf})}} = 228\,\text{Hz}$

    For Stage 2: $f_{C1} = \dfrac{1}{2\pi R_3 C_3} = \dfrac{1}{2\pi(47\,\text{k}\Omega)(15\,\text{nF})} \cong$

    226 Hz . The BW is assumed to be the lower of these values, 226 Hz.

    $A_{CL1} = \dfrac{R_{f1}}{R_{f2}} + 1 = \dfrac{27\,\text{k}\Omega}{47\,\text{k}\Omega} + 1 = 1.57$

    $A_{CL2} = \dfrac{R_{f3}}{R_{f4}} + 1 = \dfrac{30\,\text{k}\Omega}{120\,\text{k}\Omega} + 1 = 1.25$

    $A_{CL(T)} = A_{CL1}A_{CL2} = (1.57)(1.25) = 1.96$

13. $f_C = \dfrac{1}{2\pi R_1 C_1} = \dfrac{1}{2\pi(51\,\text{k}\Omega)(330\,\text{pF})} = 9.46\,\text{kHz}$

    $A_{CL} = \dfrac{R_{f1}}{R_{f2}} + 1 = \dfrac{100\,\text{k}\Omega}{10\,\text{k}\Omega} + 1 = 11$

14. $f_C = \dfrac{1}{2\pi\sqrt{R_1 R_2 C_1 C_2}}$

    $= \dfrac{1}{2\pi\sqrt{(120\,\text{k}\Omega)(62\,\text{k}\Omega)(330\,\text{pF})(330\,\text{pf})}} = 5.59\,\text{kHz}$

    $A_{CL} = \dfrac{R_{f1}}{R_{f2}} + 1 = \dfrac{5.1\,\text{k}\Omega}{20\,\text{k}\Omega} + 1 = 1.26$

15. $f_{C2} = \dfrac{1}{2\pi\sqrt{R_1 R_2 C_1 C_2}}$

    $= \dfrac{1}{2\pi\sqrt{(30\,\text{k}\Omega)(30\,\text{k}\Omega)(15\,\text{pF})(30\,\text{pF})}} = 250\,\text{kHz}$

$$f_{C1} = \frac{1}{2\pi\sqrt{R_3 R_4 C_3 C_4}}$$

$$= \frac{1}{2\pi\sqrt{(20\,\text{k}\Omega)(10\,\text{k}\Omega)(100\,\text{pF})(100\,\text{pF})}} = 113\,\text{kHz}$$

$$\text{BW} = f_{C2} - f_{C1} = 250\,\text{kHz} - 113\,\text{kHz} = 137\,\text{kHz}$$

$$f_0 = \sqrt{f_{C1} f_{C2}} = \sqrt{(113\,\text{kHz})(250\,\text{kHz})} = 168\,\text{kHz}$$

$$Q = \frac{f_0}{\text{BW}} = \frac{168\,\text{kHz}}{137\,\text{kHz}} = 1.23$$

16. $f_{C2} = \dfrac{1}{2\pi\sqrt{R_1 R_2 C_1 C_2}}$

$$= \frac{1}{2\pi\sqrt{(15\,\text{k}\Omega)(15\,\text{k}\Omega)(15\,\text{pF})(30\,\text{pF})}} = 500\,\text{kHz}$$

$$f_{C1} = \frac{1}{2\pi\sqrt{R_3 R_4 C_3 C_4}}$$

$$= \frac{1}{2\pi\sqrt{(20\,\text{k}\Omega)(10\,\text{k}\Omega)(30\,\text{pF})(30\,\text{pF})}} = 375\,\text{kHz}$$

$$\text{BW} = f_{C2} - f_{C1} = 500\,\text{kHz} - 375\,\text{kHz} = 125\,\text{kHz}$$

$$f_0 = \sqrt{f_{C1} f_{C2}} = \sqrt{(375\,\text{kHz})(500\,\text{kHz})} = 433\,\text{kHz}$$

$$Q = \frac{f_0}{\text{BW}} = \frac{433\,\text{kHz}}{125\,\text{kHz}} = 3.46$$

17. $f_0 = \dfrac{1}{2\pi\sqrt{(R_1 \parallel R_2) R_f C_1 C_2}}$

$$= \frac{1}{2\pi\sqrt{(50\,\text{k}\Omega)(300\,\text{k}\Omega)(220\,\text{pF})(100\,\text{pF})}}$$

$$= 8.76\,\text{kHz}$$

$$C = \sqrt{C_1 C_2} = \sqrt{(220\,\text{pF})(100\,\text{pF})} = 148\,\text{pF}$$

$$Q = \pi f_0 R_f C = \pi(8.76\,\text{kHz})(300\,\text{k}\Omega)(148\,\text{pF}) = 1.22$$

$$\text{BW} = \frac{f_0}{Q} = \frac{8.76\,\text{kHz}}{1.22} = 7.18\,\text{kHz}$$

Since $Q < 2$: $\quad f_{C1} \cong f_0 \sqrt{1 + \left(\dfrac{1}{2Q}\right)^2} - \dfrac{\text{BW}}{2} =$

$$(8.76\,\text{kHz})\sqrt{1 + \left(\frac{1}{2.44}\right)^2} - \frac{7.18\,\text{kHz}}{2} = 5.88\,\text{kHz},$$

and $f_{C2} \cong f_0 \sqrt{1 + \left(\dfrac{1}{2Q}\right)^2} + \dfrac{\text{BW}}{2} =$

$$(8.76\,\text{kHz})\sqrt{1 + \left(\frac{1}{2.44}\right)^2} + \frac{7.18\,\text{kHz}}{2} = 13.1\,\text{kHz}$$

18. $f_0 = \dfrac{1}{2\pi\sqrt{(R_1 \parallel R_2) R_f C_1 C_2}}$

$$= \frac{1}{2\pi\sqrt{(5\,\text{k}\Omega)(330\,\text{k}\Omega)(470\,\text{pF})(300\,\text{pF})}} = 10.4\,\text{kHz}$$

$$C = \sqrt{C_1 C_2} = \sqrt{(470\,\text{pF})(300\,\text{pF})} = 375\,\text{pF}$$

$$Q = \pi f_0 R_f C = \pi(10.4\,\text{kHz})(330\,\text{k}\Omega)(375\,\text{pF}) = 4.04$$

$$\text{BW} = \frac{f_0}{Q} = \frac{10.4\,\text{kHz}}{4.04} = 2.57\,\text{kHz}. \text{ Since } Q > 2:$$

$$f_{C1} \cong f_0 - \frac{\text{BW}}{2} = 10.4\,\text{kHz} - \frac{2.57\,\text{kHz}}{2} = 9.12\,\text{kHz},$$

$$f_{C2} \cong f_0 + \frac{\text{BW}}{2} = 10.4\,\text{kHz} + \frac{2.57\,\text{kHz}}{2} = 11.7\,\text{kHz}.$$

19. $Q = \dfrac{f_0}{\text{BW}} = \dfrac{62\,\text{kHz}}{40\,\text{kHz}} = 1.55$

$$f_{C1} \cong f_0 - \frac{\text{BW}}{2} = 62\,\text{kHz} - \frac{40\,\text{kHz}}{2} = 42\,\text{kHz}$$

$$f_{C2} \cong f_0 + \frac{\text{BW}}{2} = 62\,\text{kHz} + \frac{40\,\text{kHz}}{2} = 82\,\text{kHz}.$$

More accurately:

$$f_{C1} \cong f_0 \sqrt{1 + \left(\frac{1}{2Q}\right)^2} - \frac{\text{BW}}{2}$$

$$= (62\,\text{kHz})\sqrt{1 + \left(\frac{1}{3.1}\right)^2} - \frac{40\,\text{kHz}}{2} = 45.1\,\text{kHz}$$

$$f_{C2} \cong f_0 \sqrt{1 + \left(\frac{1}{2Q}\right)^2} + \frac{\text{BW}}{2}$$

$$= (62\,\text{kHz})\sqrt{1 + \left(\frac{1}{3.1}\right)^2} + \frac{40\,\text{kHz}}{2} = 85.1\,\text{kHz}.$$

For f_{C1},

$$\% \text{ of error} = \frac{|42\,\text{kHz} - 45.1\,\text{kHz}|}{45.1\,\text{kHz}} \times 100 = 6.87\%.$$

For f_{C2},

$$\% \text{ of error} = \frac{|82\,\text{kHz} - 85.1\,\text{kHz}|}{85.1\,\text{kHz}} \times 100 = 3.64\%$$

20. $Q = \dfrac{f_0}{\text{BW}} = \dfrac{482\,\text{kHz}}{200\,\text{kHz}} = 2.41$

$$f_{C1} \cong f_0 - \frac{\text{BW}}{2} = 482\,\text{kHz} - \frac{200\,\text{kHz}}{2} = 382\,\text{kHz}$$

$$f_{C2} \cong f_0 + \frac{\text{BW}}{2} = 482\,\text{kHz} + \frac{200\,\text{kHz}}{2} = 582\,\text{kHz}.$$

More accurately:

$$f_{C1} \cong f_0 \sqrt{1 + \left(\frac{1}{2Q}\right)^2} - \frac{BW}{2}$$

$$= (482 \text{ kHz})\sqrt{1 + \left(\frac{1}{4.82}\right)^2} - \frac{200 \text{ kHz}}{2} = 392 \text{ kHz}$$

$$f_{C2} \cong f_0 \sqrt{1 + \left(\frac{1}{2Q}\right)^2} + \frac{BW}{2}$$

$$= (482 \text{ kHz})\sqrt{1 + \left(\frac{1}{4.82}\right)^2} + \frac{200 \text{ kHz}}{2}$$

$$= 592 \text{ kHz}.$$

For f_{C1},

$$\% \text{ of error} = \frac{|382 \text{ kHz} - 392 \text{ kHz}|}{392 \text{ kHz}} \times 100 = 2.55\%.$$

For f_{C2},

$$\% \text{ of error} = \frac{|582 \text{ kHz} - 592 \text{ kHz}|}{592 \text{ kHz}} \times 100 = 1.69\%$$

21. $A_{CL} = \dfrac{R_f}{2R_1} = \dfrac{300 \text{ k}\Omega}{(2)(100 \text{ k}\Omega)} = 1.5$

22. $A_{CL} = \dfrac{R_f}{2R_1} = \dfrac{330 \text{ k}\Omega}{(2)(10 \text{ k}\Omega)} = 16.5$

23. $f_{C1} = \dfrac{1}{2\pi\sqrt{R_{1L} R_{2L} C_{1L} C_{2L}}}$

$$= \frac{1}{2\pi\sqrt{(820 \ \Omega)(820 \ \Omega)(0.1 \ \mu\text{F})(0.22 \ \mu\text{F})}}$$

$$= 1.31 \text{ kHz}$$

$$f_{C2} = \frac{1}{2\pi\sqrt{R_{1H} R_{2H} C_{1H} C_{2H}}}$$

$$= \frac{1}{2\pi\sqrt{(16 \text{ k}\Omega)(8.2 \text{ k}\Omega)(0.01 \ \mu\text{F})(0.01 \ \mu\text{F})}}$$

$$= 1.39 \text{ kHz}$$

$$BW = f_{C2} - f_{C1} = 1.39 \text{ kHz} - 1.31 \text{ kHz} = 80 \text{ Hz}$$

$$f_0 = \sqrt{f_{C1} f_{C2}} = \sqrt{(1.31 \text{ kHz})(1.39 \text{ kHz})} = 1.35 \text{ kHz}$$

$$Q = \frac{f_0}{BW} = \frac{1.35 \text{ kHz}}{80 \text{ Hz}} = 16.9$$

24. $f_{C1} = \dfrac{1}{2\pi\sqrt{R_{1L} R_{2L} C_{1L} C_{2L}}}$

$$= \frac{1}{2\pi\sqrt{(33 \text{ k}\Omega)(33 \text{ k}\Omega)(100 \text{ pF})(220 \text{ pF})}}$$

$$= 32.5 \text{ kHz}$$

$$f_{C2} = \frac{1}{2\pi\sqrt{R_{1H} R_{2H} C_{1H} C_{2H}}}$$

$$= \frac{1}{2\pi\sqrt{(68 \text{ k}\Omega)(33 \text{ k}\Omega)(47 \text{ pF})(47 \text{ pF})}}$$

$$= 71.5 \text{ kHz}$$

$$BW = f_{C2} - f_{C1} = 71.5 \text{ kHz} - 32.5 \text{ kHz} = 39 \text{ kHz}$$

$$f_0 = \sqrt{f_{C1} f_{C2}} = \sqrt{(32.5 \text{ kHz})(71.5 \text{ kHz})} = 48.2 \text{ kHz}$$

$$Q = \frac{f_0}{BW} = \frac{48.2 \text{ kHz}}{39 \text{ kHz}} = 1.24$$

25. $f_0 = \dfrac{1}{2\pi\sqrt{R_1 R_f C_1 C_2}}$

$$= \frac{1}{2\pi\sqrt{(2.7 \text{ k}\Omega)(100 \text{ k}\Omega)(0.01 \ \mu\text{F})(0.01 \ \mu\text{F})}}$$

$$= 969 \text{ Hz}$$

$$C = \sqrt{C_1 C_2} = \sqrt{(0.01 \ \mu\text{F})(0.01 \ \mu\text{F})} = 0.01 \ \mu\text{F}$$

$$Q = \pi f_0 R_f C = \pi(969 \text{ Hz})(100 \text{ k}\Omega)(0.01 \ \mu\text{F}) = 3.04$$

$$BW = \frac{f_0}{Q} = \frac{969 \text{ kHz}}{3.04} = 319 \text{ Hz}.$$

Since $Q > 2$:

$$f_{C1} \cong f_0 - \frac{BW}{2} = 969 \text{ Hz} - \frac{319 \text{ Hz}}{2} = 809.5 \text{ Hz}$$

$$f_{C2} \cong f_0 + \frac{BW}{2} = 969 \text{ Hz} + \frac{319 \text{ Hz}}{2} = 1128.5 \text{ Hz}$$

26. $f_0 = \dfrac{1}{2\pi\sqrt{R_1 R_f C_1 C_2}}$

$$= \frac{1}{2\pi\sqrt{(9.1 \text{ k}\Omega)(100 \text{ k}\Omega)(0.003 \ \mu\text{F})(0.003 \ \mu\text{F})}}$$

$$= 1.76 \text{ kHz}$$

$$C = \sqrt{C_1 C_2} = \sqrt{(0.003 \ \mu\text{F})(0.003 \ \mu\text{F})} = 0.003 \ \mu\text{F}$$

$$Q = \pi f_0 R_f C = \pi(1.76 \text{ kHz})(100 \text{ k}\Omega)(0.003 \ \mu\text{F})$$

$$= 1.66$$

$$BW = \frac{f_0}{Q} = \frac{1.76 \text{ kHz}}{1.66} = 1.06 \text{ kHz}$$

Since $Q < 2$:

$$f_{C1} \cong f_0 \sqrt{1 + \left(\frac{1}{2Q}\right)^2} - \frac{BW}{2}$$

$$= (1.76 \text{ kHz})\sqrt{1 + \left(\frac{1}{3.32}\right)^2} - \frac{1.06 \text{ kHz}}{2}$$

$$= 1.31 \text{ kHz}$$

$$f_{C2} \cong f_0 \sqrt{1 + \left(\frac{1}{2Q}\right)^2} + \frac{BW}{2}$$

$$= (1.76 \text{ kHz}) \sqrt{1 + \left(\frac{1}{3.32}\right)^2} + \frac{1.06 \text{ kHz}}{2}$$

$$= 2.37 \text{ kHz}$$

27. $f_0 = \dfrac{1}{2\pi\sqrt{LC}} = \dfrac{1}{2\pi\sqrt{(100\,\mu\text{H})(0.033\,\mu\text{F})}} = 87.6 \text{ kHz}$

$X_L = 2\pi f L = 2\pi(87.6 \text{ kHz})(100\,\mu\text{H}) = 55\ \Omega$

$Q = \dfrac{X_L}{R_W} = \dfrac{55\ \Omega}{5\ \Omega} = 11$

$R_P = Q^2 R_W = (11)^2(5\ \Omega) = 605\ \Omega$

$r_C = R_P \parallel R_L = (605\ \Omega)\parallel(5\text{ k}\Omega) = 540\ \Omega$

$Q_L = \dfrac{r_C}{X_L} = \dfrac{540\ \Omega}{55\ \Omega} = 9.82$

$\text{BW} = \dfrac{f_0}{Q_L} = \dfrac{87.6 \text{ kHz}}{9.82} = 8.92 \text{ kHz}$

Since $Q > 2$:

$f_{C1} \cong f_0 - \dfrac{\text{BW}}{2} = 87.6 \text{ kHz} - \dfrac{8.92 \text{ kHz}}{2} = 83.1 \text{ kHz}$

$f_{C2} \cong f_0 + \dfrac{\text{BW}}{2} = 87.6 \text{ kHz} + \dfrac{8.92 \text{ kHz}}{2} = 92.1 \text{ kHz}$

28. $f_0 = \dfrac{1}{2\pi\sqrt{LC}} = \dfrac{1}{2\pi\sqrt{(470\,\mu\text{H})(0.001\,\mu\text{F})}} = 232 \text{ kHz}$

$X_L = 2\pi f L = 2\pi(232 \text{ kHz})(470\,\mu\text{H}) = 685\ \Omega$

$Q = \dfrac{X_L}{R_W} = \dfrac{685\ \Omega}{20\ \Omega} = 34.3$

$R_P = Q^2 R_W = (34.3)^2(20\ \Omega) = 23.5 \text{ k}\Omega$

$r_C = R_P \parallel R_L = (23.5 \text{ k}\Omega)\parallel(12 \text{ k}\Omega) = 7.94 \text{ k}\Omega$

$Q_L = \dfrac{r_C}{X_L} = \dfrac{7.94 \text{ k}\Omega}{685\ \Omega} = 11.6$

$\text{BW} = \dfrac{f_0}{Q_L} = \dfrac{232 \text{ kHz}}{11.6} = 20 \text{ kHz}.$ Since $Q > 2$:

$f_{C1} \cong f_0 - \dfrac{\text{BW}}{2} = 232 \text{ kHz} - \dfrac{20 \text{ kHz}}{2} = 222 \text{ kHz}$

$f_{C2} \cong f_0 + \dfrac{\text{BW}}{2} = 232 \text{ kHz} + \dfrac{20 \text{ kHz}}{2} = 242 \text{ kHz}$

29. $V_{CEQ} = V_{CC} = 20 \text{ V},\ I_{CQ} = 0 \text{ A}$

30. $V_{CEQ} = V_{CC} = 12 \text{ V},\ I_{CQ} = 0 \text{ A}$

31. $V_{\text{in(pk)}} = 1 \text{ V} - V_{BB} = 1 \text{ V} - (-2 \text{ V}) = 3 \text{ V (min)}$

32. $V_{\text{in(pk)}} = 1 \text{ V} - V_{BB} = 1 \text{ V} - (-4 \text{ V}) = 5 \text{ V (min)}$

33. The loss of signal at the (+) input to the op-amp could be caused by C_1 open or R_1 shorted. (C_1 open is the more likely cause.)

34. The waveforms shown would occur only if the input to the op-amp was wired incorrectly. As shown, the first op-amp is inverting the signal.

35. As shown, the circuit has the following values:

$$f_0 = \frac{1}{2\pi\sqrt{LC}} = \frac{1}{2\pi\sqrt{(330\,\mu\text{H})(0.01\,\mu\text{F})}} = 87.6 \text{ kHz}$$

$X_L = 2\pi f L = 2\pi(87.6 \text{ kHz})(330\,\mu\text{H}) = 182\ \Omega$

$Q = \dfrac{X_L}{R_W} = \dfrac{182\ \Omega}{4\ \Omega} = 45.5,$

$R_P = Q^2 R_W = (45.5)^2(4\ \Omega) = 8.28 \text{ k}\Omega,$

$r_C = R_P \parallel R_L = (8.28 \text{ k}\Omega)\parallel(18 \text{ k}\Omega) = 5.67 \text{ k}\Omega$

$Q_L = \dfrac{r_C}{X_L} = \dfrac{5.67 \text{ k}\Omega}{182\ \Omega} = 31.2$

$\text{BW} = \dfrac{f_0}{Q_L} = \dfrac{87.6 \text{ kHz}}{31.2} = 2.81 \text{ kHz}.$ Since $Q > 2$:

$f_{C1} \cong f_0 - \dfrac{\text{BW}}{2} = 87.6 \text{ kHz} - \dfrac{2.81 \text{ kHz}}{2} = 86.2 \text{ kHz}$

$f_{C2} \cong f_0 + \dfrac{\text{BW}}{2} = 87.6 \text{ kHz} + \dfrac{2.81 \text{ kHz}}{2} = 89.0 \text{ kHz}$

When the coil is replaced,

$Q = \dfrac{X_L}{R_W} = \dfrac{182\ \Omega}{17\ \Omega} = 10.7$

$R_P = Q^2 R_W = (10.7)^2(17\ \Omega) = 1.95 \text{ k}\Omega$

$r_C = R_P \parallel R_L = (1.95 \text{ k}\Omega)\parallel(18 \text{ k}\Omega) = 1.76 \text{ k}\Omega$

$Q_L = \dfrac{r_C}{X_L} = \dfrac{1.76 \text{ k}\Omega}{182\ \Omega} = 9.67$

$\text{BW} = \dfrac{f_0}{Q_L} = \dfrac{87.6 \text{ kHz}}{9.67} = 9.06 \text{ kHz}.$ Since $Q > 2$:

$f_{C1} \cong f_0 - \dfrac{\text{BW}}{2} = 87.6 \text{ kHz} - \dfrac{9.06 \text{ kHz}}{2} = 83.1 \text{ kHz}$

$f_{C2} \cong f_0 + \dfrac{\text{BW}}{2} = 87.6 \text{ kHz} + \dfrac{9.06 \text{ kHz}}{2} = 92.1 \text{ kHz}$

$\Delta f_{C1} = 86.2 \text{ kHz} - 83.1 \text{ kHz} = 3.1 \text{ kHz}$

$\Delta f_{C2} = 92.1 \text{ kHz} - 89.0 \text{ kHz} \cong 3.1 \text{ kHz}$

36. The cutoff frequencies for the circuit are determined by the bandpass filter. When the circuit is operated below f_{C1} or above f_{C2}, the output from the bandpass filter is (ideally) zero and the input to the summing amplifier equals v_{in}. With equal resistor values (as given in the circuit), the summing amplifier has values of $A_{\text{CL}} = 1$ and $v_{\text{out}} = -v_{\text{in}}$. When the circuit is operated within its cutoff frequencies, the unity-gain bandpass filter provides an output equal to $-v_{\text{in}}$. In this case, the summing amplifier has inputs of $v_{\text{in}} + (-v_{\text{in}}) = 0 \text{ V}$, and its resulting output is 0 V.

CHAPTER 18

EXAMPLE PRACTICE PROBLEM   (CH 18)

18-1. $C_T = \dfrac{C_1 C_2}{C_1 + C_2} = \dfrac{(10\text{ nF})(1.5\,\mu\text{F})}{10\text{ nF} + 1.5\,\mu\text{F}} = 9.93\text{ nF}$

$f_r = \dfrac{1}{2\pi\sqrt{LC_T}} = \dfrac{1}{2\pi\sqrt{(10\,\mu\text{H})(9.93\text{ nF})}} = 505\text{ kHz}$

$X_{C1} = \dfrac{1}{2\pi f_r C_1} = \dfrac{1}{2\pi(505\text{ kHz})(10\text{ nF})} = 31.5\ \Omega$

$X_{C2} = \dfrac{1}{2\pi f_r C_2} = \dfrac{1}{2\pi(505\text{ kHz})(1.5\,\mu\text{F})} = 0.21\ \Omega$

$\alpha_v = \dfrac{X_{C2}}{X_{C1}} = \dfrac{0.21\ \Omega}{31.5\ \Omega} = 0.0067$

$\alpha_v = \dfrac{C_1}{C_2} = \dfrac{10\text{ nF}}{1.5\,\mu\text{F}} = 0.0067$

PRACTICE PROBLEMS   (CH 18)

1. $f_r = \dfrac{1}{2\pi RC} = \dfrac{1}{2\pi(33\text{ k}\Omega)(22\text{ pF})} = 219\text{ kHz}$

2. $f_r = \dfrac{1}{2\pi RC} = \dfrac{1}{2\pi(92\text{ k}\Omega)(0.01\,\mu\text{F})} = 173\text{ Hz}$

3. $C_T = \dfrac{C_1 C_2}{C_1 + C_2} = \dfrac{(0.1\,\mu\text{F})(1\,\mu\text{F})}{0.1\,\mu\text{F} + 1\,\mu\text{F}} = 90.9\text{ nF}$

$f_r = \dfrac{1}{2\pi\sqrt{LC_T}} = \dfrac{1}{2\pi\sqrt{(470\,\mu\text{H})(90.9\text{ nF})}} = 24.3\text{ kHz}$

4. $\alpha_v = \dfrac{C_1}{C_2} = \dfrac{0.1\,\mu\text{F}}{1\,\mu\text{F}} = 0.01$

5. $C_T = \dfrac{C_1 C_2}{C_1 + C_2} = \dfrac{(10\text{ nF})(1\,\mu\text{F})}{10\text{ nF} + 1\,\mu\text{F}} = 9.9\text{ nF}$

$f_r = \dfrac{1}{2\pi\sqrt{LC_T}} = \dfrac{1}{2\pi\sqrt{(3.3\text{ mH})(9.9\text{ nF})}} = 27.8\text{ kHz}$

$\alpha_v = \dfrac{C_1}{C_2} = \dfrac{10\text{ nF}}{1\,\mu\text{F}} = 0.01,\ A_v = \dfrac{C_2}{C_1} = \dfrac{1\,\mu\text{F}}{10\text{ nF}} = 100$

6. $C_T = \dfrac{C_1 C_2}{C_1 + C_2} = \dfrac{(1\,\mu\text{F})(10\,\mu\text{F})}{1\,\mu\text{F} + 10\,\mu\text{F}} = 909\text{ nF}$

$f_r = \dfrac{1}{2\pi\sqrt{LC_T}} = \dfrac{1}{2\pi\sqrt{(3.3\text{ mH})(909\text{ nF})}} = 2.91\text{ kHz}$

$\alpha_v = \dfrac{C_1}{C_2} = \dfrac{1\,\mu\text{F}}{10\,\mu\text{F}} = 0.1,\ A_v = \dfrac{C_2}{C_1} = \dfrac{10\,\mu\text{F}}{1\,\mu\text{F}} = 10$

7. $C_T = \dfrac{C_1 C_2}{C_1 + C_2} = \dfrac{(0.22\,\mu\text{F})(3.3\,\mu\text{F})}{0.22\,\mu\text{F} + 3.3\,\mu\text{F}} = 206\text{ nF}$

$f_r = \dfrac{1}{2\pi\sqrt{LC_T}} = \dfrac{1}{2\pi\sqrt{(330\,\mu\text{H})(206\text{ nF})}} = 19.3\text{ kHz}$

$\alpha_v = \dfrac{C_1}{C_2} = \dfrac{0.22\,\mu\text{F}}{3.3\,\mu\text{F}} = 0.067$

$A_v = \dfrac{C_2}{C_1} = \dfrac{3.3\,\mu\text{F}}{0.22\,\mu\text{F}} = 15$

8. $L_T = L_1 + L_2 = 4.7\text{ mH} + 47\,\mu\text{H} \cong 4.75\text{ mH}$

$f_r = \dfrac{1}{2\pi\sqrt{L_T C}} = \dfrac{1}{2\pi\sqrt{(4.75\text{ mH})(1\text{ nF})}} = 73\text{ kHz}$

$\alpha_v = \dfrac{L_2}{L_1} = \dfrac{47\,\mu\text{H}}{4.7\text{ mH}} = 0.01$

$A_v = \dfrac{L_1}{L_2} = \dfrac{4.7\text{ mH}}{47\,\mu\text{H}} = 100$

9. $L_T = L_1 + L_2 = 0.1\text{ H} + 1\text{ mH} = 101\text{ mH}$

$f_r = \dfrac{1}{2\pi\sqrt{L_T C}} = \dfrac{1}{2\pi\sqrt{(101\text{ mH})(22\text{ nF})}} = 3.38\text{ kHz}$

$\alpha_v = \dfrac{L_2}{L_1} = \dfrac{1\text{ mH}}{0.1\text{ H}} = 0.01,\ A_v = \dfrac{L_1}{L_2} = \dfrac{0.1\text{ H}}{1\text{ mH}} = 100$

10. $f_r = \dfrac{1}{2\pi\sqrt{LC_3}} = \dfrac{1}{2\pi\sqrt{(470\,\mu\text{H})(100\text{ pF})}} = 734\text{ kHz}$

$\alpha_v = \dfrac{C_1}{C_2} = \dfrac{0.1\,\mu\text{F}}{1\,\mu\text{F}} = 0.1,\ A_v = \dfrac{C_2}{C_1} = \dfrac{1\,\mu\text{F}}{0.1\,\mu\text{F}} = 10$

11. $f_r = \dfrac{1}{2\pi\sqrt{LC_3}} = \dfrac{1}{2\pi\sqrt{(3.3\text{ mH})(100\text{ pF})}} = 277\text{ kHz}$

$\alpha_v = \dfrac{C_1}{C_2} = \dfrac{0.1\,\mu\text{F}}{1\,\mu\text{F}} = 0.1,\ A_v = \dfrac{C_2}{C_1} = \dfrac{1\,\mu\text{F}}{0.1\,\mu\text{F}} = 10$

12. The 0 V reading at the inverting input indicates that R_4 is open or R_5 is shorted. An open R_4 is the more likely problem.

13. The dc readings are normal, despite the fact that the circuit is not working. Assuming the transistor is good, the problem is likely the result of a fault in the LC feedback network.

14. The $V_C = 0$ V reading indicates that the RF choke (RFC) is open.

15. $\alpha_v = \dfrac{L_2}{L_1}$ and $A_v = \dfrac{L_1}{L_2}$. Therefore,

$\alpha_v A_v = \dfrac{L_2}{L_1} \times \dfrac{L_1}{L_2} = 1$

16. The circuit is *emitter-feedback biased*, so

$I_B = \dfrac{V_{CC} - V_{BE}}{R_B + (h_{FE} + 1)R_E} = \dfrac{20\text{ V} - 0.7\text{ V}}{130\text{ k}\Omega + (141)(1\text{ k}\Omega)}$

$\qquad = 71.2\,\mu\text{A}$

$I_{CQ} = h_{FE} I_B = (140)(71.2\,\mu\text{A}) = 9.97\text{ mA}.$

Assuming the choke is *ideal* ($R_W = 0\ \Omega$):

$V_{CEQ} = V_{CC} - I_{CQ}R_E = 20\ \text{V} - (9.97\ \text{mA})(1\ \text{k}\Omega)$
$\qquad \cong 10\ \text{V}$

17. $C_T = \dfrac{C_1 C_2}{C_1 + C_2} = \dfrac{(100\ \text{nF})(10\ \text{nF})}{100\ \text{nF} + 10\ \text{nF}} = 9.09\ \text{nF}$

Using a transposed form of equation (18.8), the value of L required to set f_r to 22 kHz is found as

$L = \dfrac{1}{(2\pi f_r)^2 C_T} = \dfrac{1}{(2\pi \times 22\ \text{kHz})^2 (9.09\ \text{nF})}$
$\quad = 5.76\ \text{mH}$

EXAMPLE PRACTICE PROBLEM   (CH 19)

19-1. $I_{C(\text{sat})} = \dfrac{V_{CC}}{R_C} = \dfrac{10\ \text{V}}{1\ \text{k}\Omega} = 10\ \text{mA}$

$I_B = \dfrac{I_{C(\text{sat})}}{h_{FE}} = \dfrac{10\ \text{mA}}{70} = 143\ \mu\text{A}$

$+V_{\text{in}} = I_B R_B + V_{BE} = (143\ \mu\text{A})(51\ \text{k}\Omega) + 0.7\ \text{V}$
$\qquad = 7.99\ \text{V}$

19-2. When $V_{GS} = 0\ \text{V}$, $I_D = I_{DSS}$, and
$V_{\text{out}} = V_{DD} - I_{DSS}R_D = 10\ \text{V} - (5\ \text{mA})(1.8\ \text{k}\Omega) = 1\ \text{V}$
When $V_{GS} = -4\ \text{V}$, $I_D = 0\ \text{mA}$, and
$V_{\text{out}} = V_{DD} - I_D R_D = 10\ \text{V} - 0\ \text{V} = 10\ \text{V}$

19-3. When $V_{GS} = 0\ \text{V}$, $I_D = I_{DSS}$, and
$V_{\text{out}} = V_{DD} - I_{DSS}R_D = 8\ \text{V} - (500\ \mu\text{A})(2\ \text{k}\Omega) = 7\ \text{V}$

19-4. PW = (3 div)(2 µs/div) = 6 µs
$\qquad T$ = (9 div)(2 µs/div) = 18 µs

19-5. duty cycle $= \dfrac{\text{PW}}{T} \times 100 = \dfrac{6\ \mu\text{s}}{18\ \mu\text{s}} \times 100 = 33.3\ \%$

19-6. $f_C = \dfrac{0.35}{t_r} = \dfrac{0.35}{25\ \text{ns}} = 14\ \text{MHz}$

$f_{\text{max}} = \dfrac{0.35}{100 t_r} = \dfrac{0.35}{(100)(25\ \text{ns})} = 140\ \text{kHz}$

19-7. With an open load, $V_{\text{out}} = \pm 12\ \text{V}$, and

UTP $= -\dfrac{R_{\text{in}}}{R_f}(-V_{\text{out}}) = \left(-\dfrac{11\ \text{k}\Omega}{33\ \text{k}\Omega}\right)(-12\ \text{V}) = 4\ \text{V}$

LTP $= -\dfrac{R_{\text{in}}}{R_f}(V_{\text{out}}) = \left(-\dfrac{11\ \text{k}\Omega}{33\ \text{k}\Omega}\right)(+12\ \text{V}) = -4\ \text{V}$

19-8. With an open load, $V_{\text{out}} = \pm 14\ \text{V}$, and

UTP $= -\dfrac{R_{\text{in}}}{R_{f1}}(-V_{\text{out}} + 0.7\ \text{V})$

$\qquad = \left(-\dfrac{2\ \text{k}\Omega}{20\ \text{k}\Omega}\right)(-13.3\ \text{V}) = 1.33\ \text{V}$

LTP $= -\dfrac{R_{\text{in}}}{R_{f2}}(V_{\text{out}} + 0.7\ \text{V})$

$\qquad = \left(-\dfrac{2\ \text{k}\Omega}{14\ \text{k}\Omega}\right)(+13.3\ \text{V}) = -1.9\ \text{V}$

19-9. With an open load, $V_{\text{out}} = \pm 9\ \text{V}$, and

UTP $= \dfrac{R_{f2}}{R_{f1} + R_{f2}}(+V_{\text{out}}) = \left(\dfrac{1\ \text{k}\Omega}{4\ \text{k}\Omega}\right)(9\ \text{V}) = 2.25\text{V}$

LTP $= \dfrac{R_{f2}}{R_{f1} + R_{f2}}(-V_{\text{out}}) = \left(\dfrac{1\ \text{k}\Omega}{4\ \text{k}\Omega}\right)(-9\ \text{V})$
$\qquad = -2.25\text{V}$

19-10. PW $= 1.1RC = (1.1)(18\ \text{k}\Omega)(1.5\ \mu\text{F}) = 29.7\ \text{ms}$

19-11. $V_{\text{con}} = V_{CC}\dfrac{R_3}{R_2 + R_3} = (15\ \text{V})\dfrac{30\ \text{k}\Omega}{40\ \text{k}\Omega} \cong 11.3\ \text{V}$

$V_T < \dfrac{1}{2}V_{\text{con}} = \dfrac{1}{2}(11.3\ \text{V}) = 5.65\ \text{V}$

19-12.

$f_0 = \dfrac{1.44}{(R_A + 2R_B)C_1} = \dfrac{1.44}{(9.5\ \text{k}\Omega)(0.022\ \mu\text{F})}$
$\quad = 6.89\ \text{kHz}$

duty cycle $= \dfrac{R_A + R_B}{R_A + 2R_B} \times 100 = \dfrac{7.3\ \text{k}\Omega}{9.5\ \text{k}\Omega} \times 100$
$\qquad = 76.8\%$

PW $= 0.693(R_A + R_B)C_1$
$\qquad = 0.693(7.3\ \text{k}\Omega)(0.022\ \mu\text{F}) = 111\ \mu\text{s}$

PRACTICE PROBLEMS   (CH 19)

1. $I_{C(\text{sat})} = \dfrac{V_{CC}}{R_C} = \dfrac{18\ \text{V}}{9.1\ \text{k}\Omega} = 1.98\ \text{mA}$

$I_B = \dfrac{I_{C(\text{sat})}}{h_{FE}} = \dfrac{1.98\ \text{mA}}{280} = 7.07\ \mu\text{A}$

$+V_{\text{in}} = I_B R_B + V_{BE} = (7.07\ \mu\text{A})(1.5\ \text{M}\Omega) + 0.7\ \text{V}$
$\qquad = 11.3\ \text{V}$

2. $I_{C(\text{sat})} = \dfrac{V_{CC}}{R_C} = \dfrac{12\ \text{V}}{1.1\ \text{k}\Omega} = 10.9\ \text{mA}$

$I_B = \dfrac{I_{C(\text{sat})}}{h_{FE}} = \dfrac{10.9\ \text{mA}}{150} = 72.7\ \mu\text{A}$

$+V_{\text{in}} = I_B R_B + V_{BE} = (72.7\ \mu\text{A})(47\ \text{k}\Omega) + 0.7\ \text{V}$

$\qquad = 4.12\ \text{V}$

3. $I_{C(\text{sat})} = \dfrac{V_{CC}}{R_C} = \dfrac{5\ \text{V}}{3.3\ \text{k}\Omega} = 1.52\ \text{mA}$

$$I_B = \frac{I_{C(sat)}}{h_{FE}} = \frac{1.52\ \text{mA}}{300} = 5.07\ \mu\text{A}$$

$$+V_{in} = I_B R_B + V_{BE} = (5.07\ \mu\text{A})(560\ \text{k}\Omega) + 0.7\ \text{V}$$
$$= 3.54\ \text{V}$$

4. $I_{C(sat)} = \dfrac{V_{CC}}{R_C} = \dfrac{10\ \text{V}}{1\ \text{k}\Omega} = 10\ \text{mA}$

$$I_B = \frac{I_{C(sat)}}{h_{FE}} = \frac{10\ \text{mA}}{150} = 66.7\ \mu\text{A}$$

$$+V_{in} = I_B R_B + V_{BE} = (66.7\ \mu\text{A})(68\ \text{k}\Omega) + 0.7\ \text{V}$$
$$= 5.24\ \text{V}$$

5. When $V_{GS} = 0\ \text{V}$, $I_D = I_{DSS}$, and
$V_{out} = V_{DD} - I_{DSS}R_D = 6\ \text{V} - (10\ \text{mA})(510\ \Omega)$
$\qquad = 0.9\ \text{V}$

When $V_{GS} = -8\ \text{V}$, $I_D = 0\ \text{mA}$, and
$V_{out} = V_{DD} - I_D R_D = 6\ \text{V} - 0\ \text{V} = 6\ \text{V}$

6. When $V_{GS} = 0\ \text{V}$, $I_D = I_{DSS}$, and
$V_{out} = V_{DD} - I_{DSS}R_D = 20\ \text{V} - (8\ \text{mA})(2.4\ \text{k}\Omega)$
$\qquad = 0.8\ \text{V}$

When $V_{GS} = -12\ \text{V}$, $I_D = 0\ \text{mA}$, and
$V_{out} = V_{DD} - I_D R_D = 20\ \text{V} - 0\ \text{V} = 20\ \text{V}$

7. PW = (2 div)(10 μs/div) = 20 μs
$\qquad T$ = (5 div)(10 μs/div) = 50 μs

8. PW = (2.5 div)(1μs/div) = 2.5 μs
$\qquad T$ = (6 div)(1 μs/div) = 6 μs

9. duty cycle = $\dfrac{\text{PW}}{T} \times 100 = \dfrac{20\ \mu\text{s}}{50\ \mu\text{s}} \times 100 = 40\%$

10. duty cycle = $\dfrac{\text{PW}}{T} \times 100 = \dfrac{2.5\ \mu\text{s}}{6\ \mu\text{s}} \times 100 = 41.7\%$

11. $f_C = \dfrac{0.35}{t_r} = \dfrac{0.35}{15\ \text{ns}} = 23.3\ \text{MHz}$

$\qquad f_{max} = \dfrac{0.35}{100 t_r} = \dfrac{0.35}{(100)(15\ \text{ns})} = 233\ \text{kHz}$

12. $f_C = \dfrac{0.35}{t_r} = \dfrac{0.35}{20\ \text{ns}} = 17.5\ \text{MHz}$

$\qquad f_{max} = \dfrac{0.35}{100 t_r} = \dfrac{0.35}{(100)(20\ \text{ns})} = 175\ \text{kHz}$

13. $f_C = \dfrac{0.35}{t_r} = \dfrac{0.35}{29\ \text{ns}} = 12.1\ \text{MHz}$

$\qquad f_{max} = \dfrac{0.35}{100 t_r} = \dfrac{0.35}{(100)(29\ \text{ns})} = 121\ \text{kHz}$

14. $f_C = \dfrac{0.35}{t_r} = \dfrac{0.35}{25\ \text{ns}} = 14\ \text{MHz}$

$\qquad f_{max} = \dfrac{0.35}{100 t_r} = \dfrac{0.35}{(100)(25\ \text{ns})} = 140\ \text{kHz}$

15. $f_C = \dfrac{0.35}{t_r} = \dfrac{0.35}{15\ \text{ns}} = 23.3\ \text{MHz}$

$\qquad f_{max} = \dfrac{0.35}{100 t_r} = \dfrac{0.35}{(100)(15\ \text{ns})} = 233\ \text{kHz}$

16. $f_C = \dfrac{0.35}{t_r} = \dfrac{0.35}{40\ \text{ns}} = 8.75\ \text{MHz}$

$\qquad f_{max} = \dfrac{0.35}{100 t_r} = \dfrac{0.35}{(100)(40\ \text{ns})} = 87.5\ \text{kHz}$

17. $f_C = \dfrac{0.35}{t_r} = \dfrac{0.35}{65\ \text{ns}} = 5.38\ \text{MHz}$

$\qquad f_{max} = \dfrac{0.35}{100 t_r} = \dfrac{0.35}{(100)(65\ \text{ns})} = 53.8\ \text{kHz}$

18. $f_C = \dfrac{0.35}{t_{on}} = \dfrac{0.35}{15\ \text{ns}} = 23.3\ \text{MHz}$

$\qquad f_{max} = \dfrac{0.35}{100 t_{on}} = \dfrac{0.35}{(100)(15\ \text{ns})} = 233\ \text{kHz}$

19. $t_d = 20\ \text{ns}$, $t_r = 60\ \text{ns}$, $t_s = 120\ \text{ns}$, $t_f = 70\ \text{ns}$

20. $t_d = 10\ \text{ns}$, $t_r = 20\ \text{ns}$, $t_s = 50\ \text{ns}$, $t_f = 20\ \text{ns}$

21. With an open load, $V_{out} = \pm 9\ \text{V}$, and

$$\text{UTP} = -\frac{R_{in}}{R_f}(-V_{out}) = \left(-\frac{11\ \text{k}\Omega}{22\ \text{k}\Omega}\right)(-9\ \text{V}) = 4.5\ \text{V}$$

$$\text{LTP} = -\frac{R_{in}}{R_f}(V_{out}) = \left(-\frac{11\ \text{k}\Omega}{22\ \text{k}\Omega}\right)(+9\ \text{V}) = -4.5\ \text{V}$$

22. With an open load, $V_{out} = \pm 17\ \text{V}$, and

$$\text{UTP} = -\frac{R_{in}}{R_f}(-V_{out}) = \left(-\frac{100\ \text{k}\Omega}{100\ \text{k}\Omega}\right)(-17\ \text{V}) = 17\ \text{V}$$

$$\text{LTP} = -\frac{R_{in}}{R_f}(V_{out}) = \left(-\frac{100\ \text{k}\Omega}{100\ \text{k}\Omega}\right)(+17\ \text{V}) = -17\ \text{V}$$

23. With an open load, $V_{out} = \pm 9\ \text{V}$, and UTP =

$$-\frac{R_{in}}{R_{f1}}(-V_{out} + 0.7\ \text{V}) = \left(-\frac{1\ \text{k}\Omega}{5\ \text{k}\Omega}\right)(-8.3\ \text{V}) = 1.66\ \text{V}$$

$$\text{LTP} = -\frac{R_{in}}{R_{f2}}(V_{out} + 0.7\ \text{V}) = \left(-\frac{1\ \text{k}\Omega}{10\ \text{k}\Omega}\right)(+8.3\ \text{V})$$

$$= -830\ \text{mV}$$

24. With an open load, $V_{out} = \pm 7\ \text{V}$, and

$$\text{UTP} = -\frac{R_{in}}{R_{f1}}(-V_{out} + 0.7\ \text{V})$$

$$= \left(-\frac{1.1\ \text{k}\Omega}{2.2\ \text{k}\Omega}\right)(-6.3\ \text{V}) = 3.15\ \text{V}$$

$$\text{LTP} = -\frac{R_{in}}{R_{f2}}(V_{out} + 0.7\ \text{V})$$

$$= \left(-\frac{1.1\ \text{k}\Omega}{3.3\ \text{k}\Omega}\right)(+6.3\ \text{V}) = -2.1\ \text{V}$$

25. With an open load, $V_{out} = \pm 14$ V, and

$$\text{UTP} = \frac{R_{f2}}{R_{f1} + R_{f2}}(+V_{out}) = \left(\frac{10\,\text{k}\Omega}{30\,\text{k}\Omega}\right)(14\,\text{V})$$
$$= 4.67\,\text{V}$$

$$\text{LTP} = \frac{R_{f2}}{R_{f1} + R_{f2}}(-V_{out}) = \left(\frac{10\,\text{k}\Omega}{30\,\text{k}\Omega}\right)(-14\,\text{V})$$
$$= -4.67\,\text{V}$$

26. With an open load, $V_{out} = +9$ V and $+1$ V.

$$\text{UTP} = \frac{R_{f2}}{R_{f1} + R_{f2}}(+V_{out}) = \left(\frac{200\,\Omega}{1.2\,\text{k}\Omega}\right)(9\,\text{V}) = 1.5\,\text{V}$$

$$\text{LTP} = \frac{R_{f2}}{R_{f1} + R_{f2}}(+V_{out}) = \left(\frac{200\,\Omega}{1.2\,\text{k}\Omega}\right)(1\,\text{V})$$
$$= 167\,\text{mV}$$

27. With an open load, $V_{out} = \pm 15$ V, and

$$\text{UTP} = \frac{R_{f2}}{R_{f1} + R_{f2}}(+V_{out}) = \left(\frac{11\,\text{k}\Omega}{33\,\text{k}\Omega}\right)(15\,\text{V})$$
$$= 5\,\text{V}$$

$$\text{LTP} = \frac{R_{f2}}{R_{f1} + R_{f2}}(-V_{out}) = \left(\frac{11\,\text{k}\Omega}{33\,\text{k}\Omega}\right)(-15\,\text{V})$$
$$= -5\,\text{V}$$

28. With an open load, $V_{out} = +14$ V.

$$\text{UTP} = \frac{R_{f2}}{R_{f1} + R_{f2}}(+V_{out} - 0.7\,\text{V})$$

$$= \left(\frac{1\,\text{k}\Omega}{2\,\text{k}\Omega}\right)(13.3\,\text{V}) = 6.65\,\text{V}$$

$$\text{LTP} = \frac{R_{f4}}{R_{f3} + R_{f4}}(+V) - 0.7\,\text{V}$$

$$= \left(\frac{3\,\text{k}\Omega}{30\,\text{k}\Omega}\right)(15\,\text{V}) - 0.7\,\text{V} = 800\,\text{mV}$$

29. $\text{PW} = 1.1RC = (1.1)(10\,\text{k}\Omega)(1\,\mu\text{F}) = 11\,\text{ms}$

30. $\text{PW} = 1.1RC = (1.1)(33\,\text{k}\Omega)(0.47\,\mu\text{F}) = 17.1\,\text{ms}$

31. $V_{con} = V_{CC}\dfrac{R_2}{R_1 + R_2} = (8\,\text{V})\dfrac{10\,\text{k}\Omega}{57\,\text{k}\Omega} = 1.4\,\text{V}$

$$V_T < \frac{1}{2}V_{con} = \frac{1}{2}(1.4\,\text{V}) = 0.7\,\text{V}$$

32. $V_{con} = V_{CC}\dfrac{R_2}{R_1 + R_2} = (8\,\text{V})\dfrac{11\,\text{k}\Omega}{44\,\text{k}\Omega} = 2\,\text{V}$

$$V_T < \frac{1}{2}V_{con} = \frac{1}{2}(2\,\text{V}) = 1\,\text{V}$$

33. $f_0 = \dfrac{1.44}{(R_A + 2R_B)C_1} = \dfrac{1.44}{(26.4\,\text{k}\Omega)(0.01\,\mu\text{F})}$
$$= 5.45\,\text{kHz}$$

$$\text{duty cycle} = \frac{R_A + R_B}{R_A + 2R_B} \times 100 = \frac{18.2\,\text{k}\Omega}{26.4\,\text{k}\Omega} \times 100 = 68.9\%,$$
$$\text{PW} = 0.693(R_A + R_B)C_1$$
$$= 0.693(18.2\,\text{k}\Omega)(0.01\,\mu\text{F}) = 126\,\mu\text{s}$$

34. $f_0 = \dfrac{1.44}{(R_A + 2R_B)C_1} = \dfrac{1.44}{(54\,\text{k}\Omega)(0.001\,\mu\text{F})}$
$$= 26.7\,\text{kHz}$$

$$\text{duty cycle} = \frac{R_A + R_B}{R_A + 2R_B} \times 100 = \frac{32\,\text{k}\Omega}{54\,\text{k}\Omega} \times 100$$
$$= 59.3\%$$
$$\text{PW} = 0.693(R_A + R_B)C_1$$
$$= 0.693(32\,\text{k}\Omega)(0.001\,\mu\text{F}) = 22.2\,\mu\text{s}$$

35. $f_0 = \dfrac{1.44}{(R_A + 2R_B)C_1} = \dfrac{1.44}{(30\,\text{k}\Omega)(0.01\,\mu\text{F})}$
$$= 4.8\,\text{kHz}$$

$$\text{duty cycle} = \frac{R_A + R_B}{R_A + 2R_B} \times 100 = \frac{20\,\text{k}\Omega}{30\,\text{k}\Omega} \times 100$$
$$= 66.7\%$$
$$\text{PW} = 0.693(R_A + R_B)C_1$$
$$= 0.693(20\,\text{k}\Omega)(0.01\,\mu\text{F}) = 139\,\mu\text{s}$$

36. $f_0 = \dfrac{1.44}{(R_A + 2R_B)C_1} = \dfrac{1.44}{(54\,\text{k}\Omega)(0.033\,\mu\text{F})}$
$$= 808\,\text{Hz}$$
$$\text{PW} = 0.693(R_A + R_B)C_1$$
$$= 0.693(32\,\text{k}\Omega)(0.033\,\mu\text{F}) = 732\,\mu\text{s}$$

37. The 12-V drop across R_A indicates that the component has opened.

38. The 0 V reading across C_1 indicates that the component has shorted.

39. With a 700 kHz input, equation (19.3) shows that the device must have a rated value of

$$t_{on} \leq \frac{0.35}{100 f_{max}} = \frac{0.35}{(100)(700\,\text{kHz})} = 5\,\text{ns}$$

Since each of the transistors listed has a rating of $t_{on} \geq 12$ ns , none of them can be used.

40. Based on the specified duty cycle (60%),

$\dfrac{R_A + R_B}{R_A + 2R_B} = 0.6.$ Transposing and simplifying this

relationship, we get $R_B = 2R_A$. The relationship among R_A, R_B, and C_1 can be determined by using the design values in equation (19.18), as follows:

$$50\,\text{kHz} = \frac{1.44}{(R_A + 2R_B)C_1} \quad \text{or}$$

$(R_A + 2R_B)C_1 = 28.8\,\mu\text{s}$
Since $R_B = 2R_A$, the second relationship can be

rewritten as $5R_AC_1 = 28.8\,\mu\text{s}$, or $C_1 = \dfrac{5.76\,\mu\text{s}}{R_A}$.

Thus, the component requirements are $R_B = 2R_A$ and $C_1 = \dfrac{5.76\,\mu s}{R_A}$. Any combination of components that fulfills these relationships (within tolerance) can be used. (For example, $R_A = 12\ k\Omega$, $R_B = 24\ k\Omega$, and $C_1 = 470\ pF$)

41. When V_{in} goes more positive than the UTP, the op-amp output goes to -4 V. This drives the transistor into cutoff and the LED doesn't light. When V_{in} goes more negative than the LTP, the op-amp output goes to $+4$ V, saturating the transistor, and lighting the LED. Thus, the LED is off when it should be on, and vice versa. The design flaw can be corrected in one of three ways:
a. Redesign the circuit using a *noninverting* Schmitt trigger. b. Redesign the circuit so that the LED is connected in parallel with the BJT (from the BJT collector to ground). c. Rebuild the circuit using an upside-down pnp transistor.

42. According to the component spec sheet, the maximum supply voltage that can be applied to pin 8 of the LM555 timer is $+18$ V.

43. The following IC connections should be shown in the diagram:
- V_{in} to pin 2
- The feedback connection (from R_{f1} and R_{f2}) to pin 3
- The output from pin 1
- $+5$ V (supply voltage) to pin 8
- -5 V (supply voltage) to pin 4

EXAMPLE PRACTICE PROBLEM   (CH 20)

20-1. $I^2 t = (60\ A)^2 (15\ ms) = 54\ A^2 s$. The device (rated at $40\ A^2 s$) cannot withstand the surge.

20-2. $t_{max} = \dfrac{I^2 t\ (\text{rated})}{I_S^2} = \dfrac{75\ A^2 s}{(150\ A)^2} = 3.33\ ms$

20-3. $I_{S(max)} = \sqrt{\dfrac{I^2 t\ (\text{rated})}{t_s}} = \sqrt{\dfrac{75\ A^2 s}{50\ ms}} = 38.7\ A$

20-4. $\Delta V = \dfrac{dv}{dt}\Delta t = (25\ V/\mu s)(100\ ps) = 2.5\ mV$

20-5. $V_P = \eta V_{BB} + 0.7\ V = (0.75)(12\ V) + 0.7\ V = 9.7\ V$

20-6. $\lambda = \dfrac{c}{f} = \dfrac{3\times10^{17}\ nm/s}{30\times10^{12}\ Hz} = 10{,}000\ nm$

$\lambda = \dfrac{c}{f} = \dfrac{3\times10^{17}\ nm/s}{400\times10^{12}\ Hz} = 750\ nm$

20-7. $f = \dfrac{c}{\lambda} = \dfrac{3\times10^{17}\ nm/s}{940\ nm} = 319\ THz$

PRACTICE PROBLEMS   (CH 20)

1. $I^2 t = (25\ A)^2 (120\ ms) = 75\ A^2 s$. The device (rated at $2.6\ A^2 s$) cannot withstand the surge.

2. $I^2 t = (80\ A)^2 (8\ ms) = 51.2\ A^2 s$. The device (rated at $40\ A^2 s$) cannot withstand the surge.

3. $t_{max} = \dfrac{I^2 t\ (\text{rated})}{I_S^2} = \dfrac{2.6\ A^2 s}{(50\ A)^2} = 1.04\ ms$

4. $t_{max} = \dfrac{I^2 t\ (\text{rated})}{I_S^2} = \dfrac{40\ A^2 s}{(95\ A)^2} = 4.43\ ms$

5. $I_{S(max)} = \sqrt{\dfrac{I^2 t\ (\text{rated})}{t_s}} = \sqrt{\dfrac{2.6\ A^2 s}{50\ ms}} = 7.21\ A$

6. $I_{S(max)} = \sqrt{\dfrac{I^2 t\ (\text{rated})}{t_s}} = \sqrt{\dfrac{40\ A^2 s}{100\ ms}} = 20\ A$

7. $\Delta V = \dfrac{dv}{dt}\Delta t = (10\ V/\mu s)(10\ ns) = 100\ mV$

8. $\Delta V = \dfrac{dv}{dt}\Delta t = (5\ V/\mu s)(25\ ns) = 125\ mV$

9. $V_P = \eta V_{BB} + 0.7\ V = (0.56)(14\ V) + 0.7\ V = 8.54\ V$ (minimum), $V_P = \eta V_{BB} + 0.7\ V = (0.75)(14\ V) + 0.7\ V = 11.2\ V$ (maximum)

10. $V_P = \eta V_{BB} + 0.7\ V = (0.7)(12\ V) + 0.7\ V = 9.1\ V$ (minimum), $V_P = \eta V_{BB} + 0.7\ V = (0.85)(12\ V) + 0.7\ V = 10.9\ V$ (maximum)

11. $V_P = \eta V_{BB} + 0.7\ V = (0.55)(16\ V) + 0.7\ V = 9.5\ V$ (minimum), $V_P = \eta V_{BB} + 0.7\ V = (0.82)(16\ V) + 0.7\ V = 13.8\ V$ (maximum)

12. $V_P = \eta V_{BB} + 0.7\ V = (0.74)(26\ V) + 0.7\ V = 19.9\ V$ (minimum), $V_P = \eta V_{BB} + 0.7\ V = (0.86)(26\ V) + 0.7\ V = 23.1\ V$ (maximum)

13. $\lambda = \dfrac{c}{f} = \dfrac{3\times10^{17}\ nm/s}{650\times10^{12}\ Hz} = 462\ nm$

14. $\lambda = \dfrac{c}{f} = \dfrac{3\times10^{17}\ nm/s}{220\times10^{12}\ Hz} = 1364\ nm$

15. $\lambda = \dfrac{c}{f} = \dfrac{3\times10^{17}\ nm/s}{180\times10^{12}\ Hz} = 1667\ nm$

16. $\lambda = \dfrac{c}{f} = \dfrac{3\times10^{17}\ nm/s}{800\times10^{12}\ Hz} = 375\ nm$ (min) to

$\lambda = \dfrac{c}{f} = \dfrac{3\times10^{17}\ nm/s}{400\times10^{12}\ Hz} = 750\ nm$ (max)

17. $f = \dfrac{c}{\lambda} = \dfrac{3\times10^{17}\ nm/s}{0.94\ nm} = 319\ PHz$

18. $f = \dfrac{c}{\lambda} = \dfrac{3\times10^{17}\ nm/s}{0.84\ nm} = 357\ PHz$

19. At room temperature, the 2N6400 has the following maximum ratings: $V_{GT} = 1.5$ V, $I_{GT} = 30$ mA, and $I^2t = 145$ A^{2}s. The maximum value of V_{dc} required to trigger the SCR is found as

$V_{dc} = V_{GT} + V_Z = 1.5$ V $+ 33$ V $= 34.5$ V

When the device triggers, the zener current (I_Z) equals the sum of I_{GT} and I_{RG}. Assuming that the SCR triggers at $V_{GT} = 1.5$ V

$I_{RG} = \dfrac{V_{GT}}{R_G} = \dfrac{1.5\,\text{V}}{100\,\Omega} = 15$ mA

$I_Z = I_{GT} + I_{RG} = 30$ mA $+ 15$ mA $= 45$ mA (max). The circuit fuse can withstand a 4 A surge for 5 seconds. Using these values,

$I^2t = (4\ \text{A})^2(5\ \text{s}) = 90$ A^{2}s

Since this value is lower than the SCR rating of 145 A^{2}s, the fuse will blow.

20. At room temperature, the 2N6400 has maximum ratings of $V_{GT} = 1.5$ V and $I_{GT} = 30$ mA. Taking the diode voltage into account,

$V_A = V_{GT} + 0.7$ V $= 1.5$ V $+ 0.7$ V $= 2.2$ V (max).

Using this voltage,

$I_{R2} = \dfrac{2.2\,\text{V}}{27\,\Omega} = 81.5$ mA

$I_{R1} = I_{R2} + I_{GT} = 81.5$ mA $+ 30$ mA $= 111.5$ mA

The value of v_{in} required to trigger the SCR is found as

$v_{in} = V_A + I_{R1}R_1 = 2.2$ V $+ (111.5\ \text{mA})(820\ \Omega)$
$\quad = 93.6$ V

The peak input is found as $V_{in} = \dfrac{120\,\text{V}}{0.707} \cong 170$ V$_{pk}$

The firing angle is found as

$\theta_F = \sin^{-1}\dfrac{v_{in}}{V_{pk}} = \sin^{-1}\dfrac{93.6\,\text{V}}{170\,\text{V}} = 33.4°$

Finally, $\theta_C = 180° - 33.4° \cong 147°$

21. V_{BB} for the UJT equals V_Z (51 V). The minimum value of V_P is found as

$V_P = \eta V_{BB} + 0.7$ V $= (0.7)(51\ \text{V}) + 0.7$ V $= 36.4$ V

22. The 2N5060 has a circuit fusing rating of 0.4 A^{2}s. For the circuit described,

$I^2t = (7\ \text{A})^2(8\ \text{ms}) = 0.392$ A^{2}s

Therefore, the component can be used (though it can be argued that the component leaves little room for error.)

23. This is an open-ended question with a variety of possible answers. The only requirement for the chosen photodiode a *wavelength of peak spectral response* rating that is within ±10% of 470 nm (between 423 and 517 nm).

CHAPTER 21

EXAMPLE PRACTICE PROBLEM

21-1. Line regulation $= \dfrac{\Delta V_{out}}{\Delta V_{in}} = \dfrac{100\,\mu\text{V}}{4\,\text{V}} = 25\ \mu\text{V/V}$

21-2. Load regulation $= \dfrac{V_{NL} - V_{FL}}{\Delta I_L} = \dfrac{8\,\text{V} - 7.996\,\text{V}}{40\,\text{mA}}$
$\qquad\qquad = 100\ \mu\text{V/mA}$

21-3. $V_{in(max)} = V_{outadj)} + V_d = 6$ V $+ 32$ V $= 38$ V

21-4. $V_{dc} = 1.25\left(\dfrac{R_2}{R_1} + 1\right) = (1.25)\left(\dfrac{1.68\,\text{k}\Omega}{240\,\Omega} + 1\right) = 10$ V

21-5. $V_{ave} = V_{in}\dfrac{T_{on}}{T_{on} + T_{off}} = (36\ \text{V})\dfrac{6\,\mu\text{s}}{6\,\mu\text{s} + 9\,\mu\text{s}} = 14.4$ V

PRACTICE PROBLEMS (CH 21)

1. Line regulation $= \dfrac{\Delta V_{out}}{\Delta V_{in}} = \dfrac{20\,\mu\text{V}}{4\,\text{V}} = 5\ \mu\text{V/V}$

2. Line regulation $= \dfrac{\Delta V_{out}}{\Delta V_{in}} = \dfrac{14\,\mu\text{V}}{10\,\text{V}} = 1.4\ \mu\text{V/V}$

3. Line regulation $= \dfrac{\Delta V_{out}}{\Delta V_{in}} = \dfrac{15\,\mu\text{V}}{5\,\text{V}} = 3\ \mu\text{V/V}$

4. Line regulation $= \dfrac{\Delta V_{out}}{\Delta V_{in}} = \dfrac{12\,\text{mV}}{12\,\text{V}} = 1\ \text{mV/V}$

5. Load regulation $= \dfrac{V_{NL} - V_{FL}}{\Delta I_L} = \dfrac{6\,\text{V} - 5.98\,\text{V}}{150\,\text{mA}}$
$\qquad = 133\ \mu\text{V/mA}$

6. Load regulation $= \dfrac{V_{NL} - V_{FL}}{\Delta I_L} = \dfrac{20\,\text{mV}}{50\,\text{mA}}$
$\qquad = 400\ \mu\text{V/mA}$

7. Load regulation $= \dfrac{V_{NL} - V_{FL}}{\Delta I_L} = \dfrac{1.5\,\text{mV}}{20\,\text{mA}}$
$\qquad = 75\ \mu\text{V/mA}$

8. Load regulation $= \dfrac{V_{NL} - V_{FL}}{\Delta I_L} = \dfrac{14\,\text{mV}}{100\,\text{mA}}$
$\qquad = 140\ \mu\text{V/mA}$

9. $V_L = V_Z - V_{BE} = 6.8$ V $- 0.7$ V $= 6.1$ V

10. $V_L = V_Z - 2V_{BE} = 20$ V $- 1.4$ V $= 18.6$ V

11. $I_{L(max)} = \dfrac{V_{BE(Q3)}}{R_S} = \dfrac{0.7\,\text{V}}{0.2\,\Omega} = 3.5$ A

12. $I_{L(\text{max})} = \dfrac{V_{BE(Q3)}}{R_S} = \dfrac{0.7\,\text{V}}{1.2\,\Omega} = 583\,\text{mA}$

13. $V_{\text{in(max)}} = V_{\text{outadj}} + V_d = 3\,\text{V} + 32\,\text{V} = 35\,\text{V}$

14. $V_{\text{in(max)}} = V_{\text{outadj}} + V_d = 6\,\text{V} + 24\,\text{V} = 30\,\text{V}$

15. $V_{\text{dc}} = 1.25\left(\dfrac{R_2}{R_1} + 1\right) = (1.25)\left(\dfrac{2.848\,\text{k}\Omega}{330\,\Omega} + 1\right) = 12\,\text{V}$

16. $V_{\text{dc}} = 1.25\left(\dfrac{R_2}{R_1} + 1\right) = (1.25)\left(\dfrac{6.834\,\text{k}\Omega}{510\,\Omega} + 1\right) = 18\,\text{V}$

17. $V_{\text{ave}} = V_{\text{in}}\dfrac{T_{\text{on}}}{T_{\text{on}} + T_{\text{off}}} = (36\,\text{V})\dfrac{12\,\mu s}{12\,\mu s + 48\,\mu s} = 7.2\,\text{V}$

18. $V_{\text{ave}} = V_{\text{in}}\dfrac{T_{\text{on}}}{T_{\text{on}} + T_{\text{off}}} = (24\,\text{V})\dfrac{10\,\mu s}{10\,\mu s + 40\,\mu s} = 4.8\,\text{V}$

19. 420 ppm/V (parts per million per volt) equals
420 μV/V. For $\Delta V_{\text{in}} = 10\,\text{V}$,
$V_{\text{out}} = 12\,\text{V} + \Delta V_{\text{out}} = 12\,\text{V} + (10\,\text{V})(420\,\mu\text{V/V})$
$\quad = 12\,\text{V} + 4.2\,\text{mV} = 12.0042\,\text{V}$

20. Line reg $= \dfrac{\Delta V_{\text{out}}}{\Delta V_{\text{in}}} = \dfrac{12.002\,\text{V} - 12\,\text{V}}{30\,\text{V} - 20\,\text{V}} = 200\,\mu\text{V/V}$

In mV: 200 μV/V = 0.2 mV
In %:

$\qquad$ Line reg $= \dfrac{\Delta V_{\text{out}}}{\Delta V_{\text{in}}} \times 100 = \dfrac{2\,\text{mV}}{10\,\text{V}} \times 100 = 0.02\%$

In %/V:

$\qquad$ Line reg $= \dfrac{\text{Line reg (\%)}}{\Delta V_{\text{in}}} = \dfrac{0.02\%}{10\,\text{V}} = 0.002\,\%/\text{V}$

21. The change in load voltage over the range of I_L is
$\Delta V_{\text{out}} = (2\,\Omega)(100\,\text{mA}) = 200\,\text{mV}$
In V/mA:

$\qquad$ Load reg $= \dfrac{\Delta V_{\text{out}}}{\Delta I_L} = \dfrac{200\,\text{mV}}{100\,\text{mA}} = 0.002\,\text{V/mA}$

In %:

$\qquad$ Load reg $= \dfrac{\Delta V_{\text{out}}}{V_{NL}} \times 100 = \dfrac{200\,\text{mV}}{5\,\text{V}} \times 100 = 4\%$

In %/mA:

$\qquad$ Load reg $= \dfrac{\text{Load reg (\%)}}{\Delta I_L} = \dfrac{4\%}{100\,\text{mA}} = 0.04\,\%/\text{mA}$

22. Load reg = (15 V)(0.02 %/mA) = 3 mV/mA,
$\quad V_{L(\text{max})} = V_{\text{dc(rated)}} + (\Delta V_{\text{out}})$
$\qquad = 15\,\text{V} + (3\,\text{mV/mA})(50\,\text{mA}) = 15.15\,\text{V}$
$\quad P_{L(\text{max})} = V_{L(\text{max})}I_{L(\text{max})} = (15.15\,\text{V})(50\,\text{mA})$
$\qquad = 757.5\,\text{mW}$

Part II

Lab Manual Solutions

Note: The results obtained for almost all of these exercises were obtained using circuit simulations. **These results are ideal and are intended only as guidelines.** Your students' results may (and probably will) vary above and below those provided in this manual. In those cases where simulation was not an option, physical circuit measurements provided the bases for the solutions.

Exercise 1

Diode Characteristics

Table 1.1 Diode Test Measurements

Diode	V_F	V_R
1N4148	0.56 V	O/R
1N4001	0.55 V	O/R

Table 1.2 Diode Forward Current and Voltages

I_F (mA)	V_F (1N4148)	V_F (1N4001)
0.5	0.578 V	0.412 V
1.0	0.598 V	0.456 V
1.5	0.608 V	0.481 V
2.0	0.617 V	0.500 V
2.5	0.623 V	0.513 V
3.0	0.629 V	0.525 V
3.5	0.634 V	0.534 V
4.0	0.638 V	0.543 V
4.5	0.642 V	0.550 V
5.0	0.645 V	0.557 V

Step 9

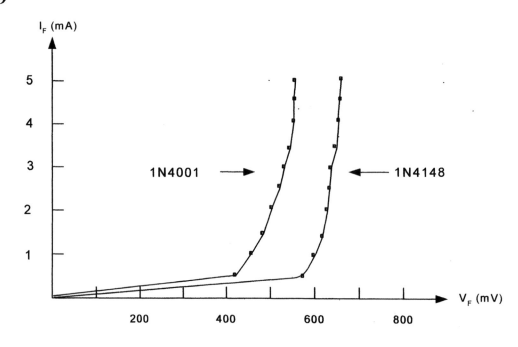

Step 11 $V_{R2} = 12\ \mu V$

$I_{R2} = 12\ nA$

Step 12 $R_{D\ (reverse)} = \dfrac{V_D}{I_{R2}} = \dfrac{12V}{12\ nA} = 1\ G\Omega$

Step 13 $V_{R2} = 682\ \mu V$

$I_{R2} = 682\ nA$

$R_{D\ (reverse)} = \dfrac{V_D}{I_{R2}} = \dfrac{12V}{682\ nA} = 17.6\ M\Omega$

QUESTIONS & PROBLEMS

1. As the temperature of the *pn*-junction increases, there is an increase in thermally produced charge carriers. Therefore, when the *pn*-junction is heated, there is an increase in I_F and a decrease in V_F.

2. The forward characteristics of the two diodes are similar since we are looking at a forward biased pn-junction in both cases. The doping levels are different, and therefore the actual V_F values differ, but the general characteristics are very similar.

3. Since we are dealing with very low current levels, any current calculated in the nano-amp range is within expected values. If the temperature were to increase, we would expect I_R to increase as well. An increase in temperature results in an increase in reverse saturation current, therefore, an increase in I_R.

SIMULATION RESULTS

TABLE 1.3 V_F Measurements

Diode	V_F (mV) Diode Checker	V_F (mV) Voltmeter
1N4001	456	613
1N4148	597	680
1N4944	536	606
1N5395	337	570

5. $V_{F(open)}$: Meter reads "OPEN". (Diode checker)
   $V_{F(open)}$ = Meter reads 12 V (Voltmeter)

6. $V_{F(short)}$: Meter reads 0 V. (Diode checker)
   $V_{F(short)}$ = Meter reads 0 V. (Voltmeter)

QUESTIONS

1. The default current of 1 mA that the meter employs for measuring forward diode drop is quite low compared to most diode applications. The forward current is much higher in the voltmeter circuit, so the value of V_F would also be higher.

2. When the diode is open, the voltmeter measures the source voltage across the open diode. The diode checker simply sees this as an open circuit. When the diode is shorted, in both cases, there is no voltage across the short.

Exercise 2

Zener Diodes

Step 1

Nominal zener voltage (V_Z) = 10 V

Zener test current (I_{ZT}) = 20 mA

Table 28.3 Zener Voltage Measurements

I_Z (mA)	V_Z	I_Z (mA)	V_Z
1.0	9.918 V	10	9.982 V
2.0	9.937 V	15	9.995 V
3.0	9.947 V	20	10.001 V
4.0	9.955 V	25	10.013 V
5.0	9.962 V	30	10.021 V

Step 14

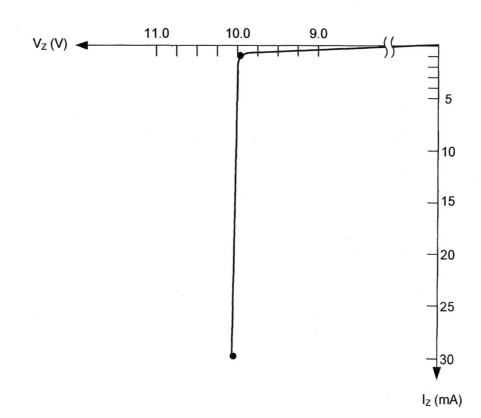

QUESTIONS & PROBLEMS

1. $I_{ZT} = 20$ mA

    $V_Z = 10.001$ V @ I_{ZT}

    % Variation: This answer will vary from student to student.

2. The student should choose the two voltage measurements for 15 mA and 25 mA to determine their ΔV value. They can calculate an approximation of Z_Z using

    $$Z_Z = \frac{\Delta V_Z}{\Delta I_Z} = \frac{18\,\text{mV}}{10\,\text{mA}} = 1.8\,\Omega$$

    where ΔV_Z is the change in zener voltage from $I_Z = 15$ mA to 25 mA.

    Note: Since we are dealing with very small variations in V_Z the value of Z_Z determined by the student may vary by a wide margin. If the V_Z value at $I_Z = 15$ mA were 1% lower, and the V_Z value at $I_Z = 25$ mA were 1% higher, then $Z_Z = 33.9\,\Omega$! The rated value of $Z_{ZT} = 17$ Ω. For this reason the percent variation from the nominal rated value may be quite significant.

SIMULATION EXERCISE

Table 2.2

Condition	I_S	I_Z	I_L	V_{OUT}
$V_S = 25$ V, $R_L = 2.2$ kΩ	68 mA	63 mA	4.57 mA	10.057 V
$V_S = 20$ V, $R_L = 2.2$ kΩ	45 mA	41 mA	4.56 mA	10.034 V
$V_S = 25$ V, $R_L = 3.3$ kΩ	68 mA	65 mA	3.04 mA	10.059 V

QUESTIONS & PROBLEMS

1. The zener diode will no longer regulate the output voltage if V_S is less than +11 V. When the input voltage is low enough so that the zener no longer operates below its knee voltage, we can treat the zener (effectively) as an open circuit. This means that if we calculate the value of V_S at which the voltage divider of R_S and R_L produces a load

voltage of less than 10 V, this will be (approximately) the input voltage below which the 1N5240 will no longer regulate. Thus, this input voltage is found as:

$$V_S = 10\,\text{V}\,\frac{2.42\ \text{k}\Omega}{2.2\ \text{k}\Omega} = 11\ \text{V}$$

Note: This is only an approximation since the zener is not a true open circuit when operated just above the knee voltage. In practice the actual value will be closer to 12 V.)

2. $\Delta I_S = 33.8\ \%$ $\Delta I_Z = 34.9\ \%$

          $\Delta I_L = 0.22\ \%$ $\Delta V_{OUT} = 0.23\ \%$

The graph that was plotted in Figure 2.2, and the results above, show that as long as the zener current is greater than I_{ZK}, significant changes in zener current result in very small changes in zener voltage. Thus, as the input voltage decreased, so did the zener current, compensating for the change in V_S.

3. $\Delta I_S = 0.00\ \%$ $\Delta I_Z = 3.17\ \%$

          $\Delta I_L = 33.5\ \%$ $\Delta V_{OUT} = 0.02\ \%$

Even though the load resistance decreased, zener current remained almost the same. This allowed load current to increase, and thus, maintain a constant load voltage.

4. When source voltage increases, zener current *increases* to compensate, keeping load current (and thus load voltage) constant. The opposite is true when V_S *decreases*. When load resistance *increases*, zener current (and thus zener voltage) remain relatively constant allowing load current to *decrease* keeping load voltage constant. The opposite is true when R_L *decreases*.

Exercise 3

Diode Rectifier Circuits

Step 2 The waveforms in Figure 3.3 should resemble those shown in Figure 3.1a.

Step 3 $V_{S(pk)} = 35.1$ V $\qquad V_{ave} = 11$ V

Step 4 $V_{ave} = -11$ V. The positive alternation of the waveform has been removed (clipped.)

Step 5 The waveforms in Figure 3.5a should be resemble those shown in Figure 3.1b.

Step 6 $V_{S(pk)} = 17.8$ V $\qquad V_{ave} = 10.8$ V

Step 7 $V_{ave} = -10.8$V

Step 8 The waveforms in Figure 3.5b should be resemble those shown in Figure 3.1b.
$V_{S(pk)} = 34.6$ V $\quad V_{ave} = 21.6$ V

QUESTIONS & PROBLEMS

1. This is due to the fact that the load is only across one half of the secondary. The load is connected between the junction of the two diodes and ground. The center tap is also connected to ground. This means that for the positive alternation of the signal, the load is coupled across one half of the secondary through D_1. During the negative alternation, the load is coupled to the other side of the secondary through D_2.

2. Slight variations may be due to the tolerance of the component values. If an analog meter is used to make the voltage readings, this will also contribute to differences due to parallax and meter loading.

   V_{ave} (half-wave) $= 11.1$ V $\qquad V_{ave}$ (full-wave) $= 10.9$ V

   V_{ave} (bridge-wave) $= 21.8$ V

   All of the measured values are within expected variations from the calculated ones.

3. The bridge rectifier doesn't need a center-tapped transformer, however it requires more components than the full-wave rectifier.

4. Place a ground between diodes D_3 and D_4, and take the output from between diodes D_1 and D_2. This will swap the load and ground connections to the bridge.

SIMULATION EXERCISE

Fault 3-1: Open transformer primary (T1) in the half-wave rectifier.

Symptom(s):	$V_P = 0$ V. There is no waveform display.
Analysis:	Since the primary is open, there is no primary current. Thus, no voltage is induced in the secondary. As a result, there is no ac or dc load voltage.

Fault 3-2: Shorted transformer secondary (T3 to T4) in the half-wave rectifier

Symptom(s):	$V_{dc} = 0$ V. There is no waveform display. The fuse opened.
Analysis:	The fuse opened as soon as the circuit was activated. This would suggest that there was an over-current condition caused by the shorted secondary. The shorted secondary means that the primary is trying to drive a $0 \, \Omega$ load, thus the over-current condition.

Fault 3-3: Shorted diode in the half-wave rectifier

Symptom(s):	The dc meter reads a load voltage of close to 0 V. Load voltage is an ac waveform with approximately the same amplitude as the secondary.
Analysis:	The shorted diode means that there is no rectification. Thus almost all of the secondary voltage is dropped across the load.

Fault 3-4: Open diode in the full-wave rectifier

Symptom(s):	The dc meter reads a load voltage of approx. 5.4 V_{dc}. The waveform is that of a half-wave rectifier.
Analysis:	Since one of the diodes is open, the circuit has now become a half-wave rectifier. Note that the V_{ave} value is approximately one half of the half-wave rectifier circuit in Figure 29.2. The reason is that the load is still only connected across one-half of the transformer secondary.

Fault 3-5: Open transformer secondary (T4) in the full-wave rectifier

Symptom(s):	The dc meter reads a load voltage of approx. 5.4 V_{dc}. The waveform is that of a half-wave rectifier.
Analysis:	With one terminal of the secondary open, this is effectively the same circuit as in the previous simulation. The load is connected across both halves of the secondary and ground. Opening one terminal of the secondary still leaves a current path through one diode, the non-faulted secondary terminal, and the grounded center tap.

Fault 3-6: Open transformer secondary center tap (T5) in the full-wave rectifier

Symptom(s):	The dc meter reading is close to 0 V. There is no waveform display.
Analysis:	As mentioned earlier, the load is connected to both sides of the secondary and the grounded center tap. By opening the center tap of the transformer there is no current path through the load. This means that load voltage must be 0 V.

Fault 3-7: Open D_3 in the bridge rectifier

Symptom(s):	The dc meter reads approx. 10.8 V_{dc}. The waveform is that of a half-wave rectifier. It has a peak voltage of 33.8 V.
Analysis:	Opening D_3 means that the $D_1 - D_3$ current path is lost for the load. This means that the circuit acts like a half-wave rectifier. Note that there are two diode drops, so the peak load voltage is approximately 1.8 volts below the peak secondary voltage.

Fault 3-8: Open D_4 in the bridge rectifier

Symptom(s):	The dc meter reads approx. 10.8 V_{dc}. The waveform is that of a half-wave rectifier. It has a peak voltage of 33.8 V.
Analysis:	Opening D_4 means that the $D_2 - D_4$ current path is lost. This means that the circuit acts like a half-wave rectifier. Note that there are two diode drops, so the peak load voltage is approximately 1.8 volts below the peak secondary voltage.

Exercise 4

A Basic Power Supply

Step 2 $V_{ave} = 36.3$ V

Step 3 $V_r = 4.1.$ V$_{pp}$ @ C = 10 μF

Step 4 $V_{ave} = 33.6$ V $V_r = 400$ V$_{pp}$ @ C = 100 μF

Step 5 $V_{ave} = 10.02$ V $V_r = 45$ mV$_{pp}$ @ C = 10 μF

Step 6 $V_{ave} = 10.04$ V $V_r = 6.5$ mV$_{pp}$ @ C = 100 μF

Step 7 $R_L \cong 200$ Ω (Note: this value may vary significantly from student to student, as it is a judgment call as to when a "significant" drop in load voltage occurs).

QUESTIONS & PROBLEMS

1. The ripple voltage dropped from 4.1 V to .4 V as C changed from 10 to 100 μF. This decrease occurred because the larger capacitor has a longer discharge time ($\tau = RC$), and hasn't nearly enough time to discharge. This maintains a high voltage and reduces ripple.
2. DC load voltage was increased, because the larger capacitor decreased the ripple voltage.
3. Changing the filter capacitor had less of an effect on ripple voltage in the regulated circuit. This is because the zener regulator is doing a significant amount of the ripple suppression, and thus, the change in the filter had less of an effect.
4. If you reduce the value of the load resistance to a point where most of the current flows through the load, then I_Z will drop below I_{ZK} (the knee current of the zener) and voltage regulation will be lost.
5. Two 1 kΩ resistors in parallel were needed for power handling. A single 510 Ω ¼ W. resistor would not handle the power. Referring back to Step 4, the voltage across the two resistors is approximately 34 V – 10 V = 24 V. Thus the power dissipated is $(24$ V$)^2 \div$ 1000 Ω = 576 mW. If it was a single 510 Ω resistor, power dissipation would be 1.3 W.

SIMULATION EXERCISE

Step 3 $V_r = 4.45$ mV$_{PP}$

Step 4 $V_r = 460$ mV$_{PP}$

QUESTIONS & PROBLEMS

1. Student responses will vary, but you are looking for a response that recognizes that the zener diode maintains a nearly constant voltage (V_{OUT}) across its terminals even when there is a change in source voltage. In this case, the ripple voltage can be viewed as a change in source voltage.

Exercise 5

Common Diode Applications: Clippers, Clampers, and Voltage Multipliers

Step 2   Figure 5.2a is shown below.

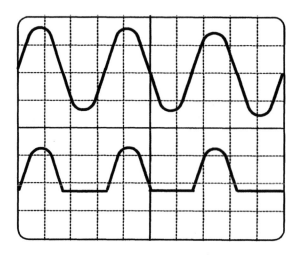

Step 3   Figure 5.2b is shown below.

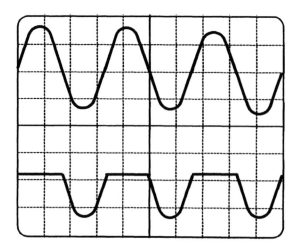

Step 5   Both waveforms in Figure 5.4a are sinusoidal. The output waveform (Ch2) is shifted above the 0 V reference.

Step 6   Both waveforms in Figure 5.4b are sinusoidal. The output waveform (Ch2) is shifted below the 0 V reference.

Step 7 $V_{ave} = 9.5$ V

Step 9 $V_{dc} = 19.3$ V $V_r = 1.6$ mV$_{PP}$

QUESTIONS & PROBLEMS

1. R_S is a current limiting resistor. When the diode is forward biased, it drops less than a volt. This means that if R_S was too small, or was not there at all, circuit current would be too high.

2. No, it was clipped at a level that was approximately equal to the forward voltage drop across a diode. Because the diode is in parallel with the load, and since the clipping action occurs when the diode is forward biased, then the minimum voltage that the load can ever reach is the forward voltage across the forward biased diode.

3. The dc offset was close to the value of the peak input voltage. It was slightly lower due to the voltage across the diode.

4. The dc offset will be approximately equal to the negative peak value plus the diode drop.

5. No, it was slightly lower, once again due to the diode drops.

6. In order to convert Figure 5.5 into a negative voltage doubler, simply reverse the direction of the two diodes. The cathode of D_1 is now facing the source and the cathode of D_2 goes to ground. The capacitors must also be reversed if they are electrolytic.

SIMULATION EXERCISE

Fault 5-1: Open diode in the shunt clipper

Symptoms:	There is no clipping action
Analysis:	Since the diode is open, the input is directly connected to the load and the waveform is not affected in any way.

Fault 5-2: Open diode in the Clamper

Symptoms:	There is no clamping action. The input and output seem almost the same.
Analysis:	Since the diode is open, the capacitor and the load form an RC voltage divider. But, at 2 kHz the reactance of the capacitor is only about 80 Ω. This means that almost all of the input is coupled to the load with no phase shift.

Fault 5-3: Open shunt diode (D_2) in the voltage multiplier

Symptoms:	The dc voltage has dropped to about half of what it was before the fault.
Analysis:	Opening the shunt diode means that C_1 never charges on the negative alternation of the input cycle. Thus, the output only reaches approximately one half of the input peak voltage.

Fault 5-4: Open output capacitor (C_3) in the voltage multiplier

Symptoms:	The output is almost identical to the input in amplitude, but it has a positive dc offset of approximately ½ $V_{in(pk)}$.
Analysis:	With the filter capacitor open, the circuit is now acting like a positive voltage clamper. The shunt diode and the series capacitor form the voltage clamper. The series diode simply introduces another forward voltage drop.

Fault 5-5: Shorted output diode (D_3) in the voltage multiplier

Symptoms:	The output is a sine wave with approximately half the amplitude of the input. It has a positive dc offset close to one-half of the peak-input voltage.
Analysis:	The shunt diode and the series capacitor form a voltage clamper, just like in Fault 5-4. Once the series capacitor is charged, the shunt diode cannot conduct. This means that the two capacitors form a voltage divider. Since they are equal in value, the output voltage has a peak voltage that is one half of the input.

Exercise 6

Bipolar Junction Transistors

Step 1 $R_1 = 100$ kΩ (Obviously, this value will vary from student to student).

Step 3 $V_{R1} = 0.5$ V

Table 6.1 I_C for various values of I_B and V_{CE} for the circuit in Figure 6.1

V_{CE} (V)	$I_B = 5$ μA	$I_B = 10$ μA	$I_B = 20$ μA	$I_B = 40$ μA
0.5	0.80	1.55	3.20	6.60
1.0	0.85	1.60	3.30	6.80
5	0.90	1.65	3.40	7.00
10	1.05	1.70	3.50	7.30
15	1.05	1.70	3.60	7.70
20	1.10	1.75	3.75	8.20
		I_C (mA)		

Step 9 Your curves should be similar to those in Figure 6.25 of *Introductory Electronic Devices and Circuits*.

Step 10 **2N3904 test results**
For the forward test: $V_{BE} = 707$ mV, $V_{BC} = 697$ mV, V_{CE} is out of range.
For the reverse test: all reading are out of range.

Step 11 **2N3906 test results**
For the forward test: $V_{BE} = 742$ mV, $V_{BC} = 735$ mV, V_{CE} is out of range.
For the reverse test: all reading are out of range.

Note: The results for Steps 10 and 11 were not the result of a simulation, but are actual values measured for two randomly chosen transistors. Student results will vary, but they should be in the range of 700 mV for all forward biased BE and BC junctions. All other measurements should be out of range.

QUESTIONS & PROBLEMS

1. The value of I_C is primarily determined by the value of I_B. If you refer to Table 6.1 you will see that when I_B is held constant, I_C increases very little with an increase in V_{CE}. But,

I_C increases dramatically with an increase in I_B. I_C and I_B are directly related as stated by $I_C = \beta I_B$.

2. If you use $I_B = 20 \, \mu A$ and $I_C = 3.50 \, mA$ beta is found as

$$\beta_{dc} = \frac{I_C}{I_B} = \frac{3.50 \, mA}{20 \, \mu A} = 175$$

This is well within expected values.

3. When I_B is held constant and V_{CE} is increased over a wide range, the value of I_C increases slowly. This shows that I_C is controlled primarily by I_B and not by V_{CE}.

4. The reason that it was not necessary to show meter polarity is because there are two *pn* junctions between the CE terminals. Thus, no matter what the polarity of the meter, the reading will always be out of range for an undamaged transistor.

SIMULATION EXERCISE

Table 6.2 Fault Analysis

Fault	I_C	I_B	V_{CE}
No Fault	5.08 mA	29.2 μA	9.83 V
6-1 R_B Open	0 mA	0 μA	20 V
6-2 R_B Shorted	9.95 mA	1.9 A	105 mV
6-3 R_C Open	3.5 μA	29.4 μA	22.3 mV
6-4 R_C Shorted	5.7 mA	29.2 μA	20 V
6-5 Transistor shorted (C-E)	10 mA	29.4 μA	10 pV
6-6 Transistor shorted (B-E)	3.6 μA	30.3 μA	20 V
6-7 Transistor open (B-E)	0 mA	0 μA	20 V

Fault 6-1: R_B Open

Symptom(s):	There is no base or collector current. $V_{CE} = V_{CC}$.
Analysis:	With R_{B2} open, there is no path for base current. Since collector current is dependent upon base current, this explains why there is no collector current. Since there is no collector current, there is no voltage across R_C thus all of V_{CC} is across V_{CE}.

Fault 6-2: R_B Shorted

Symptom(s):	Both I_B and I_C increase dramatically. $V_{CE} \cong 0$ V.
Analysis:	With both base resistors shorted, V_{CC} has a direct path to ground through the forward biased base-emitter junction. This explains the very high base current. It should be noted that in a real-world situation, the transistor would be destroyed. The collector current is limited by V_{CC}/R_C. V_{CE} is close to 0 V since most of V_{CC} is across R_C.

Fault 6-3: R_C Open

Symptom(s):	I_B is close to the no-fault condition. $I_C \cong 0$ mA and $V_{CE} \cong 0$ V.
Analysis:	With R_C open there is no path for collector current, thus $I_C \cong 0$ mA. V_{CE} is close to 0 V as well since all of V_{CC} is across the open collector resistor. I_B is close to the no-fault reading since the base circuit is not affected. The base-emitter junction is still forward biased, so I_B is still determined by $I_B = \dfrac{V_{CC} - V_{BE}}{R_{B1} + R_{B2}}$.

Fault 6-4: R_C Shorted

Symptom(s):	I_B and I_C are close to the no-fault condition. $V_{CE} \cong V_{CC}$.
Analysis:	With R_C shorted, I_B is still determined by the base circuit as mentioned in Fault 6-3. I_C does not change too much since I_C is determined by βI_B and is not affected by changes in R_C. $V_{CE} \cong V_{CC}$ since there is no voltage across the shorted R_C.

Fault 6-5: Transistor Shorted (C-E)

Symptom(s):	I_B is close to the no-fault condition. I_C has increased and $V_{CE} \cong 0$ V.
Analysis:	With the collector-emitter shorted, I_C is determined by V_{CC}/R_C. V_{CE} is close to 0 V since this junction is shorted. I_B is still close to normal since the base-emitter junction and the base circuit are not affected.

Fault 6-6: Transistor Shorted (B-E)

Symptom(s):	I_B is slightly higher than the no-fault condition. $I_C \cong 0$ A and $V_{CE} \cong V_{CC}$.
Analysis:	With the base-emitter shorted, I_B is determined by V_{CC} and the total resistance in the base circuit. The only difference between this and the no-fault base current is the loss of the base-emitter voltage drop. Thus, I_B is slightly higher. The almost 0A value of I_C is a little harder to explain. With the shorted base-emitter junction, all of the emitter current will take the path of least resistance (through the base) and ignore the path through the collector. This is why $I_C \cong 0$ mA. With no collector current, $V_{RC} = 0$ V so all of V_{CC} is across V_{CE}.

Fault 6-7: Transistor Open (B-E)

Symptom(s):	$I_B \cong I_C \cong 0$ A. $V_{CE} \cong V_{CC}$
Analysis:	With the base-emitter open, there is no path for I_B and it is zero. Since I_C is determined by βI_B, it too is zero. With no collector current, $V_{RC} = 0$ V so all of V_{CC} is across V_{CE}

Exercise 7

Base Bias

Step 1

Component	Nominal value	Measured value
R_{B2}	10 kΩ	10 kΩ
R_C	2 kΩ	2 kΩ

Don't forget: The simulator provides measured values identical to the nominal values.

Table 7.1 Current Values for the Transistor in   Figure 7.1

I_C	I_B	V_{CE}	h_{FE}
2 mA	11.6 μA	16.04 V	172
4 mA	22.4 μA	12.14 V	178
6 mA	34.4 μA	8.12 V	174
8 mA	48.2 μA	3.99 V	167

Step 7 $I_{C(sat)}$ = 10 mA. $V_{CE(off)}$ = 20 V. Figure 7.2 appears below.

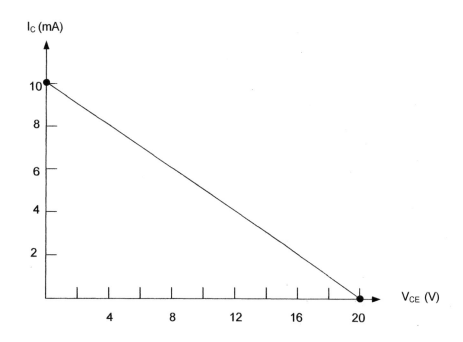

Table 7.2 Predicted and Measured Current Values

V_{CE}	I_C (Predicted)	I_C (Measured)
2 V	9 mA	8.8 mA
8 V	8 mA	5.8 mA
16 V	2.1 mA	2.0 mA

Note: All of the answers to the questions in Part 3 will vary from student to student with the exception of Step 12. Here is an example of what a student might discover:

Table 7.3 Bias Instability Test

Value	1st transistor	2nd transistor	% Change
V_{CEQ}	10.05 V	12.18 V	17.5 %
I_{CQ}	4.8 mA	3.6 mA	25.1 %

Step 12 The heating of the emitter of the transistor should result in I_C increasing and V_{CE} decreasing.

QUESTIONS & PROBLEMS

1. The h_{FE} values were within the expected range.

2. Yes, β did change with I_C. The change was not proportional in that β first increased and then decreased as I_C increased.

3. As I_C increased, V_{CE} decreased. This means that they have an *inverse* relationship. This can be shown by the data collected in table 7.1.

4. When I_C doubled, I_B doubled and V_{CE} decreased by 25%. When I_C increased by 50% I_B increased by almost the same amount. V_{CE} decreased by about 33%. When I_C increased by 33% so did I_B, but V_{CE} decreased by more than 50%. From these results we can make the following assertions:

   - I_B is directly proportional to I_C.
   - I_C and V_{CE} have an inverse relationship that is <u>not</u> proportional. At lower values of I_C a given increase in I_C produces a relatively small decrease in V_{CE}. For higher values of I_C that same amount of change in collector current produces a larger decrease in V_{CE}.

5. Yes the load line values agreed with the measured values.

6. This must be a student response.

7. a. The response will vary from student to student, but the instability of the base-bias circuit should have been demonstrated. Even the circuit itself, during operation, can increase the temperature enough to effect the circuit stability.
   b. Again, the response will vary, but an increase in temperature should result in an
   I increase in h_{FE}.

SIMULATION EXERCISE

1. $I_C = 4.94$ mA, $I_B = 28$ μA, $V_{CE} = 10.13$ V

Fault Simulations

Fault 7-1: R_B Open

Symptom(s):	There is no base or collector current. $V_{CE} = V_{CC}$.
Analysis:	With R_B open, there is no path for base current. Since collector current is dependent upon base current, this explains why there is no collector current. Since there is no collector current, there is no voltage across R_C thus all of V_{CC} is across V_{CE}.

Fault 7-2: R_C Open

Symptom(s):	I_B is close to the no-fault condition. $I_C \cong 0$ mA and $V_{CE} \cong 0$ V.
Analysis:	With R_C open there is no path for collector current, thus $I_C \cong 0$ mA. V_{CE} is close to 0 V as well since all of V_{CC} is across the open collector resistor. I_B is close to the no-fault reading since the base circuit is not affected. The base-emitter junction is still forward biased, so I_B is still determined by $I_B = \dfrac{V_{CC} - V_{BE}}{R_{B1} + R_{B2}}$.

Fault 7-3: Shorted R_B

Symptom(s):	I_B is much higher than the no-fault condition. I_C has increased and $V_{CE} \cong 0$ V.
Analysis:	With R_B shorted, V_{CC} has a direct path to ground through the forward biased base-emitter junction. This explains the very high base current. It should be noted that in a real-world situation, the transistor would be destroyed. The collector current is limited by V_{CC}/R_C. V_{CE} is close to 0 V since most of V_{CC} is across R_C.

Fault 7-4: Shorted BE Junction

Symptom(s):	I_B is slightly higher than the no-fault condition. $I_C \cong 0$ A and $V_{CE} \cong V_{CC}$.
Analysis:	With the base-emitter shorted, I_B is determined by V_{CC} and the total resistance in the base circuit. The only difference between this and the no-fault base current is the loss of the base-emitter voltage drop. Thus, I_B is slightly higher. The almost 0A value of I_C is a little harder to explain. With the shorted base-emitter junction, all of the emitter current will take the path of least resistance (through the base) and ignore the path through the collector. This is why $I_C \cong 0$ mA. With no collector current, $V_{RC} = 0$ V so all of V_{CC} is across V_{CE}.

Fault 7-5: Shorted CE Junction

Symptom(s):	I_B is close the no-fault condition. I_C has increased and $V_{CE} \cong 0$ V.
Analysis:	With the collector-emitter shorted, I_C is determined by V_{CC}/R_C. V_{CE} is close to 0 V since this junction is shorted. I_B is still close to the no-fault condition since the base-emitter junction and the base circuit are not affected.

Fault 7-6: Shorted R_C

Symptom(s):	I_B and I_C are close to the no-fault condition. $V_{CE} \cong V_{CC}$.
Analysis:	With R_C shorted, I_B is still determined by the base circuit as mentioned in the answer to Fault 7-2. I_C does not change too much since I_C is determined by βI_B and is not affected by changes in R_C. $V_{CE} \cong V_{CC}$ since there is no voltage across the shorted R_C.

Exercise 8

Voltage-Divider Bias

Step 1

Component	Nominal Value	Measured Value
R_1	33 kΩ	33 kΩ
R_2	6.8 kΩ	6.8 kΩ
R_E	560Ω	560 Ω
R_C	1.5 kΩ	1.5 kΩ

Don't forget: The simulator provides measured values identical to the nominal values.

Steps 2 & 3

Table 8.1. Values for the circuit in Figure 8.1.

Value	Calculated	Measured
V_{R1}	16.6 V	16.7 V
V_B	3.42 V	3.3 V
V_E	2.72 V	2.64 V
I_{CQ}	4.85 mA	4.56 mA
V_{RC}	7.28 V	7.03 V
V_{CEQ}	9.99 V	10.34 V

$$V_{R1} = V_{CC} \frac{R_1}{R_1 + R_2} = 16.6 \text{ V} \qquad V_B = V_{CC} \frac{R_2}{R_1 + R_2} = 3.42 \text{ V},$$

$$V_E = V_B - V_{BE} = 2.72 \text{ V} \qquad I_C \cong I_E = \frac{V_E}{R_E} = 4.85 \text{ mA},$$

$$V_{RC} = I_C R_C = 7.28 \text{ V} \qquad V_{CEQ} = V_{CC} - I_C(R_C + R_E) = 9.99 \text{ V}$$

Step 4 $V_{R1} = 17.6$ V $V_B = 2.41$ V
$V_{RE} = 1.72$ V $V_{RC} = 4.57$ V
$V_{CEQ} = 13.7$ V

Step 5   The results from this step will vary from student to student. None the less, in all cases, there should not be a large change in circuit values, when compared to the results in Table 8.1. This step should illustrate that voltage-divider bias is relatively stable (compared to base bias) and is not severely affected by changes in beta (which is what will happen when one transistor is substituted for another).

Step 6   As was the case in Step 5, results will vary from student to student, depending on how much they heat up the device. The object here is to once again demonstrate the superior stability of the voltage-divider bias circuit.

QUESTIONS & PROBLEMS

1. The measured values were very close to the calculated values. Component tolerances explain most of the variations.

2.

$$I_C = \frac{V_{RC}}{R_C} = 4.56 \text{ mA} \qquad I_{R1} = \frac{V_{R1}}{R_1} = 506 \text{ μA}$$

$$I_{R2} = \frac{V_B}{R_2} = 485 \text{ μA} \qquad I_B = I_{R1} - I_{R2} = 21 \text{ μA}$$

$$h_{FE} = \frac{I_C}{I_B} = 217 \qquad \text{This value of β falls within the spec sheet values.}$$

3.

$$I_{CQ} = \frac{V_{RC}}{R_C} = 3.05 \text{ mA} \qquad I_{R1} = \frac{V_{R1}}{R_1} = 53.3 \text{ μA}$$

$$I_{R2} = \frac{V_B}{R_2} = 35.4 \text{ μA} \qquad I_B = I_{R1} - I_{R2} = 17.9 \text{ μA}$$

$$h_{FE} = \frac{I_C}{I_B} = 171$$

The value of h_{FE} changed due to a change in I_{CQ}. This is a result of the larger bias resistors. The emitter circuit is loading down the bias circuit changing the value of V_B and thus I_B and I_{CQ}.

4. $V_{TH} = V_{CC} \dfrac{R_2}{R_1 + R_2} = 3.42\,\text{V}$ $\qquad R_{TH} = R_1 \,\|\, R_2 = 56.4\,\text{k}\Omega$

$I_{CQ} = \dfrac{V_{TH} - V_{BE}}{\dfrac{R_{TH}}{h_{FE}} + R_E} = 3.06\,\text{mA}$ $\qquad V_{CEQ} = V_{CC} - I_{CQ}(R_C + R_E) = 13.7\,\text{V}$

The calculated value of V_{CEQ} is approximately equal to the measured value.

5. This must be a student response, but results should show a circuit that is much more stable than the base-bias circuit.

SIMULATION EXERCISE

Table 8.1 Simulation Results

Current	Measured value	Voltage	Measured value
I_{R1}	504 µA	V_B	3.30 V
I_{R2}	485 µA	V_C	12.97 V
I_B	20.9 µA	V_E	2.64 V
I_E	4.71 mA	V_{BE}	666 mV
I_C	4.68 mA	V_{CE}	10.34 V

Fault 8-1: Open biasing resistor (R_1)

Symptom(s):	All currents drop to near zero. $V_C = V_{CC}$ and all other voltages are 0 V.
Analysis:	With R_2 open, there is no path for bias current. This means that $V_B = 0$ V and therefore I_C and I_E are zero. $V_C = V_{CC}$ because $I_C = 0$ A. Therefore there is no voltage across R_C or R_E.

Fault 8-2: Open transistor base lead

Symptom(s):	I_C and $I_E \cong 0$ mA. $I_{R1} = I_{R2}$. $I_B \cong 0$ μA. $V_C \cong V_{CC}$. $V_E = 0$ V. $V_B = V_{BE} = 3.42$ V.
Analysis:	With the base open, I_B has no current path. This is why $I_{R1} = I_{R2}$. With no base current I_C and I_E must be close to 0 mA. $V_C = V_{CC}$ since $I_C = 0$ A and therefore there is no voltage across R_C or R_E. Note that $V_{BE} = V_B$. Since there is no emitter current, the emitter is at ground potential, so measuring the voltage across R_2 is the same as measuring V_{BE}.

Fault 8-3: Open transistor emitter lead

Symptom(s):	$I_C = I_E = I_B \cong 0$. $I_{R1} = I_{R2}$. $V_C \cong V_{CC}$. $V_B = V_{BE} = 3.42$ V.
Analysis:	With the emitter open, there is no current path for either I_B, I_C or of course I_E. $I_{R1} = I_{R2}$ because there is no I_B.

Fault 8-4: Open transistor collector lead

Symptom(s):	$I_E = I_B$ and the value is quite high (450 μA). $I_C = 0$. I_{R2} is quite low (129 μA). $V_E = 252$ mV and $V_B = 878$ mV. $V_C \cong V_{CC}$.
Analysis:	With the collector open, there is still a path for I_E and I_B, but all of I_E must flow through the base. This is why $I_B = I_E$ and the value of I_B is so high. The high I_B explains why I_{R2} is low.

Fault 8-5: Open biasing resistor (R_2)

Symptom(s):	$I_B = I_{R1}$. $I_{R2} = 0$. $V_{CE} = 87$ mV, a very low value. I_C is quite high (9.55 mA).
Analysis:	With R_2 open, this is now a base bias circuit. The problem is that R_1 is too low and the circuit is saturated. This is why $V_{CE} \cong 0$ V.

Fault 8-6: Shorted collector resistor

Symptom(s):	$V_C \cong V_{CC}$. $I_E \cong I_C + I_B$. $I_C = 4.7$ mA which is very close to the no-fault condition as are all other currents.
Analysis:	This fault illustrates how I_B and I_C are independent of R_C. The bias circuit is not affected, so V_B is unchanged and so is I_C. With R_C shorted there is no voltage across it, which is why $V_C \cong V_{CC}$.

Fault 8-7: Shorted transistor (collector-to-emitter)

Symptom(s):	$I_C = I_E$ and $I_{R1} = I_{R2}$. $I_B = 0$. $V_C = V_E$ and therefore $V_{CE} = 0$ V.
Analysis:	The reason that I_B is zero is because all of I_E flows through the shorted emitter-collector. With $I_B = 0$, this explains why $I_{R1} = I_{R2}$.

Fault 8-8: Shorted transistor (base to emitter)

Symptom(s):	$I_E = I_B$ and the value of I_B is quite high (550µA). $I_C = 0$. I_{R2} is quite low (45 µA). $V_{BE} = 0$ V. $V_B = V_E \cong 309$ mV. $V_C \cong V_{CC}$.
Analysis:	The shorted base-emitter junction explains why $V_{BE} = 0$ V. Because the junction is shorted, this explains why all of I_E flows through the base and none of I_E flows through the collector.

QUESTIONS

1. Yes, they are nearly equal. They should be because we want I_B (which is the difference between the two) to be at least 10 times lower than the bias current. If this is not the case, then the emitter circuit loads down R_2.

2. Yes, they are nearly equal. They should be because $I_E = I_C + I_B$, and I_B is quite small compared to the other two currents.

3. Yes, Kirchoff's current law is supported because $I_E = I_C + I_B$. From Table 8.2, $I_E = 4.71$ mA, $I_C = 4.68$ mA, and $I_B = 20.9$ µA. 4.68 mA + 20.9 µA = 4.70 mA which is very close to the measured value of I_E. Rounding explains the slight difference.

4. $V_{CC} = I_C R_C + V_{CE} + I_E R_E = 7.02$ V + 10.34 V + 2.64 V = 20 V

Exercise 9

Emitter Bias

Part 1: Emitter Bias DC Analysis

Step 1

Component	Nominal value	Measured value
R_B	1 kΩ	1 kΩ
R_C	3.3 kΩ	3.3 kΩ
R_E	6.2 kΩ	6.2 kΩ

Don't forget: The simulator provides measured values identical to the nominal values.

Step 2

$$I_{CQ} = \left| \frac{V_{EE} - V_{BE}}{R_E} \right| = 1.82 \text{ mA}$$

$$V_{CEQ} = V_{CC} - I_{CQ}R_C + V_{BE} = 6.71 \text{ V}$$

Step 3

$$V_B = -12 \text{ mV}$$

$$V_E = -691 \text{ mV}$$

$$V_C = 6.02 \text{ V}$$

Step 4

$$I_B = \frac{V_B}{R_B} = 12 \text{ μA} \qquad I_E = \frac{|V_{EE} - V_E|}{R_E} = 1.82 \text{ mA}$$

$$I_{CQ} = \frac{V_{CC} - V_C}{R_C} = 1.81 \text{ mA} \qquad V_{CEQ} = V_C - V_E = 6.71 \text{ V}$$

Part 2: Emitter Bias Stability

Steps 5 through 7

The results for all of these questions will vary from student to student and cannot be determined through simulations. The beta of the two transistors and the amount of heat applied by each student introduce too many variables. Nonetheless, what these steps are intended to demonstrate is that the emitter-bias circuit has fairly good Q-point stability, especially when compared to the base-bias circuit.

QUESTIONS & PROBLEMS

1. Calculated and measured results should be fairly close.

2. The h_{FE} for the second transistor will depend on the results of step 5. For the first transistor:

$$h_{FE} = \frac{I_C}{I_B} = \frac{1.82 \text{mA}}{12\mu2} = 151.7$$

Keep in mind that this result is based upon a simulation. Student results should fall within the rated beta value for the 2N3904.

3. These results should illustrate the fact that when beta changes (due to a change in transistors) the dc operating characteristics of the emitter-bias circuit remain relatively stable. This is why this circuit is called a *"beta independent circuit"*. In terms of circuit operation, this can be explained as follows: Since the base of the transistor is

approximately at ground, I_{CQ} is found from $I_{CQ} = \dfrac{V_{EE} - V_{BE}}{R_E}$. Beta does not enter into the

equation, therefore it is a beta independent circuit.

SIMULATION EXERCISE

Step 2

$$V_C = 6.02 \text{ V}$$

$$V_E = 691 \text{ mV}$$

$$V_B = 12 \text{ mV}$$

$$I_C = 1.81 \text{ mA}$$

$$I_B = 12 \text{ }\mu\text{A}$$

Fault 9-1: Open R_C

Symptom(s):	I_C and V_{CE} dropped to near zero. $I_E = I_{CB} =$ 1.57 mA.
Analysis:	With R_C open, there is no path for collector current. The only path for emitter current is through the base circuit, so $I_B = I_E$. With V_{EE} being a negative voltage, and with the base tied to ground via R_B, *the BE junction is forward biased.*

Fault 9-2: Open R_B

Symptom(s):	I_C and I_E =195 μA. $I_B \cong 1.8$ μA. $V_{CE} =$ 22.2 V. V_{CC}.
Analysis:	With the base resistor open, you would think that I_B has no current path *and I_B* would be zero. This is almost true, but the voltmeter used to monitor V_B is now the current path for I_B. Because it is much higher than R_B, base current is much lower, and so are I_E and I_C. If the meter was not connected to the base, all current would be closer to zero.

Fault 9-3: Open R_E

Symptom(s):	$I_C = I_E = I_B \cong 0$. $V_C \cong V_{CC}$. $V_E \cong 0$ V.
Analysis:	With the emitter resistor open, there is no current path for either I_B, I_C or of course I_E. Thus, there is no current drop across R_C and $V_C \cong V_{CC}$. Due to the meters in the circuit, the emitter current is close to, but not quite zero.

Fault 9-4: Open transistor (collector-to-emitter)

Symptom(s):	All current are close to zero. V_{CE} is close to $V_{CC} - V_{EE}$ or 24 V.
Analysis:	With the emitter open, there is no path for I_E. Since I_B is really just a portion of I_E, it is also close to zero. Since the collector is open, $I_C \cong 0$ A. With no currents flowing, there is no voltage drop across R_E or R_C so $V_{CE} \cong V_{CC} - V_{EE}$.

Fault 9-5: Shorted transistor (base-to-emitter)

Symptom(s):	$I_B = I_E = 1.7$ mA. I_C is close to zero. $V_C \cong V_{CC}$. $V_E = V_B \cong 1.7$ V.
Analysis:	With the BE junction shorted, all of I_E flows through the base and none through the collector. That is why I_B is so high and I_C is close to zero.

Fault 9-6: Open transistor (base-to-emitter)

Symptom(s):	All currents are close to zero. $V_{CE} \cong 24$ V.
Analysis:	With the BE junction open, there is no base current, so no collector or emitter current. With no I_C or I_E, there is no voltage drop across R_E or R_C, so $V_{CE} \cong V_{CC} - V_{EE}$ or 24 V.

Exercise 10

Feedback Bias Circuits

Part 1: Collector-feedback Bias

Step 2 $I_B = 26\ \mu A$

$I_{CQ} = 4.53\ mA$

$V_{CEQ} = 9.99\ V$

Step 3 $h_{FE} = \dfrac{I_C}{I_B} = 174$

Step 4 $I_B = 23\ \mu A$

$I_{CQ} = 5.09\ mA$

$V_{CEQ} = 8.75\ V$

$h_{FE} = \dfrac{I_C}{I_B} = 221$

Part 2: Emitter-feedback Bias

Step 6 $I_B = 23.98\ \mu A$

$I_C = 4.00\ mA$

$V_{CE} = 9.98\ V$

$h_{FE} = \dfrac{I_C}{I_B} = 167$

Step 7 $I_B = 22.2\ \mu A$

$I_C = 4.87\ mA$

$V_{CE} = 7.80\ V$

$$h_{FE} = \frac{I_C}{I_B} = 219$$

Step 8 $\Delta I_B = 1.78 \ \mu A$ $\Delta I_C = 0.87 \ mA$

$\Delta V_{CE} = 2.18 \ V$ $\Delta h_{FE} = 52$

Step 10 $I_B = 35.3 \ \mu A$ $I_C = 6.21 \ mA$

$V_{CE} = 10.06 \ V$ $h_{FE} = 176$

Step 11 $I_B = 35.1 \ \mu A$ $I_C = 7.70 \ mA$

$V_{CE} = 7.68 \ V$ $h_{FE} = 219$

Step 12 $\Delta I_B = 0.22 \ \mu A$ $\Delta I_C = 1.49 \ mA$

$\Delta V_{CE} = 2.38 \ V$ $\Delta h_{FE} = 43$

QUESTIONS & PROBLEMS

1. $\Delta I_B = 11.5\%$ $\Delta I_C = 12.4\%$ $\Delta V_{CE} = 12.4\%$ $\Delta h_{FE} = 27\%$

    These results show that due to the feedback circuit, the percent change in Q-point values was less than half of the change in beta.

2. Student responses will vary, however, the emitter-bias circuit should show that it, like the collector feedback circuit, limits the affect that changes in h_{FE} have on the Q-point stability of the circuit.

3. The emitter feedback circuit with the larger emitter resistor had a more stable $Q-$ point (based on the results found in steps 8 and 12). This is because as beta increases, the initial resulting increase in I_E causes V_E to increase, decreasing V_{BE} and thereby decreasing I_B. This is how the feedback works. Thus, a larger value emitter resistor results in a greater change in V_E as beta changes.

SIMULATION EXERCISE

Collector-feedback Bias Faults

Fault 10-1: Open collector resistor (R_C)

Symptom(s):	All currents drop to near zero. And all voltages are 0 V.
Analysis:	With R_C open, there is no path for bias current. This means that $V_B = 0$ V and therefore I_C and I_E are zero. $V_C = 0$ since $I_C = 0$ A and therefore there is no voltage across V_{CE}.

Fault 10-2: Open base resistor R_B (R_{B1} or R_{B2})

Symptom(s):	All current are close to zero. $V_{CE} \cong V_{CC}$.
Analysis:	With the base resistor open, there is no path for bias current. This is why the transistor is not conducting. With no collector current, there is no voltage drop across R_C and $V_{CE} \cong V_{CC}$.

Fault 10-3: Shorted transistor, base-to-emitter

Symptom(s):	$V_{CE} = 19.9$ V. $I_B = 55$ μA. $I_C \cong$ zero.
Analysis:	With the base-to-emitter shorted, the base circuit is now the path of least resistance for current. This is now a totally resistive circuit with the transistor (effectively) removed. Base current is determined by V_{CC} and the sum of $R_C + R_{B1} + R_{B2}$.

Fault 10-4: Open transistor emitter lead

Symptom(s):	All currents $\cong$ zero. $V_{CE} \cong V_{CC}$.
Analysis:	With the emitter open, there is no path for current. With no voltage drop across R_C $V_{CE} \cong V_{CC}$.

Emitter-feedback Bias Faults

Fault 10-5: Open collector resistor (R_C)

Symptom(s):	I_C and $V_{CE} \cong 0$ zero. $I_B = 30$ μA.
Analysis:	With R_C open, there is no path for collector current so $I_C \cong$ zero. The base circuit is not really changed, so I_B is close to the no-fault condition.

Fault 10-6: Open base resistor R_B (R_{B1} or R_{B2})

Symptom(s):	All currents drop to near zero. $V_C \cong V_{CC}$.
Analysis:	With the base open, I_B has no current path, so $I_B = 0$. With no base current I_C and I_E must be close to zero. With no I_C, $V_{RC} = 0$ V, so $V_C \cong V_{CC}$.

Fault 10-7: Shorted transistor, base-to-emitter

Symptom(s):	$I_B = 30.7$ μA. $I_C \cong 0$ mA. $V_{CE} \cong V_{CC}$.
Analysis:	With the BE shorted, all of I_E flows through the base circuit, so $I_C \cong 0$ mA. With no collector current, $V_{RC} = 0$ V so $V_{CE} \cong V_{CC}$.

Fault 10-8: Open emitter resistor (R_E)

Symptom(s):	All current drop to near zero, $V_{CE} \cong 0$ V.
Analysis:	With R_E open, there is no path for current. With no collector or emitter current, the emitter and collector are at the same potential, so $V_{CE} \cong 0$ V.

Exercise 11

The Common-Emitter Amplifier

Step 1 $V_B = 1.86$ V $V_E = 1.16$ V $I_E = 2.97$ mA

$$r'_e \cong \frac{25\,\text{mV}}{I_E} = 8.4\ \Omega \qquad\qquad r_C = 1.3\ \text{k}\Omega$$

$$A_v = \frac{r_C}{r'_e} = 155 \qquad\qquad Z_{in} = R_1 \parallel R_2 \parallel h_{fe}r'_e = 808\ \Omega$$

> **Note:** These calculations ignore the loading
> effect of the transistor (because $10R_2 < h_{FE}R_E$).

Step 3 $v_{in} = 20$ mV$_{PP}$ $v_{out} = 2.4$ V$_{PP}$ $A_v = \dfrac{v_{out}}{v_{in}} = 120$

Step 4   The waveforms are sinusoidal and 180° out of phase.

Step 5 $Z_{in} = 820\ \Omega$

Step 6 $v_{in} = 20$ mV$_{PP}$ $v_{out} = 1.2$ V$_{PP}$ $A_v = \dfrac{v_{out}}{v_{in}} = 60$

Step 7 $v_{in} = 20$ mV$_{PP}$ $v_{out} = 65$ mV$_{PP}$ $A_v = \dfrac{v_{out}}{v_{in}} = 3.25$

QUESTIONS & PROBLEMS

1. The two values were close. Variations can be attributed to component tolerance, the assumed value of β and the approximation of r'_e.

2. From Step 1 we see that $I_C \cong 2.97$ mA. This means that $V_{CE} \cong 12$ V $- (2.97$ mA $\times$ 1.89 k$\Omega) = 6.39$ V. Therefore, the circuit is not midpoint biased, but it is close.

3. When v_{in} *increases* (goes more positive) base current increases, so collector current also *increases* ($I_C = \beta I_B$). As I_C *increases* so does V_{RC}. This means that V_C, which is also the voltage across the load, must *decrease* due to increased voltage across the collector resistor. When v_{in} *decreases*, the opposite is true. This explains the 180° phase relationship.

4. The measured and calculated values were close. Variations can be attributed to component tolerance, the assumed value of β, and the approximation of r'_e.

5. $r'_e = \dfrac{r_C}{A_V} = 10.8 \ \Omega$. This value is about 25% higher than the calculated value in Step 1. Considering the number of calculations, assumptions, and approximations involved in the original calculation, this is very close.

6. Decreasing the load resistance means that r_C has also decreased ($r_C = R_L \parallel R_C$). Since $A_v = \dfrac{r_C}{r'_e}$, this explains why the gain decreased.

7. Removing the bypass capacitor means that R_E is now a part of the ac emitter circuit. Since voltage gain is calculated from the *total* ac collector resistance divided by the *total* ac emitter resistance, making R_E a part of the ac emitter circuit will significantly decrease the voltage gain. The difference between R_E and r'_e illustrates just how much change can be expected.

SIMULATION EXERCISE

Table 11.2 Simulation Results for ac Measurements

R_L	C_2	v_{in}	v_{out}	A_v
10 kΩ	Normal	300 mV$_{PP}$	2.5 V$_{PP}$	8.33
10 kΩ	Open	300 mV$_{PP}$	545 mV$_{PP}$	1.82
1 kΩ	Normal	300 mV$_{PP}$	1.4 V$_{PP}$	4.67

Step 3   Removing the bypass capacitor caused the voltage gain to decrease.

Step 4   Lowering the value of R_L caused the voltage gain to decrease.

Step 5   The student should observe severe nonlinear distortion and both cutoff and saturation clipping. Voltage gain has increased significantly.

QUESTIONS & PROBLEMS

1. Removing the bypass capacitor caused the voltage gain to decrease, because R_{E2} is now part of the ac emitter circuit. Since voltage gain is calculated from the *total* ac collector resistance divided by the *total* ac emitter resistance, making R_{E2} a part of the ac emitter circuit will decrease the voltage gain.

2. Lowering the value of R_L caused the voltage gain to decrease for reasons similar to those stated in Question 1. Since voltage gain is calculated from the *total* ac collector resistance divided by the *total* ac emitter resistance, lowering R_L also lowers r_C. Since $A_v = r_C \div (r'_e + R_{E1})$, lowering r_C must decrease A_v.

3. Clipping was observed when the bypass capacitor was connected between the emitter terminal and ground in Step 5. The reason is that now the total ac emitter resistance is only r'_e. Assuming $r'_e \cong 11 \ \Omega$, this means that the voltage gain of the amplifier is found as $A_v = \dfrac{r_C}{r'_e} = \dfrac{1.3\,k\Omega}{11\Omega} = 118$. With an input of 300 mV$_{PP}$, the amplifier is trying to produce an output voltage of 300 mV $\times$ 118 = 35.4 V$_{PP}$. Since V$_{CC}$ = 12 V, this is clearly not possible. This explains why the output is so distorted.

Exercise 12

The Common-Collector Amplifier (Emitter Follower)

Step 1 $V_B = 6.95$ V $V_E = 6.25$ V $I_E = 6.25$ mA

$$r'_e \cong \frac{25\,\text{mV}}{I_E} = 4.0\ \Omega \qquad r_E = R_E \parallel R_L = 500\ \Omega$$

$$A_v = \frac{r_E}{r'_e + r_E} = 0.992 \qquad Z_{in} = R_1 \parallel R_2 \parallel h_{fc}(r'_e + r_E) = 8.31\ \text{k}\Omega$$

> **Note:** The loading effect of the transistor was not taken into account in these calculations.

Step 3

v_{in} (*Measured*)	v_{out} (*Measured*)	A_v (*Calculated*)
1 V_{PP}	1 V_{PP}	1

Step 4

v_{in} (*Measured*)	v_{out} (*Measured*)	A_v (*Calculated*)
1 V_{PP}	925 mV_{PP}	0.925

Step 5 $Z_{in} = 8.1$ kΩ

Step 6 $Z_{in} = 5.9$ kΩ

Step 9 $$V_{L(pk)} = V_{S(pk)} \frac{R_L}{R_S + R_L} = 45.5\ \text{mV}$$

$$V_L = 0.707 V_{L(pk)} = 32.1\ \text{mV}$$

$$P_L = \frac{V_L^2}{R_L} = 10.3\ \mu\text{W}$$

Step 10 $V_{L(pk)} = 405$ mV $V_L = 0.707 V_{L(pk)} = 286$ mV

$$P_L = \frac{V_L^2}{R_L} = 820 \ \mu W$$

QUESTIONS & PROBLEMS

1. The two values were very close. Component tolerances and various assumptions and approximations (h_{FE} and r'_e) and the resolution of the scope explain any variations.

2. Since $I_E = 6.25$ mA this means that $V_{CE} = 12$ V $- (6.25$ mA $\times 1$ k$\Omega) = 6.25$ V. Therefore this circuit is close to being midpoint biased.

3. The gain of the amplifier decreased. The reason for this can be seen from the gain equation: $A_v = \dfrac{r_E}{r'_e + r_E}$. Since $r_E = R_E \parallel R_L$ decreasing R_L decreased r_E. As we can see from the gain equation, this will decrease A_v.

4. The two results were close. Once again, component tolerance and assumptions and approximations explain any variations.

5. Decreasing the load decreased the input impedance. The reason can be seen from the equation for calculating input impedance: $Z_{in} = R_1 \parallel R_2 \parallel h_{fc}(r'_e + r_E)$. Since input impedance varies directly with r_E, and as we saw in Question 4, r_E decreases if R_L decreases, this explains why input impedance decreases when R_L decreases.

6. Yes, the circuit was very effective. This can be seen if we calculate load power if it was coupled directly to the high-impedance source, as follows:

$$V_{L(pk)} = 500 mV \frac{100\Omega}{1100\Omega} = 45.45 mV$$

Converting to rms: $V_L = 0.707 \times 45.45$ mV $= 32.14$ mV

$$P_L = \frac{V_L^2}{R_L} = \frac{32.14 mV^2}{100\Omega} = 10.3 \ \mu W.$$

Thus, the buffer amplifier did a very good job of coupling the high-impedance source to a low-impedance load.

SIMULATION EXERCISE

Step 2 $V_B = 6.62$ V $v_{in} = 1$ V$_{PP}$

$V_E = 5.91$ V $v_{out} = 989$ mV$_{PP}$

$I_C = 5.87$ mA $A_v = 0.989$

Fault 12-1: Open input coupling capacitor

Symptoms:	All dc measurements are normal. The input signal is unaffected, but there is no output signal.
Analysis:	The open input capacitor prevents the input signal from reaching the amplifier, therefore there is no output signal.

Fault 12-2: Open R_1 in the base circuit

Symptoms:	Both V_B and V_E are close to 0 V. The input signal is unaffected, but there is no output signal.
Analysis:	The open R_1 causes V_B to equal 0 V which means that the BE junction is not forward biased. Further, the input signal is not high enough to bias the junction, even for a portion of the positive alternation.

Fault 12-3: Open transistor emitter lead

Symptoms:	V_B has increased slightly, $V_E \cong 0$ V. The input signal is unaffected, but there is no output signal.
Analysis:	The open emitter means that $I_E = 0$ A. This also means that the input signal cannot reach the load. V_B has increased slightly since the emitter circuit is no longer loading down the bias circuit.

Fault 12-4: Shorted transistor (collector-to-emitter)

Symptoms:	V_B has increased slightly (6.95 V) and V_E has increased to 12 V. The input signal is unaffected, but there is no output signal.
Analysis:	With the C-E shorted, all of V_{CC} is across R_E. V_B has increased slightly since there is no base current. With the emitter held at V_{CC} there can be no output signal.

Fault 12-5: Open output coupling capacitor

Symptoms:	There is no change in dc levels. The input signal is unaffected, but there is no output.
Analysis:	With the output capacitor open, there can be no output signal since the signal cannot be coupled to the load.

Fault 12-6: Shorted transistor (base to emitter)

Symptoms:	V_{R1} has increased to 11.3 V. $V_B = V_E = 677$ mV. The input and output signals are unaffected.
Analysis:	With the base-emitter shorted, R_E is in parallel with R_2 which means that V_B decreases. The output signal is unaffected since the input is applied to the parallel combination of $R_2 \parallel R_E$.

Fault 12-7: Open load

Symptoms:	There is no change in dc levels. The input and output signals are unaffected.
Analysis:	With the load open, it is like a very high resistance load is connected to the amplifier. Thus, no dc levels are changed, and the ac output will be slightly higher, but the difference is very small.

Fault 12-8: Open R_2 in the base circuit

Symptoms:	V_{R1} has dropped to 1.01 V. $V_{R2} = 11$ V. V_E = 10.3 V. The input and output signal are unaffected.
Analysis:	With R_2 open, this is a base bias circuit. It is not saturated though, so with this low-level input, there is still an output signal.

Questions & Problems

1. These two faults are not the same at all. When R_1 is open, all biasing is lost since the open bias resistor blocks any dc voltage at the base. On the other hand, when R_2 is open, the voltage at the base increases. Depending on the bias resistor values, it may even be saturated.

2. Although there is no voltage gain (actually a loss) there is current gain. If the current *gain* is greater than the voltage *loss* ($A_P = A_v \times A_i$), then there must be power gain. The student should be referred to the current gain equation for the CC amplifier that follows (and is introduced in Chapter 10 of the text).

$$A_i = h_{fc} \left(\frac{Z_{in} r_E}{Z_{in(base)} R_L} \right)$$

Exercise 13

The Common-Base Amplifier

Step 1 $I_E = \dfrac{|V_{EE} + 0.7\,\text{V}|}{R_E} = 930\,\mu\text{A}$

$r'_e \cong \dfrac{25\,\text{mV}}{I_E} = 26.9\,\Omega$

$r_c = R_C \parallel R_L = 6\text{k}\Omega \parallel 10\text{k}\Omega = 3.75\ \text{k}\Omega$

$A_v = \dfrac{r_C}{r'_e} = 139$

Step 3 $v_{in} = 8\,\text{mV}$

$v_{out} = 1\text{V}$

$A_v = 125$

Step 4 $v_{in} = 11.5\,\text{mV}$

$v_{out} = 1\text{V}$

$A_v = 87$

Step 5 $Z_{in} = 32\,\Omega$

Step 6 $R_{C2} = 2.8\ \text{k}\Omega$

$R_C = R_{C1} + R_{C2} = 6.1\ \text{k}\Omega$

QUESTIONS & PROBLEMS

1. Student answers may vary significantly. This is due to the fact that the method used to calculate r'_e is not very accurate. None the less, student results should give A_v results in the range of 100 to 175.

2. Both input and output signals were in phase. When the input at the emitter goes more positive, the BE junction becomes *less* forward biased. This decreases base current, and therefore, collector current. With less collector current, V_{RC} decreases, which means that V_C (and therefore V_L) increases. The only amplifier configuration that exhibits a out of phase relationship between input and output is the CE amplifier. r'_e

3. The r'_e value below was close to that calculated in Step 1, but student responses may well vary be a sizable margin. As stated in the answer to Question 1 above, the method used to calculate r'_e is not that accurate.

   $A_v = 125$ (from Step 3)

   $R_C = 6.1$ kΩ (from Step 6)

   $$r'_e \cong \frac{R_C \| R_L}{A_v} = 30.3$$

4. When the value of load resistance was decreased from 10 kΩ to 4.7 kΩ A_v decreased. The reason is obvious from the equation for calculating voltage gain:

   $A_v = \dfrac{r_C}{r'_e}$. If R_L decreases, then r_C must decrease and therefore, so does A_v.

5. Our Z_{in} results were close our calculations for r'_e, but for reasons mentioned before, student results may vary by a wide margin.

SIMULATION EXERCISE

Step 2

Table 13.1 Simulation Results for ac and dc Measurements

Current	Measured Value	Voltage	Measured Value
I_E	1.096 mA	V_E	898 mV
I_C	1.088 mA	V_{CE}	8.00 V
I_B	7.541 μA	V_B	1.56 V

Step 3 $v_{in} = 5 \text{ mV}_{PP}$

$v_{out} = 750 \text{ mV}_{PP}$

$$A_v = \frac{v_{out}}{v_{in}} = 150$$

Step 4 $v_{in} = 5 \text{ mV}_{PP}$

$v_{out} = 1.1 \text{ V}_{PP}$

$$A_v = \frac{v_{out}}{v_{in}} = 220$$

There was no change in the dc values.

Step 6 $v_{in} = 5 \text{ mV}_{PP}$

$v_{out} = 95.4 \text{ mV}_{PP}$

$$A_v = \frac{v_{out}}{v_{in}} = 19.1$$

There was no change in the dc values.

Step 7   Amplitude of positive alternation = 370 mV

Amplitude of negative alternation = 383 mV

Step 8   Amplitude of positive alternation = 1.4 V

Amplitude of negative alternation = 1.6 V

The positive alternation waveform has become more blunted at its peak, and the amplitude has decreased relative to the negative alternation. The negative alternation seems normal.

Step 9   Amplitude of positive alternation = 4 V

Amplitude of negative alternation = 7.4 V

The positive alternation has become extremely distorted. It is very blunt at the top and seem to occupy much more than 180°. The negative alternation is narrow and seems to occupy much less than 180°.

Questions & Problems

1. a. Opening the load is the same as increasing the load to a very high value. The voltage gain equation for the CB amplifier $\left(A_v = r_C/r'_e\right)$ show us that if R_L increases, then so does r_C and therefore, so does A_v.

   b. There were no changes in the dc values since the load is isolated by the coupling capacitor.

2. a. Decreasing the load resistance caused a decrease in r_C and a decrease in A_v.

   b. There were no changes in the dc values since the load is isolated by the coupling capacitor.

3. As the input voltage goes more positive, it biases the BE junction more and more *off*. (Remember, the emitter must be more negative than the base in order to conduct). As the junction is driven below its knee voltage, this means that for a given change in voltage, there is a smaller and smaller change in current. It is due to this nonlinear change in current, as a result of a change in voltage, that this type of distortion is called *nonlinear distortion*. All of the above discussion refers to the positive alternation of the output waveform only.

   Referring to the negative alternation of the waveform, as the input voltage goes more negative, it is biasing the BE junction more and more *on*. Since in its quiescent condition the BE junction is already biased above the knee voltage, this means that a change in voltage results in a relatively linear change in current. The student should refer back to the basic diode characteristic curve in Section 2.5 of the text. They should also review their results from Exercise 1.

4. Nonlinear distortion always precedes clipping. If the student increases the input signal they will see that eventually, the output will clip, first on the negative alternation, and then on the positive.

Exercise 14

Class B and Class AB Amplifiers

Step 1

Label	Measured value
$V_{BE(Q1)}$	165 mV
$V_{BE(Q2)}$	200 mV
$V_{CE(Q1)}$	4.95 V
$V_{CE(Q2)}$	5.07 V

Figure 14.2a There should be two waveforms, in phase, with crossover distortion appearing in the output. The output is slightly lower than the input.

Step 3

Label	Measured value
$V_{BE(Q1)}$	590 mV
$V_{BE(Q2)}$	627 mV
$V_{CE(Q1)}$	4.9 V
$V_{CE(Q2)}$	5.01 V

Step 4 $v_{in} = 8\ V_{PP}$ $v_{out} = 7.5\ V_{PP}$

Figure 14.2b There should be two waveforms, in phase, with no crossover distortion in the output waveform.

Step 5 $A_v = 0.94$ $P_L = \dfrac{V_L^2}{R_L} = 260\ \text{mW}$

Step 6 $I_{CC} = 43\ \text{mA}$ $P_S = I_{CC}V_{CC} = 430\ \text{mW}$

Step 7 $\eta = \dfrac{P_L}{P_S} \times 100 = 60.5\%$

1. The class AB amplifier had the higher values of V_{BE}. The reason is that the two diodes in the class AB circuit cause the base-emitter junctions of the two transistors to be more forward biased.

2. This type of voltage gain ($A_v < 1$) is consistent with an emitter-follower.

3. The circuit is very close to being midpoint biased. The use of matched diode and transistor pairs would help make the circuit closer to ideal.

4. One would think that changing the two bias resistors would have no significant effect on voltage gain. Voltage gain is not affected since this is determined by $A_v = \dfrac{R_L}{R_L + r_e'}$. Since the bias resistors appear to have no affect on any of the determining factors, one would assume that voltage gain is unaffected. This is not the case though. One needs to look at the bias current. With $R_1 = R_3 = 10 \text{ k}\Omega$, this means that the bias current would be $(10 \text{ V} - 1.4 \text{ V}) \div 20 \text{ k}\Omega = 430 \text{ }\mu\text{A}$. This means that the diodes would not be fully conducting. The result would be that some amplitude is lost at the output and crossover distortion would appear.

   Input impedance is increased if the two bias resistor values are increased. They are in parallel with $Z_{in(base)}$.

5. This value is slightly lower than the theoretical maximum efficiency, but that is to be expected. It is well within expected values.

SIMULATION EXERCISE

Table 14.1 Class AB Amplifier Simulation Results

v_{in} (Measured)	v_{out} (Measured)	A_v (Calculated)
8 V_{PP}	7.5 V_{PP}	0.94

Figure 14.4 There should be two waveforms, in phase, with crossover distortion appearing in the output.

Table 14.2 Class AB Amplifier Simulation Results

i_{in} (Measured)	i_{out} (Measured)	A_i (Calculated)
3.71 mA	97.1 mA	26.17

Table 14.3 Class AB Amplifier Simulation Results

i_{in} (*Measured*)	i_{out} (*Measured*)	A_i (*Calculated*)
6.8 mA	98 mA	14.41

Step 6 $I_{CC} = 43$ mA $P_S = 430$ mW

Step 7 $I_{CC} = 144$ mA $P_S = 1.44$ W

Step 8   The output waveform seems unaffected. There is no cross-over distortion.

QUESTIONS

1. By increasing the value of R_1 and R_2 the bias current was decreased. If we assume that the diodes are forward biased, the bias current (ignoring base current) can be found from,

$$ I_{Bias} = \frac{V_{CC} - 1.4 \text{ V}}{R_1 + R_2} = \frac{8.6 \text{ V}}{20 \text{ k}\Omega} = 430 \text{ } \mu\text{A} $$

   This is not enough forward current for the two diodes to be fully forward biased. This means that the diodes are no longer compensating for the base-emitter voltage drops of the two transistors. Thus, the two transistors are not biased slightly into conduction and the circuit acts like a class B amplifier.

2. The bias resistors are in parallel with Z_{base}. This means that there are effectively three current branches at the input to the amplifier. The lower the value of the bias resistors, the more input current passes through the R_1 and R_2 branches and less of the current enters the transistor bases. This is why current gain has decreased.

3. The opening of the diode means that both transistors are now base biased. In other words, they are biased well into conduction. This explains why I_{CC} is so much higher. There is a significant amount of I_{CQ}. Although the circuit does not distort the output, all of the efficiency advantages of the class AB circuit have been lost.

Exercise 15

A Multi-Stage Amplifier

Step 2 $V_{B(Q1)} = 1.98$ V $V_{B(Q3)} = 6.39$ V

$V_{C(Q1)} = 6.94$ V $V_{C(Q3)} = 12.00$ V

$V_{E(Q1)} = 1.31$ V $V_{E(Q3)} = 5.81$ V

$V_{B(Q2)} = 1.98$ V $V_{B(Q4)} = 5.20$ V

$V_{C(Q2)} = 5.20$ V $V_{C(Q4)} = 0$ V

$V_{E(Q2)} = 1.32$ V $V_{E(Q4)} = 5.81$ V

Step 4 $v_A = 200$ m V_{PP} $v_D = 5.9$ V_{PP}
$v_B = 1.8$ V_{PP} $v_E = 5.9$ V_{PP}
$v_C = 1.8$ V_{PP} $v_F = 5.5$ V_{PP}

Step 5 The two signals are in phase with each other.

Step 6 A_v (A to B) = 9
A_v (C to D) = 3.3
A_v (E to F) = 0.93

Step 7 Varying the amplitude causes the sound to get louder and softer.

Step 8 As the frequency was increased it caused the sound to get higher (more treble). As the frequency was lowered it caused the sound to get lower (more bass). The loudness remained constant.

Step 9 $V_{out} = 4.5$ V_{PP} (200 Hz)
$V_{out} = 5.4$ V_{PP} (20 kHz)
$V_{out} = 4.6$ V_{PP} (2 MHz)

QUESTIONS & PROBLEMS

1. $A_{vT} = 27.5$

2. The first stage (Q_1) is a CE amplifier so it inverts its output. The second stage (Q_2) is also an inverting amplifier, so its output is in phase with the input to Stage 1. The final stage (Q_3 and Q_4) is a class AB amplifier, which has the characteristics of an emitter follower, so its output is in phase with its input. Thus, the output of the entire circuit is in phase with its input.

3. At 200 Hz, the 10 μF coupling capacitors have a reactance of 80 Ω. This is high enough to cause some signal loss. Also, the bypass capacitor (C_B) will not be as effective at this frequency and the gain of the first stage will be lower.

    The losses at 2 MHz. are harder to explain to the student, as they have not studied Chapter 14 of the text on amplifier frequency response. It should be enough to simply have them state that any shunt capacitance (to ground) will cause higher losses at higher frequencies. It might not be a bad idea to suggest that the student look ahead to Chapter 14 if they want to know more.

4. These resistors are used to bias Q_2, which in turn balances the voltage at point F.

Exercise 16

JFET Operation

Part 1: Drain Current and V$_{DS}$

Step 1 $V_P = -2.0$ V to -6.0 V $I_{DSS} = 8.0$ mA to 20 mA

Table 16.1 Voltage and Current Values for the JFET Test Circuit

V_{DS} (V)	I_D (mA)	V_{DS} (V)	I_D (mA)
0.0	0	4.0	12.7
0.5	2.8	4.5	12.8
1.0	5.3	5.0	13.0
1.5	7.5	6.0	13.2
2.0	9.3	7.0	13.4
2.5	10.7	8.0	13.6
3.0	11.8	10.0	14
3.5	12.5	15.0	15.1

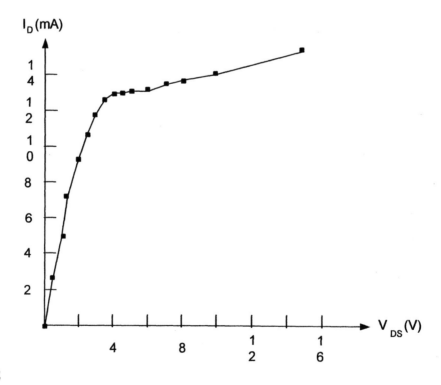

Figure 16.2

Step 5 $V_P = 2.8$ V $I_{DSS} = 13$ mA

Step 6 $I_{DSS} = 12.7$ mA

Step 7 $V_{GS(off)} = -3.86$ V

**Table 16.2 Measured
combinations of V_{GS} and I_D**

V_{GS}	I_D
-0.5 V	9.7mA
-1.0 V	7.1 mA
-2.0 V	3.0 mA
-3.0 V	0.61 mA

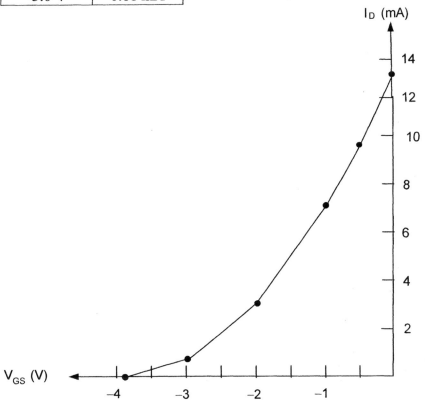

Figure 16.4

QUESTIONS & PROBLEMS

1. The values are within the rated values for the device.

2. Below V_P there is a relationship between V_{GS} and I_D that is directly proportional. This region is known as the ohmic region.

3.

Table 16.2   Calculated and Measured Drain Current Values

V_{GS}	I_D (Calculated)	I_D (Measured)	% Variation
−0.5 V	9.62mA	9.7 mA	0.8%
−1.0 V	6.97 mA	7.1 mA	1.8%
−2.0 V	2.95 mA	3.0 mA	1.7%
−3.0 V	0.63 mA	0.61 mA	3.3%

It should be noted that although the results listed above in Table 16.2 show variations of less than 5 %, it will not be uncommon for student results to show errors of 20, 30, or even 50%. This is due to the fact that so much depends on student interpretation. They have to interpret the values for I_{DSS} and $V_{GS(off)}$ from their test results, and this is very subjective.

SIMULATION EXERCISE

Step 2 $I_{DSS} = 15.12$ mA

Step 3 $V_{GS(off)} = -3.82$ V

Table 16.4   Measured combinations of V_{GS} and I_D

V_{GS}	I_D
−3.2 V	480 μA
−2.6 V	1.70 mA
−2.0 V	3.63 mA
−1.4 V	6.30 mA
−0.8 V	9.54 mA
−0.2 V	13.65 mA

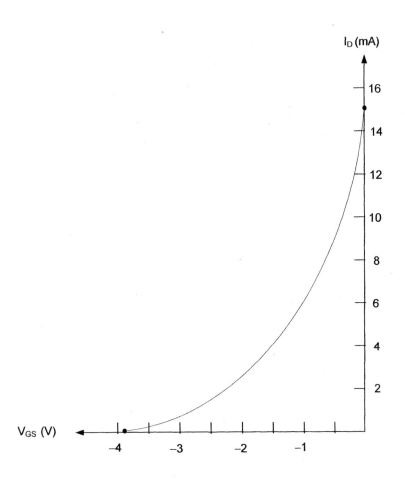

Figure 16.6

Exercise 17

Gate Bias and Self-Bias Circuits

Step 1 $V_P = 2.0$ V to 6.0 V $I_{DSS} = 8.0$ mA to 20 mA

Step 2 $I_D = 2$ mA to 13.89 mA

Step 4 $I_D = 7.78$ mA $V_{DS} = 10$ V

Step 5   Results will vary, but I_D should increase and V_{DS} should decrease.

Step 6   Results will vary, but there may be significant variations from one device to another.

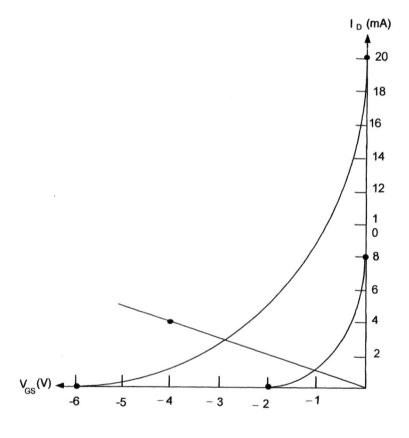

Figure 17.2

Step 9 $V_{GS} = $ -1.0 V to -2.8 V $I_D = $ 1.2 mA to 3 mA

Step 10 $V_{GS} = -2.58$ V $I_D = 1.57$ mA $V_{DS} = 10.05$ V

Step 11   These values will vary. As before, there may be significant variations from one device to another.

QUESTIONS & PROBLEMS

1. Yes, the measured values fell within the rated range of values.

2. When the circuit heated up, I_D increased. This is most likely a result of an increase in thermally induced majority charge carriers in the channel.

3. Due to the large range of possible Q-points, this circuit would have poor stability.

4. There may be a significant difference in the value of I_D obtained from the bias line and the measured value. The bias line was plotted using $R_S = 1$ kΩ. To midpoint bias the circuit, the value of R_S may be quite a different value. If the bias line was redrawn using the actual value of R_S the point should fall on the line.

SIMULATION EXERCISE

Step 2

V_{GS}	V_{DS}	I_D	I_G
0 V	6.68 V	13 mA	0 A
−4 V	20 V	0 A	450nA

Step 3

R_S	V_{GS}	I_D	I_G
0 Ω	893 nV	4.1 mA	0.74 pA
2.5 kΩ	−2.80 V	1.12 mA	3.04 nA
5 kΩ	−3.08 V	618 μA	347 nA

Steps 4 & 5

Device	V_{GS}	V_{DS}	I_D
2N5486	−2.58 V	10.05 V	1.57 mA
2N5485	−1.49 V	14.28	901 μA
2N5484	−812 mV	16.87	494 μA

QUESTIONS

1. There were very large changes in I_D in conjunction with very small changes in I_G. In Step 2, there was drain current when I_G was zero. This shows that gate current has no real relationship to drain current. On the other hand, changes in V_{GS} caused significant changes in drain current. This leads us to the conclusion that JFET drain current is controlled by voltage, not by gate current.

2. These results show that it is the positive voltage across R_S that establishes the negative V_{GS} voltage necessary to bias the FET. When $R_S = 0\ \Omega$, V_{GS} was close to 0 V and I_D was at its maximum. As the value of R_S increased, V_{GS} became more negative and I_D decreased.

3. As the results show, replacing the devices resulted in significant changes in I_D and V_{DS}. This shows that these biasing circuits are not very stable.

Exercise 18

The Common-Source Amplifier

Step 2 $V_{GS} = -2.28$ V $I_D = 2.28$ mA

Step 3 $V_{GS} = -2.53$ V $I_D = 1.69$ mA

Step 4 $\Delta V_{GS} = V_{GS(max)} - V_{GS(min)} = 250$ mV

$\Delta I_D = I_{D(max)} - I_{D(min)} = 590$ µA

$g_m = \dfrac{\Delta I_D}{\Delta V_{GS}} = 1475$ µS

Step 5 $A_v = g_m R_D = 6.9$

Step 7   The input and output signals are 180° out of phase.

Step 8 $v_{in} = 400$ mV$_{PP}$ $v_{out} = 4.2$ V$_{PP}$ $A_v = \dfrac{v_{out}}{v_{in}} = 10.5$

Step 9 $v_{in} = 400$ mV$_{PP}$ $v_{out} = 1.4$ V$_{PP}$ $A_v = \dfrac{v_{out}}{v_{in}} = 3.5$

Step 10 $R \cong Z_{in} = 980$ kΩ

QUESTIONS & PROBLEMS

1. There is approximately a 35% variation between the two A_v values. This is within the acceptable range. Student results may vary significantly. The main causes for the variation is that using the delta V and I values to calculate g_m is an approximation of g_m. Component tolerances and measurement accuracy will also have some affect.

2. The voltage gain decreased when the load was added. This was because $A_v = g_m r_D$. When the load was not connected, $r_D = R_D$. With the addition of the load,

$r_D = R_D \| R_L$. Thus A_v must decrease.

3. As stated, the input and output were 180° out of phase. This is also the case for the common-emitter BJT amplifier.

4. The input impedance of the amplifier was very close the value of the gate resistor. This means that the input impedance of the JFET has little bearing on the input impedance of the amplifier.

SIMULATION EXERCISE

Normal circuit operation: $V_{GS} = -2.28$ V $v_{in} = 500$ mV$_{PP}$

$V_{DS} = 9.24$ V $v_{out} = 2.0$ V$_{PP}$

Fault 1: Shorted gate resistor (R_G)

Symptoms:	There is no significant change in the dc readings. The input is unaffected, but there is no output signal.
Analysis	Since there is no dc gate current, having a shorted R_G makes no difference in the dc values. The gate is still at dc ground, but the shorted R_G also shorts the input signal to ground. This is why there is no output signal.

Fault 2: Open JFET source terminal

Symptoms:	V_{GS} is close to 0 V. V_{DS} is close to V_{DD}. The input is unaffected, but there is no output signal.
Analysis:	With the source open, there can be no channel current, so V_D must equal V_{DD}. This is also why $V_{GS} \cong 0$ V. Since $g_m = \dfrac{\Delta I_D}{\Delta V_{GS}}$ and there is no I_D, there can be no output.

Fault 3: Shorted JFET gate-source junction

Symptoms:	The input signal is unaffected. The output has dropped to about 20 mV$_{PP}$. V_{GS} is 0 V and $V_{DS} = 609$ mV.
Analysis:	Since the GS-junction is shorted, $V_{GS} = 0$ V. V_{DS} is simply a function of I_D and the channel resistance. Explaining the ac output is a little more complex. This circuit is no longer an amplifier. It is a series-parallel ac circuit. The ac signal is applied to $R_G \parallel R_S$ tied to ground. This is in series with the channel resistance and the parallel combination of R_D and R_L, also tied to ground. The voltage across the load is simply a function of the voltage division in the series-parallel circuit.

Fault 4: Shorted JFET (drain to source)

Symptoms:	V_{DS} is close to 0 V. V_{GS} has increased to -3.51 V. The input is unaffected, but there is no output signal.
Analysis:	With the drain and source shorted there can be no V_{DS}. V_{GS} has become more negative because the shorted DS-channel means that I_D has increased, and therefore, so has V_S. Since the DS-channel is shorted, the load is in parallel with the source, and therefore the bypass capacitor. Since the bypass cap is an ac path to ground, there can be no ac output.

Fault 5: Shorted bypass capacitor

Symptoms:	The $V_{GS} \cong 0$ V, $V_{DS} = 750$ mV. The input is unaffected, but the output has dropped to 96 mV$_{PP}$.
Analysis:	Shorting the capacitor means that there is no dc voltage across R$_S$ and therefore no V_{GS}. With $V_{GS} = 0$ V, $I_D = I_{DSS}$ and V_{GS} is very low due to the resulting high voltage across R$_D$. Just as in a CE amplifier, shorting the bypass capacitor causes the voltage gain of the amplifier to decrease.

Fault 6: Open source resistor (R_S)

Symptoms:	Both V_{GS} and V_{DS} are close to 10 V. The input is unaffected, but there is no output signal.
Analysis:	The dc values are misleading. Since there is no path for I_D with R_S open, this means that there is no ground reference to measure V_{DS}, and thus it is floating. Since there is no I_D, there can be no output signal.

Exercise 19

E-MOSFETs

Steps 2 & 3

TABLE 19.1

V_{GS}	I_D
$V_{GS(th)} = 1.88$ V	450 μA
$V_{GS(th)} + 100$ mV = 2.0 V	1.85 mA
$V_{GS(th)} + 200$ mV = 2.1 V	4.46 mA
$V_{GS(th)} + 300$ mV = 2.2 V	8.13 mA
$V_{GS(th)} + 400$ mV = 2.3 V	12.81 mA
$V_{GS(th)} + 500$ mV = 2.4 V	14.6 mA
$V_{GS(th)} + 600$ mV = 2.5 V	14.7 mA
$V_{GS(th)} + 700$ mV = 2.6 V	14.8 mA

Step 4

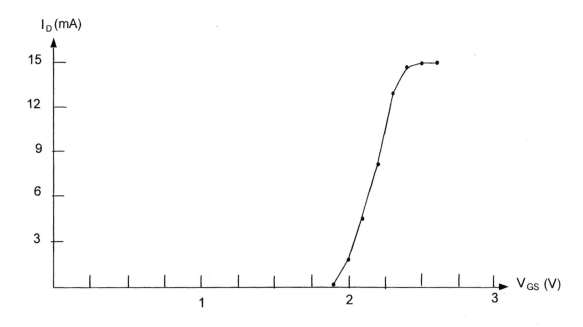

Step 5 $V_{GSQ} = 2.12$ V @ $I_{DQ} = 4.93$ mA

Step 7 $v_{in} = 40$ mV$_{pp}$ $v_{out} = 2.2$ V$_{PP}$ $A_v = 55$

The input and output signals are 180° out of phase.

Step 8 $v_{in} = 40$ mV$_{pp}$ $v_{out} = 870$ mV$_{PP}$ $A_v = 21.75$

QUESTIONS & PROBLEMS

1. Yes, the value of $V_{GS(th)}$ was within the rated range. Student responses will vary, but they should still fall with specifications.

2. The reason the output signal is out of phase with the input is for the same reason as a common emitter amplifier. As Table 19.1 illustrates, as V_{GS} increases, so does I_D. As I_D increases, V_{RD} increases and V_D (and therefore V_L) decreases.

3. Lowering the load resistance also lowered the voltage gain. This is due to the fact that voltage gain is the product of the g_m of the MOSFET multiplied by the total ac drain resistance r_D. By lowering R_L we lower r_D and thus A_v.

Exercise 20

Amplifier Bandwidth and Roll-off Rates

Part 1: BJT Amplifier Bandwidth

Step 3 $v_{out} = 3.3$ V$_{PP}$ (based upon an input of 30 mV$_{PP}$)

Step 4 $v_{out} = 2.3$ V$_{PP}$ $f_{C1} = 125$ Hz

Step 5 $v_{out} = 2.3$ V$_{PP}$ $f_{C2} = 95$ kHz

Step 6   BW $= f_{C2} - f_{C1} = 94.875$ kHz $f_0 = \sqrt{f_{C1}f_{C2}} = 3.45$ kHz

Part 2: BJT Amplifier Roll-off Rates

Step 7 $v_{out} = 1.3$ V$_{PP}$ @ ½ f_{C1} $v_{out} = 545$ mV$_{PP}$ @ ¼ f_{C1}

Step 8 $v_{out} = 1.4$ V$_{PP}$ @ $2f_{C2}$ $v_{out} = 790$ V$_{PP}$ @ $4f_{C2}$

Step 9 $R_{1b} = 6.3$ kΩ $R_1 = R_{1a} + R_{1b} = 11$ kΩ

QUESTIONS & PROBLEMS

1. $f_{C1} = 93.74$ Hz
2. % variation $= 1.2\%$
3. $f_{C2} = 94.06$ kHz
4. % variation $= 1\%$

Note: Due to capacitor tolerances and stray capacitance, it is not surprising to have high percentages of error in this lab. A 50% variation is not unusual. To minimize this, you can hardwire the circuit and measure all caps if you have the proper facility.

SIMULATION EXERCISE

Step 2 $A_{v(dB)} = 45.62$ dB

Step 3 $A_v = \log^{-1}\left(\dfrac{45.62}{20}\right) = 191$

Step 4 $f_{C1} = 190.55$ Hz $A_{v(dB)} = 42.66$ dB

Step 5 $A_v = 18.3$ dB $f = 19.1$ Hz

Step 7   Phase $= -179.5°$ (10 kHz)

               Phase $= -124.4°$ (190.55 Hz.)

               Phase difference $= 55.1°$

Questions

1. The base circuit was the dominant network.

$$f_{C1} = \frac{1}{2\pi R_{in} C_{C1}} = \frac{1}{2\pi (10k\Omega \parallel 2k\Omega \parallel 3k\Omega)1\mu F} = 148.5 \text{ Hz} \quad (\text{assume } h_{ie} = 3 \text{ k}\Omega)$$

2. The phase difference was close to 45° (55.1°) as expected for a one-pole network.

3. They were as nearly equal as could be expected. The calculated frequencies are based on approximations of the transistor parameters.

Exercise 21

Op-Amp Slew Rates

Step 3 $\Delta V = 5$ V

Step 4 $\Delta t = 10.5$ μs

Step 5   Slew rate $= 0.48$ V/μs

Step 6   As the amplitude decreases, the output waveform started to look more like a rectangular waveform, i.e. the slope on the transitions becomes less pronounced.

Step 7   As the frequency decreased, the slope on the transitions became less pronounced, as was the case in Step 6.

Step 8 $f_{max} = 32$ kHz.

Step 9 $f_{max} = 22$ kHz (**Note**: student response for Steps 8 and 9 may vary significantly as these are both subjective evaluations.)

QUESTIONS & PROBLEMS

1. The KA741 has a rated slew rate of 0.5 V/μs. The % variation is less than 1% but student response may vary significantly due to measurement error.

2. $f_{max} = 31.8$ kHz for a 5 V_{pp} sine wave input. This is very close to our measured value from Step 8. Student responses may vary significantly as distortion may occur before it is visible or noticed by the student. $f_{max} = 25.1$ kHz for an 8 V_{PP} input.

3. An increase in input voltage will cause a decrease in the maximum frequency. This is obvious from our results and from the f_{max} equation.

4. 140 times higher, $f_{max} = 4.5$ MHz

SIMULATION EXERCISE

Step 2   Slew rate $= \dfrac{\Delta V}{\Delta t} = 0.53$ V/μs

Step 3   Slew rate $= \dfrac{\Delta V}{\Delta t} = 11.9$ V/μs

Questions:

1. The (−) and (+) terminals on the op-amp symbol represent the inverting and noninverting inputs respectively. The op-amp will not work if either the inverting (pin 2) or the noninverting (pin 3) inputs are left open.

2. An op-amp with a faster slew rate will have a higher value of f_{max}, and thus, a wider bandwidth.

3. The measured and specified rates should be very close.

4. The LM308D is a much faster op-amp than the 741 (approximately 12 V/μs vs. 0.5 V/μs respectively). Based upon the f_{max} equation, $\left(f_{max} = \dfrac{\text{slew rate}}{2\pi V_{pk}} \right)$ we can see that maximum frequency is directly proportional to slew rate. Thus, a higher slew rate means a wider bandwidth.

Exercise 22

Inverting Amplifiers

Step 1 $A_{CL} = \dfrac{R_f}{R_i} = 1$

Step 3 $v_{in} = 500 \text{ mV}_{PP}$ $v_{out} = 500 \text{ mV}_{PP}$

Figure 22.2: There should be two waveforms that are 180° out of phase.

Step 4 $A_{CL} = \dfrac{v_{out}}{v_{in}} = 1$

Table 22.1 Voltage measurements and calculations

$R_f(\text{k}\Omega)$	v_{in}	v_{out}	A_{CL} (Calculated)	A_{CL} (Measured)
27	1V_{PP}	2.7 V_{PP}	2.7	2.7
39	1V_{PP}	3.9 V_{PP}	3.9	3.9
47	1V_{PP}	4.7 V_{PP}	4.7	4.7
82	1V_{PP}	8.2 V_{PP}	8.2	8.2

Table 22.2

R_L	v_{in}	v_{out}	A_{CL}
10 kΩ	5 V_{PP}	5 V_{PP}	1
1 kΩ	5 V_{PP}	5 V_{PP}	1
470 Ω	5 V_{PP}	5 V_{PP}	1

Step 8 $R_L = 90 \ \Omega$

QUESTIONS & PROBLEMS

1. The input and output are 180° out of phase. The reason is that the input signal is applied to the inverting input.

2. The two values were identical, or close enough to make no significant difference. Any variation is a function of component tolerances.

3. The change in load had very little if any affect on amplifier gain. This is very different from CE and CS amplifiers. Load resistance can significantly affect the voltage gain of these amplifiers.

4. The output impedance of the 741 op-amp is close to 75 Ω. This explains why the signal began to distort at a load value of 90 Ω. As the load approaches the output impedance of the amplifier's output impedance, the voltage division between the two is such that the amplifier cannot produce enough voltage swing to maintain the 5 V_{PP} output. It begins to clip.

SIMULATION EXERCISE

Fault 22-1: Open op-amp input (pin 2)

Symptoms:	The input is unaffected, but there is no output signal.
Analysis:	With inverting input open, the input signal never reaches the op-amp. Therefore, there can be no output.

Fault 22-2: Open op-amp input (pin 3)

Symptoms:	The input is unaffected, but there is no output signal.
Analysis:	As stated in the introduction to the exercise, if either inputs of the op-amp are left open, it will not work.

Fault 22-3: Open feedback resistor (R_f)

Symptoms:	The input is unaffected, but the output is a square-wave with a peak-to-peak value of approximately 22 V. The two waveforms are 180° out of phase.
Analysis:	The open feedback resistor means that the gain of the circuit is now the open loop gain of the op-amp. This is why the output is driven into clipping.

Fault 22-4: Shorted feedback resistor (R_f)

Symptoms:	The input is unaffected, but there is no output signal.
Analysis:	Since $A_v = R_f/R_i$ if $R_f = 0\ \Omega$, the gain of the circuit is zero and the output is also zero.

Fault 22-5: Shorted input resistor (R_{in})

Symptoms:	The input is unaffected, but the output is a square-wave with a peak-to-peak value of approximately 22 V. The two waveforms are 180° out of phase.
Analysis:	Since $A_v = R_f/R_i$ if $R_i = 0\ \Omega$, the gain of the circuit is infinite and the output is driven into clipping.

Fault 22-6: Open input resistor (R_{in})

Symptoms:	The input is unaffected, but there is no output signal.
Analysis:	The open input resistor blocks the input signal from reaching the inverting input. This is why there is no output signal.

Exercise 23

Noninverting Amplifiers

Part 1: Noninverting Amplifier Characteristics

Step 1 $A_{CL} = \dfrac{R_f}{R_i} + 1 = 2$

Step 3 $v_{in} = 1 \text{ V}_{PP}$ $v_{out} = 2 \text{ V}_{PP}$

Figure 23.2 The grid should contain two sinusoidal waveforms that are in phase.

Step 4 $A_{CL} = \dfrac{v_{out}}{v_{in}} = 2$

Table 23.1 Voltage Measurements and Calculations

R_f (kΩ)	v_{in}	v_{out}	A_{CL} (Calculated)	A_{CL} (Measured)
27	1 V$_{PP}$	3.7 V$_{PP}$	3.7	3.7
39	1 V$_{PP}$	4.9 V$_{PP}$	4.9	4.9
47	1 V$_{PP}$	5.7 V$_{PP}$	5.7	5.7
82	1 V$_{PP}$	9.2 V$_{PP}$	9.2	9.2

Step 6 $f_{max} \cong 50 \text{ kHz at } R_L = 27 \text{ k}\Omega$

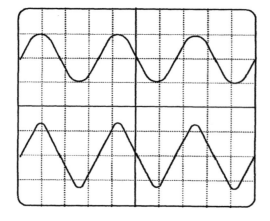

The output magnitude is approximately 3.44 V$_{PP}$.

Figure 23.3a

Step 7 $f_{\text{max}} \cong 35$ kHz at $R_L = 47$ kΩ (*Note*: as this is a subjective evaluation, student responses to Steps 6 and 7 may vary.)

The waveforms in Figure 23.3b should be similar to Figure 23.3a.

Part 2: The Voltage Follower

Step 9 $v_{in} = 1$ V$_{\text{pp}}$ $v_{out} = 1$ V$_{\text{pp}}$

$A_{CL} = 1$ $P_L = 1.25$ mW

Step 10 $P_L = 10.3$ μW

QUESTIONS & PROBLEMS

1. In all cases the calculated and measured values of A_{CL} agreed.

2. Since $v_{out} = 1.85$ V$_{\text{pk}}$

$$f_{\text{max}} = \frac{0.5V/\mu s}{2\pi(1.85V)} = 43.02 \, kHz \, .$$

   The difference between the measured and calculated values can be explained in a number of ways. First of all, the point at which the output starts to distort is a subjective evaluation. Secondly, the 0.5 V/μs slew rate is a typical value.

3. As the value of R_f increased, the cutoff frequency decreased. As R_f increases so does the gain of the amplifier. The increase in gain means that the output voltage also increases. Since f_{max} is inversely proportional to the peak output voltage, the upper cutoff frequency of the amplifier must decrease as voltage gain increases.

4. The op-amp buffer increased load power by more than 120 times. This illustrates the effectiveness of the circuit.

SIMULATION EXERCISE

Fault 23-1: Open op-amp input (pin 2)

Symptoms:	The input is unaffected, but there is no output signal.
Analysis:	As we learned in Exercise 39, an op-amp will not work if either of the two inputs is left open.

Fault 23-2: Open op-amp input (pin 3)

Symptoms:	The input is unaffected, but there is no output signal.
Analysis:	With noninverting input open, the input signal never reaches the op-amp. Therefore, there can be no output.

Fault 23-3: Open feedback resistor (R_f)

Symptoms:	The input is unaffected, but the output is a square-wave with a peak-to-peak value of approximately 22 V. The two waveforms are in phase.
Analysis:	The open feedback resistor means that the gain of the circuit is now the open loop gain of the op-amp. This is why the output is driven into clipping.

Fault 23-4: Shorted feedback resistor (R_f)

Symptoms:	The input is unaffected, but the output signal, has dropped to 1 V$_{PP}$.
Analysis:	Since $A_{CL} = \dfrac{R_f}{R_i} + 1$, if $R_f = 0 \ \Omega$, the gain of the circuit is 1 and the output is 1 V$_{PP}$.

Fault 23-5: Open input resistor (R_{in})

Symptoms:	The input is unaffected, but the output signal, has dropped to 1 V_{PP}.
Analysis:	Since $A_{CL} = \dfrac{R_f}{R_{in}} + 1$, if $R_{in} \cong$ infinity, the gain of the circuit is 1 and the output is 1 V_{PP}.

Fault 23-6: Shorted input resistor (R_{in})

Symptoms:	The input is unaffected, but the output is a square-wave with a peak-to-peak value of approximately 22 V. The two waveforms are 180° out of phase.
Analysis:	Since $A_{CL} = \dfrac{R_f}{R_{in}} + 1$, if R_f is 0 Ω, the gain of the circuit is infinite. This is why the output is clipped.

Exercise 24

Comparators and Summing Amplifiers

Part 1: Comparators

Step 3 V_{out} changes state when $V_{in} = 1.1$ V.

Figure 24.2a

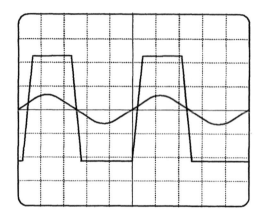

Step 5 V_{out} changes state when $V_{in} = -1.1$ V.

Figure 24.2b

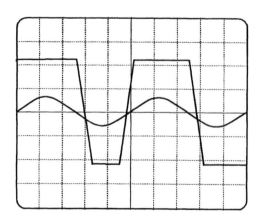

Part 2: Summing Amplifiers

Step 7 $v_{out} = 4\ V_{PP}$

Step 8 $v_{out} = 2.9\ V_{PP}$

Step 9 $v_{out} = 8.8\ V_{PP}$

QUESTIONS & PROBLEMS

1. $V_{ref} = +V\ \dfrac{R_2}{R_1 + R_2} = 1.09\ V.$

   This is very close to the measured value of 1.1 V.

2. For the circuit in Figure 24.1a, a positive dc voltage of 1.09 V is applied to the inverting input, while a 2.5 V peak sine wave is applied to the noninverting input. This means that so long as the voltage at the noninverting input is more negative than +1.09 V, the output stays low. As soon as the sine wave goes more positive than 1.09 V, the output is driven high. For Figure 24.1b, the opposite is true. Since a negative dc voltage is applied to the inverting input, the output remain high so long as the sine inverting input is more positive than −1.09 V.

3. Increasing R_1 means that the overall output decreases. The reason is found in the formula used to determine the output of this two-input summing amplifier:

   $$V_{out} = -R_f\left(\frac{V_1}{R_1} + \frac{V_2}{R_2}\right).$$

   Thus, if R_1 is increased, the overall output from the summing amplifier decreases.

4. Increasing R_f increases the gain of the summing amplifier. This means that the output is increased in *magnitude*, but it still represents a voltage that is *proportional* to the sum of the two inputs.

SIMULATION EXERCISE

Fault 24-1: Open R_1 (Circuit 24.1a)

Symptoms:	The inverting input reads approximately 0 V. The input signal is not affected. The output waveform is a square wave that is in phase with the sine wave input at the noninverting terminal. The amplitude is ± 11.1 V.
Analysis:	Since R_1 is open, the inverting input is tied to ground via R_2. The sine wave input is applied to the noninverting input, so all that is needed to drive the output either positive or negative is a very small (μVs) differential voltage between the two inputs. When the noninverting input starts to go positive, the output goes positive. It stays in that state until the sine wave starts to go negative. When the input differential is just slightly negative (remember, the inverting input is tied to ground) the output also goes negative.

Fault 24-2: Open R_2 (Circuit 24.1a)

Symptoms:	The noninverting input reads approximately 12 V_{dc}. The input sine wave is unaffected. The output is a constant dc value of -11.1 V.
Analysis:	With R_2 open, the inverting input is tied to the +12 V supply. Since the input signal is only 2.5 V peak, the output will always stay negative.

Fault 24-3: Shorted resistor (R_1) (Circuit 24.1b)

Symptoms:	The voltage at the inverting input reads -12 V. The input signal at the noninverting input is unaffected. The output is a constant dc value of $+11.1$ V.
Analysis:	With R_1 shorted, the full -12 V is across R_2, which means that this is the voltage at the inverting input. This causes the output to stay positive.

Fault 24-4: Open resistor (R_2) (circuit 24.1b)

Symptoms:	The voltage at the inverting input reads −12 V. The input signal at the noninverting input is unaffected. The output is a constant dc value of +11.1V.
Analysis:	With R_2 open, the full −12 V is connected to the inverting input. This causes the output to stay positive.

Fault 24-5: Open feedback resistor (R_f) in the summing amplifier

Symptoms:	The input signal is unaffected. The output is a square wave 180° out of phase with the input with a peak value of 11.1 V.
Analysis:	With the feedback resistor open, the amplifier now has no feedback and its gain will be its open-loop gain. This means that with the slightest differential voltage at its inputs it will be driven to either its positive or negative maximum output voltages. It is still an inverting amplifier, (input applied to the inverting input) so the two waveforms are 180° out of phase.

Fault 24-6: Open input resistor (R_1) in the summing amplifier

Symptoms:	The input waveform is not affected. The output is identical to the input but is 180° out of phase. It has an amplitude of 2 V_{PP}.
Analysis:	With R_1 open, the amplifier has only one input. It is now simply an inverting amplifier with a gain of 1 (unity).

Exercise 25

Integrators and Differentiators

Part 1: Integrators

Step 2   The input square wave and the output ramp (triangle waveform) are 180° out of phase. In other words, when the input square wave goes positive, the output triangle wave goes negative.

$V_{out} = 606$ mV$_{PP}$

Step 3 $V_{out} = 315$ mV$_{PP}$

Step 4 $V_{out} = 1.2$ V$_{PP}$

Part 2: Differentiators

Step 5   The input ramp (triangle waveform) is 180° out of phase with the output square wave. In other words, when the input triangle wave goes positive, the output rectangle wave goes negative.

$V_{out} = 8$ V$_{PP}$

Step 6 $V_{out} = 16.2$ V$_{PP}$

Step 7 $V_{out} = 4$ V$_{PP}$

QUESTIONS & PROBLEMS

1. The input is a square wave and the output is a ramp (triangle waveform). This is because the output signal of an integrator is proportional to the area of the input signal. Since the input is a square wave, as long as it is high, the magnitude of the output continues to increase at a constant rate (ramp higher). As soon as the input

goes low, the output amplitude continues to decrease at a constant rate (ramp lower). But, the two waveforms are 180° out of phase. This is because the op-amp is wired as an inverting amplifier (the input is applied to the inverting input of the op-amp.)

2. Students may come up with several possible answers to this question, but the simplest is to connect a unity gain inverting amplifier to the output of the circuit.

3. The output signal decreased in amplitude as the frequency increased. It increased as input frequency decreased. This is because the output signal of an integrator is proportional to the area of the input signal. At higher frequencies, the input stays in a given state for a shorter period of time, thus, the area of the square wave is smaller. The opposite is true when frequency decreases.

4. The output of the differentiator is a function of the *rate of change* of the input. This means that so long as the input ramp (triangle wave) continues to increase in amplitude at a constant rate of change, the output of the differentiator will remain at whatever output voltage this rate of change produces for the differentiators gain. The reason that output amplitude increases as frequency increases is because, assuming a constant input amplitude, the rate of change of the input (the slope of the ramp) increases as frequency increases. An increase in rate of change produces an increase in output signal amplitude. The opposite is true when frequency decreases.

SIMULATION EXERCISE

Part 1: Integrators Fault Simulations

Fault 25-1: Open Input Resistor R_1

Symptoms:	There was no output signal. The input was unaffected.
Analysis:	By opening R_1, the input cannot reach the inverting input of the op-amp, so the output must be 0.

Fault 25-2: Shorted Feedback Resistor R_f

Symptoms:	There is no output signal. The input is unaffected.
Analysis:	With R_f shorted, the gain of the circuit becomes zero, so there is no output.

Fault 25-3: Short Input Resistor R_1

Symptoms:	Input is unchanged, however the output is a square wave that has the same amplitude and phase as the input.
Analysis:	By shorting R_1 this effectively bypasses the op-amp. The feedback capacitor has an almost instantaneous charge time, so the output follows the input.

Fault 25-4: Open Feedback Capacitor C_f

Symptoms:	Input is unchanged, however the output increases to $10V_{PP}$.
Analysis:	With C_f open, this is simply an inverting amplifier, with a gain of 10.

Part 2: Differentiators Fault Simulations

Fault 25-5: Open Feedback Resistor (R_f)

Symptoms:	The input is unaffected. The output is a rectangular waveform of 18.2 V_{PP}.
Analysis:	With R_f open, the gain of the differentiator has increased to its open loop gain and the output is driven to the supply rails.

Fault 25-6: Open Input Capacitor (C_1)

Symptoms:	Input is unchanged. There is no output signal.
Analysis:	With C_1 open, there is no path for the input signal. It is blocked from reaching the inverting input of the op-amp.

Fault 25-7: Short Feedback Resistor (R_f)

Symptoms:	The input is unaffected. There is no appreciable output signal.
Analysis:	With R_f shorted, gain for the circuit (R_f/R_i) is $0\Omega/220\Omega = 0$. This is why there is no output.

Fault 25-8: Shorted Input Capacitor (C_1)

Symptoms:	Output is a clipped triangular waveform. Input is unchanged.
Analysis:	With C_1 shorted, this is simply an inverting amplifier, with a gain of 45.5. With an input of 1 V_{PP} this explains why the output is clipped.

Exercise 26

Low-Pass and High-Pass Active Filters

Step 1 $f_C = \dfrac{1}{2\pi RC} = 1.06 \text{ kHz}$

Table 26.1 Voltage and Gain Values for the Circuit in Figure 26.1

f_{in}	v_{in}	v_{out}	A_{CL}	$A_{CL(dB)}$
$\frac{1}{4}f_C$	1 V	970 mV	0.97	−0.26 dB
f_C	1 V	700 mV	0.7	−3.1 dB
$2f_C$	1 V	445 mV	0.445	−7.03 dB
$4f_C$	1 V	235 mV	0.235	−12.6 dB

Step 6 $f_C = \dfrac{1}{2\pi\sqrt{R_1 R_2 C_1 C_2}} = 715 \text{ Hz.}$

Table 26.2 Voltage and Gain Values for the Circuit in Figure 26.2

f_{in}	v_{in}	v_{out}	A_{CL}	$A_{CL(dB)}$
$\frac{1}{4}f_C$	1 V	1 V	1	0 dB
f_C	1 V	740 mV	0.74	−2.6 dB
$2f_C$	1 V	240 mV	0.24	−12.4 dB
$4f_C$	1 V	62 mV	0.06	−24.1 dB

Step 8 $f_C = 1.06 \text{ kHz}$

Table 26.3 Voltages and Gains for the Circuit in Figure 26.3a

f_{in}	v_{in}	v_{out}	A_{CL}	$A_{CL(dB)}$
$4f_C$	1 V	965 mV	0.965	−0.31 dB
f_C	1 V	720 mV	0.72	−2.85 dB
$\frac{1}{2}f_C$	1 V	455 mV	0.455	−6.84 dB
$\frac{1}{4}f_C$	1 V	245 mV	0.245	−12.2 dB

Step 13 $f_C = 1.07$ kHz

Table 26.4 Voltages and Gains for the Circuit in Figure 26.3b.

f_{in}	v_{in}	v_{out}	A_{CL}	$A_{CL(dB)}$
$4f_C$	1 V	1 V	1	0 dB
f_C	1 V	740 mV	0.74	−2.6 dB
$\frac{1}{2} f_C$	1 V	250 mV	0.25	−12.04 dB
$\frac{1}{4} f_C$	1 V	62 mV	0.062	−24.2 dB

QUESTIONS & PROBLEMS

1. a. The two values were very close. The most likely source of variations would be component tolerances. At these low frequencies, stray reactances should be minimal.

    b. The two-stage filter had the greatest variations. This is as expected as there are more components and it is component tolerance that will introduce the variations.

2 - 3.   In all cases the calculation should be made at 2 times to 4 times f_C for the low-pass filter or ½ to ¼ f_C for the high-pass filter. Using these values we get the following:

Single-pole LPF: $\Delta A_{v(dB)} = -12.6$ dB $- (-7.03$ dB$) = -5.57$ dB/octave
Two-pole LPF: $\Delta A_{v(dB)} = -24.1$ dB $- (-12.4$ dB$) = -11.7$ dB/octave

Single-pole HPF: $\Delta A_{v(dB)} = -12.2$ dB $- (-6.84$ dB$) = -5.36$ dB/octave
Two-pole HPF: $\Delta A_{v(dB)} = -24.1$ dB $- (-12.4$ dB$) = -11.7$ dB/octave

All of the roll-off rates were close to expected values.

SIMULATION EXERCISE

Fault 26-1: R_1 out of tolerance (1.5 kΩ in Figure 26.1)

Symptoms:	The cutoff frequency increased by a factor of 10, but the rolloff rate was unchanged.
Analysis:	Since $f_c = \dfrac{1}{2\pi RC}$, decreasing R_1 by a factor of 10 increases the cutoff frequency by the same factor.

Fault 26-2: Open Filter Capacitor (C_1 in Figure 26.1)

Symptoms:	No filter action at all.
Analysis:	With C_1 open, this is simply a non-inverting amplifier.

Fault 26-3: Shorted Filter Resistor (R_2 in Figure 26.2)

Symptoms:	f_C increased while the roll-off rate decreased.
Analysis:	By shorting R_2 this effectively produces a single pole filter. This is why the roll-off rate decreased.

Fault 26-4: Open Filter Capacitor (C_2 in Figure 26.2)

Symptoms:	The cutoff frequency decreased as did the roll-off rate.
Analysis:	With C_2 open, this also produces a single-pole filter. This is why the roll-off rate decreased.

Fault 26-5: Shorted Filter Capacitor (C_1 in Figure 26.3a)

Symptoms:	No filter action at all.
Analysis:	With C_1 shorted, this is simply a non-inverting amplifier.

Fault 26-6: Open Filter Resistor (R_1 in Figure 26.3a)

Symptoms:	No output.
Analysis:	With R_1 open, there is no current path for the input signal.

Fault 26-7: Open Filter Capacitor (C_1 in Figure 26.3b)

Symptoms:	No output.
Analysis:	With C_1 open, there is no current path for the input signal.

Fault 26-8: Shorted Filter Capacitor (C_2 in Figure 26.3b)

Symptoms:	The cutoff frequency decreased to approximately 720 Hz. and the roll off rate decreased.
Analysis:	With C_2 shorted, this effectively becomes a single-pole filter. Note that the cutoff frequency is lower than in Figure 26.3a since both R_1 and R_2 must be taken into account.

Exercise 27

The Multiple-Feedback Bandpass Filter

Step 1
$$f_0 = \frac{1}{2\pi\sqrt{(R_1 \| R_2)R_f C_1 C_2}} = 12.44 \text{ kHz}$$

$$Q = \pi f_0 R_f C = 7.03 \qquad \text{(where } C = \sqrt{C_1 C_2}\text{)}$$

Step 2
$$\text{BW} = \frac{f_0}{Q} = 1.78 \text{ kHz}$$

$f_{C1} = 11.55$ kHz $\qquad\qquad\qquad f_{C2} = 13.33$ kHz

Step 5 $\quad f_{C1} = 10.55$ kHz $\qquad\qquad\qquad f_{C2} = 12.15$ kHz

Step 6 $\quad f_0 = \sqrt{f_{C1}f_{C2}} = 11.32$ kHz $\quad$ BW $= f_{C2} - f_{C1} = 1.6$ kHz

Step 7 $\quad Q = \dfrac{f_0}{\text{BW}} = 7.08$

Step 8 $\quad f_{C1} = 10.55$ kHz $\qquad f_{C2} = 12.15$ kHz $\qquad$ BW $= f_{C2} - f_{C1} = 1.6$ kHz

QUESTIONS & PROBLEMS

1. Theoretical values should be close to the calculated values, but expect variations from student to student. Discrepancies could be due to: component tolerance, stray reactances, instrument tolerance, or a student's inability to interpret instrument values accurately.

2. If R_f was increased from 180kΩ to 220 kΩ, the gain of the circuit would increase from $A_v = 9$ to $A_v = 11$. Then f_0 would decrease since it is inversely related to R_f. The bandwidth would decrease since Q is directly related to R_f. If Q increases, then BW decreases.

3. Driving the circuit with a high-impedance source would have very little effect on the value of f_0. The reason is that the resistive value used in the calculation of f_0 is $R_1 \| R_2$. Increasing the effective value of R_2 (R_2 is in series with the source resistance) would have little effect as R_1 is the dominant value in the parallel

network (it is much smaller). Therefore, the change in the value of $R_1 \| R_2$ would be negligible.

4. Connecting the load should have very little effect on the BW. This illustrates that this filter has good stability.

SIMULATION EXERCISE

Step 3 $f_0 = 1.66$ kHz. $A_{CL} = 13.97$ dB

Step 4 $f_{C1} = 1.51$ kHz. $f_{C2} = 1.82$ kHz.

Step 5 $BW = f_{C2} - f_{C1} = 310$ Hz.

Step 6 $f_0 = \sqrt{f_{C1}f_{C2}} = 1.67$ kHz

Step 7 $Q = \dfrac{f_0}{BW} = 5.39$

Step 8   The values are the same for the 1 kΩ load as for the 10 kΩ load. This, once again, shows the stability of this filter.

Questions:

1. The calculated and measured values were equal.
2. There was no measurable change in circuit performance for the lower value load.

Exercise 28

The Discrete Tuned Amplifier

Step 1 $\qquad f_0 = \dfrac{1}{2\pi\sqrt{L_1 C_1}} = 112.54 \text{ kHz}$

Step 2 $\qquad V_E = 1.98 \text{ V} \qquad V_{CE} = 13.01 \text{ V}$

Step 4 $\qquad f_0 = 111 \text{ kHz}$

Step 5 $\qquad v_{in} = 20 \text{ mV}_{PP} \qquad\qquad v_{out} = 27.1 \text{ V}_{PP} \qquad\qquad A_v = 1355$

Step 6 $\qquad f_{C1} = 108.2 \text{ kHz} \qquad\quad f_{C2} = 113.9 \text{ kHz}$

Step 7 $\qquad \text{BW} = f_{C2} - f_{C1} = 5.7 \text{ kHz}$

Step 8 $\qquad Q = \dfrac{f_0}{\text{BW}} = 19.5$

Step 9 $\qquad f_0 = 111 \text{ kHz} \qquad\qquad\qquad A_v = 1000$

$\qquad\qquad\quad f_{C1} = 105.8 \text{ kHz} \qquad\qquad\qquad f_{C2} = 117.2 \text{ kHz}$

Step 10. $\qquad \text{BW} = f_{C2} - f_{C1} = 11.4 \text{ kHz} \qquad Q_L = \dfrac{f_0}{\text{BW}} = 9.74$

> **Note**: It is very likely that student results will vary significantly from these solutions, and from student to student. The reason is simply that these solutions are the result of simulations and do not take into account the loading effect of the test equipment, and most especially, stray reactances. Component tolerance, especially the capacitors, will also have a significant effect.

QUESTIONS & PROBLEMS

1. There is very little difference between the measured and calculated values in these results, but you should expect significant variations from the students.

2. These results show a decrease in Q and a resulting increase in bandwidth. Since the load is in parallel with the tank circuit, this parallel resistance will decrease the Q of the circuit. The lower the value of R_L, the lower the Q of the circuit and the wider the bandwidth. The student should be directed to Section 17.6.4 of the text for information on loaded-Q.

3. Adding the load also decreased the gain of the circuit. This is because the impedance of the tank circuit is in parallel with the load. The load therefore lowered the overall impedance of the total ac collector circuit. As in any CE amplifier, the gain of the amplifier is the total ac collector impedance divided by the total ac emitter impedance.

4. No, such a circuit could not be built due to the gain-bandwidth limitation of the op-amp.

SIMULATION EXERCISE

Fault 28-1: Open Load Resistor R_L

Symptoms:	The amplitude of the output signal increases causing a slight clipping. Bandwidth has decreased.
Analysis:	An open load is the same as dramatically increasing the value of R_L. This means that the Q of the circuit will increase, the gain will increase, and the BW will decrease.

Fault 28-2: Changed value of Load ($R_L = 2k\Omega$)

Symptoms:	The amplitude of the output signal has decreased. Bandwidth has increased.
Analysis:	This is simply the opposite of Fault 28-1. The Q of the circuit has decreased due to the lower value of R_L.

Fault 28-3: Shorted Emitter Resistor R_E

Symptoms:	f_0 remains approximately the same. The gain has increased, but the output shows some signs of distortion.
Analysis:	With R_E shorted the ac emitter impedance is lowered and the circuit gain has increased.

Fault 28-4: Open Inductor L_T

Symptoms:	The output signal at f_0 has dropped to about 1.5 mV$_{PP}$.
Analysis:	With the inductor open, the ac collector impedance is now the reactance of the 2 nF capacitor in parallel with the load. As input frequency decreases, the circuit gain will increase as the capacitor's reactance increases.

Fault 28-5: Open Coupling Capacitor C_{C1}

Symptoms:	There is no output signal
Analysis:	With C_{C1} open, the amplifier has no input to the base of the transistor, and therefore, no output.

Fault 28-6: Shorted Capacitor C_T

Symptoms:	There is no output signal
Analysis:	With C_T shorted, this essentially removes both the capacitor and inductor from the circuit, meaning that the ac collector impedance is close to 0 Ω. As stated earlier, the gain of the circuit is found from the total ac collector impedance divided by the total ac emitter impedance. If the collector impedance is zero, the output will be zero as well.

Exercise 29

The Class C Amplifier

Step 1 $f_0 = \dfrac{1}{2\pi\sqrt{L_1 C_1}} = 50.33 \text{ kHz}$

Step 2 $V_E = 0.0 \text{ V}$ $V_B = -1 \text{ V}$ $V_C = 15 \text{ V}$

Step 4 $f_0 = 50.25 \text{ kHz}$

Step 5 $v_{in} = 3.6 \text{ V}_{PP}$ $v_{out} = 32.3 \text{ V}_{PP}$ $A_v = 8.97$

Step 7 $V_{in\,(positive)} = 800 \text{ mV}$

Step 8 The input waveform is centered 1 volt below the center of the grid.

Step 10 $f_{in} = 25.125 \text{ kHz}$ $f_{out} = 50.5 \text{ kHz}$

Step 11 The waveforms will appear as sine waves. The input frequency should be approximately half the output frequency. The output waveform may appear slightly distorted.

QUESTIONS & PROBLEMS

1. There is very little difference between the measured and calculated values, expect much larger variations from student results. Component tolerance, stray reactances, and measurement error will be the main causes.
2. The output signal is 180° out of phase with the input signal. This is because this is a common emitter amplifier, and like any CE amplifier, it has a 180° phase difference between its input and output signals.
3. Assuming 700 mV is used simply to turn the BE junction fully on, this means that only the most positive 100 mV of the input signal is actually being used to drive the transistor during full conduction. This represents about 10% of the input waveform; obviously, a very efficient amplifier.
4. The input frequency is half the output frequency. The tank circuit is tuned to its first harmonic. When tuned to a harmonic of its resonant frequency, the circuit can function as a frequency multiplier.

Fault 29-1: Open Load Resistor (R_L)

Symptoms:	There is little if any change in the output signal, either in amplitude, or frequency.
Analysis:	Since the load was already a fairly high value resistor, opening the load had very little effect. The bandwidth of the circuit should narrow slightly as well, since the Q of the circuit should increase slightly.

Fault 29-2: Change value of Load (R_L = 22 kΩ)

Symptoms:	The amplitude of the output signal has decreased slightly.
Analysis:	The change in load decreases the gain of the circuit slightly, and should widen the bandwidth, since the Q of the circuit would decrease.

Fault 29-3: Shorted Base Resistor (R_B)

Symptoms:	The input signal is unaffected, but there is no output signal.
Analysis:	With the base resistor shorted, there can be no ac voltage at the base of the transistor. This explains why there is no input signal.

Fault 29-4: Open Inductor (L_T)

Symptoms:	The input signal is unaffected. $V_B = -1.16$ V, $V_{CE} = 1.607$ V, and at 50 kHz, the output is distorted. The output consists of 28 mV spikes that occur at the rate of 50kHz.
Analysis:	With the inductor open, the amplifier is no longer discretely tuned. If you sweep the amplifier with the bode plotter, from 1 kHz to 500 kHz, you will see that the gain never varies from -71 dB.

Fault 29-5: Open Coupling Capacitor (C_{C1})

Symptoms:	The input waveform is not affected, but there is no output.
Analysis:	With C_{C1} open, the amplifier has no input to the base of the transistor.

Fault 29-6: Shorted Capacitor (C_T)

Symptoms:	The input waveform is not affected, but there is no output.
Analysis:	With C_T shorted, the ac impedance of the collector circuit is approximately zero. This means that the gain of the amplifier is also zero, explaining why there is no output signal.

Exercise 30

Wien-Bridge and Colpitts Oscillators

Part 1: The Wien-bridge Oscillator

Step 2 $f_{out} = 1.05$ kHz

Step 3   When R_4 was decreased, the amplitude of the output decreased, and eventually became distorted. When R_4 was increased, the output increased and eventually was clipped.

Step 4   Removing the diodes caused the output to clip.

Step 5   Varying R_4 with the diodes removed changes the level of clipping.

Part 2: The Colpitts Oscillator

Step 6 $C_T = \dfrac{C_1 C_2}{C_1 + C_2} = 99.55$ pF $f_{out} = \dfrac{1}{2\pi\sqrt{LC_T}} = 504$ kHz

Step 8 $f_{out} = 535$ kHz

Step 9 $f_{out} = 770$ kHz.

QUESTIONS & PROBLEMS

1. $f_{out} = \dfrac{1}{2\pi RC} = 1.06$ kHz

   This is very close to the measured value. It should be noted however, that student results may vary significantly.

2. The negative feedback path controls the gain of the circuit. The results from Step 3 show that when the value of the feedback resistor (R_4) was increased, the gain of

the circuit also increased. When R_4 was decreased, the output decreased.

3. The diodes limit the output swing of the circuit and thus prevent the output from clipping.

4. Yes, there was a discrepancy, especially at the higher frequency. This can be attributed to an accumulation of component tolerances, stray reactance, and loading from the scope. The reason that the higher frequency circuit is most affected is because the 51 pF capacitor is a lower value and therefore, stray capacitance and scope lead capacitance will represent a much greater percentage of the total circuit capacitance.

5. It is inversely related. As capacitance decreased, the output frequency increased. This is evident from the equation for solving for the oscillator frequency:

$$f_{out} = \frac{1}{2\pi\sqrt{LC_T}}$$

SIMULATION EXERCISE

Step 1 f_{out} = 1.05 kHz

Step 2 The oscillation action of the circuit slowly died out after four or five passes of the trace.

Step 3 f_{out} = 1.57 kHz

Step 4 f_{out} = 478 Hz

Questions

1. Because the oscillation slowly dies out, we can assume that the attenuation factor is too high. As each oscillation cycle occurs, the attenuation is higher than the gain of the circuit, and eventually the oscillation action ceases. This type of action is called damping.

2. Output frequency is inversely related to resistance in the positive feedback path.

3. Output frequency is inversely related to capacitance in the positive feedback path.

Exercise 31

BJT Switching Circuits

Figure 31.2   The display should show two rectangular waveforms that are 180° out of phase.

Step 3 $t_d = 40$ ns $t_r = 35$ ns

Step 4 $t_s = 120$ ns $t_f = 40$ ns

Step 5 $t_d = 15$ ns $t_r = 35$ ns
              $t_s = 20$ ns $t_f = 40$ ns

Step 6   This is a subjective measurement that has no set answer. However, the response should be between 100 kHz and 150 kHz..

Step 7   This is a subjective measurement that has no set answer. However, the response should be close to the answer to Step 6.

QUESTIONS & PROBLEMS

1. Storage time was by far the longest delay. This is consistent with the information in Section 19.2.2 of the text.

2. % of change in $t_d = 62.5\%$
   % of change in $t_r = 0\%$
   % of change in $t_s = 83.3\%$
   % of change in $t_f = 0\%$

   These results are consistent with the information in Section 19.2.3 of the text.

3. The reason is that the input is applied to the base of the transistor and the output is taken from the collector. As we saw in the CE amplifier, when this is the case, there is a 180° phase relationship between input and output waveforms.

4. The speedup capacitor improves the transistor switching time, but has no significant effect on the maximum circuit operating frequency.

175

SIMULATION EXERCISE

Step 1 $t_d = 340$ ns $t_r = 175$ ns

               $t_s = 25.5$ ns $t_f = 170$ ns

Step 2 $f_{max} = \dfrac{0.35}{100t_r} = 20$ kHz

Step 3 $t_d = 12.5$ ns $t_r = 7.8$ ns

               $t_s = 6.3$ ns $t_f = 11.4$ ns

Step 4 $f_{max} = \dfrac{0.35}{100t_r} = 449$ kHz

QUESTIONS

1. The 2SC2001 transistor has a lower f_{C2} than the 2N3904.

2. The BFS17 transistor has a higher f_{C2} than the 2N3904.

Exercise 32

Op-Amp Schmitt Triggers

Part 1: Symmetrical Trigger Points

Step 1 $UTP = (+V - 1\ V) \times 0.091 = 8.2\ V$

$LTP = (-V + 1\ V) \times 0.091 = -8.2\ V$

Figure 32.2 There should be two waveforms drawn, one sinusoidal and one rectangular. They appear to be approximately 180° out of phase. The output (rectangular) waveform is changing states when the sine wave reaches levels of ±800 mV.

Step 4 $UTP = 800\ mV$ $LTP = -800\ mV$

Step 5 $V = 830\ mV_{PP}$

Part 2: Asymmetrical Trigger Points

Step 6 $UTP = (+V - 1.7\ V) \times 0.33 = 2.77\ V$

$LTP = (-V + 1.7\ V) \times 0.25 = -2.08\ V$

Figure 32.5a There should be two waveforms drawn, one sinusoidal and one rectangular, that appear to be approximately 180° out of phase. The output (rectangular) waveform is changing states at approximately +3 V and −2 V.

Step 8 $UTP = 2.8\ V$ $LTP = -2.1\ V$

Figure 32.5b These waveforms should be similar to those in Figure 32.5a. However, the output (rectangular) waveform is now switching states at approximately 1 V and −2 V

Step 10 $UTP = 900\ mV$ $LTP = -2.1\ V$

1. The measured values were very close to the calculated values. There should be no significant variation other than that introduced by component tolerances.

2. The output stopped changing state because the input voltage never reached the trigger points of the circuit.

3. Again, the measured and calculated values were very close.

4. The upper trigger point was affected. This is because of the polarity of diode D_1. The diode only allows conduction when the output of the op-amp is positive. This is why D_1 and R_1 determine the UTP. When D_1 is conducting, a positive reference voltage is established.

SIMULATION EXERCISE

Fault 32-1: Open R_1 (Symmetrical Schmitt Trigger)

Symptoms:	The Schmitt trigger changes state as soon as the input crosses the zero axis.
Analysis:	With R_1 open, the voltage at the noninverting input is tied to ground via R_2. Thus, as soon as the inverting input goes either slightly positive of negative, the output changes state.

Fault 32-2: Shorted R_1 (Symmetrical Schmitt Trigger)

Symptoms:	The output stays negative, regardless of the input level.
Analysis:	With R_1 shorted, the voltage at the noninverting input is at whatever initial value the output goes to. Since the simulator always starts with a positive going input sine wave, the output initially goes negative. Since the input amplitude is only ± 2.5 V, it is never enough to change this initial output state.

Fault 32-3: Open R_2 (Symmetrical Schmitt Trigger)

Symptoms:	The output stays negative, regardless of the input level.
Analysis:	This condition is very similar to that discussed in Fault 2. Once again, the reference voltage is determined by the initial state of the output.

Fault 32-4: Shorted R_2 (Symmetrical Schmitt Trigger)

Symptoms:	The Schmitt trigger changes state as soon as the input crosses the zero axis.
Analysis:	This condition is similar to that in Fault 1. Since R_2 is shorted, the reference voltage is zero, so the output changes state as soon as the input does.

Fault 32-5: Open D_1 (Asymmetrical Schmitt Trigger)

Symptoms:	The LTP is unaffected, but the UPT is close to 0 V.
Analysis:	With D_1 open, R_3 ties the noninverting input to ground. Thus as soon as the input goes even slightly positive, the output immediately goes negative. The LTP is unaffected since D_2 and R_2 determine this value.

Fault 32-6: Shorted D_1 (Asymmetrical Schmitt Trigger)

Symptoms:	The UTP = 2.9 V. The LPT = –4.0 V.
Analysis:	The UPT is easily calculated since with D_1 shorted, the voltage division between R_1 and R_3 determines the UPT. Determining the LPT is much more complex. Since D_1 is shorted, R_1 is conducting even when the output goes negative. This means that R_1 is in parallel with the combination of R_2 in series with a conducting D_2. This parallel combination, in conjunction with R_3, determines the LTP.

Fault32-7: Open R_3 (Asymmetrical Schmitt Trigger)

Symptoms:	The output stays negative regardless of the state of the input.
Analysis:	With R_3 open, the voltage at the noninverting input is whatever the initial state of the output is. As stated earlier, the simulator always starts with a positive going input signal. This drives the output negative. It stays in this state since the input voltage is never high enough change the output state.

Exercise 33

The 555 Timer

Part 1: The 555-Timer One-Shot

Step 1   PW = $1.1RC$ = 2.43 s

Step 2 V_T (pin 2) = 12 V V_{out} (pin 3) = 0 V

Step 3   PW = 2.5 seconds

Step 4   PW = 1.2 seconds

Step 5   PW = 5 seconds

Part 2: The 555-Timer Free-Running Multivibrator

Step 6 f_0 = 272 Hz   duty cycle = 81%

Figure 33.3a   The input is a sawtooth wave and the output is a rectangular wave. The measurements for the waveforms are listed in Step 8 (below).

Step 8 T = 3.7 ms   PW = 3 ms
              f_0 = 270 Hz   duty cycle = 81%

Step 9 T = 4.7 ms   PW = 4 ms
              f_0 = 213 Hz   duty cycle = 85%

Step 10 T = 1.5 ms   PW = 770 μs
              f_0 = 667 Hz   duty cycle = 51%

Figure 33.3b   These waveforms are similar to those shown in Figure 33.3a. However, the waveforms have the measured values shown in Step 12 (below).

Step 12 T = 850 μs   PW = 90 μs
              f_0 = 1.18 kHz   duty cycle = 11%

QUESTIONS & PROBLEMS

1. The calculated and measured values were close. Discrepancies would be primarily due to component tolerances, especially the capacitors.

2. Pulse duration is directly proportional to R and C. This can be seen from the equation: $PW = 1.1RC$.

3. When R_A was increased, f_0 decreased. The opposite was also true. This relationship can be seen from the equation for calculating output frequency:
$f_0 = \dfrac{1.44}{(R_A + 2R_B)C_1}$. Frequency is inversely related to R_A, R_B, and C_1.

4. When the capacitor is charging, R_B is effectively shorted by the conducting diode. When the threshold voltage is reached, pin 7 is shorted to ground and the capacitor is discharged via R_B. The diode does not conduct in this state since it is reverse biased by the capacitor. This means that in the charge path, there is only R_A and the forward biased diode. In the discharge path, there is only R_B. This is why the duty cycle can be less than 50%.

SIMULATION EXERCISE

Step 3 $R_2 = 4.9 \text{ k}\Omega$

Step 4 $R_2 = 4.9 \text{ k}\Omega$

Step 7 $V_{min} = 4.1$ V $f_0 = 1.38$ kHz
                $V_{max} = 8.0$ V $V_{out} = 12$ V$_{PP}$

Step 8 $V_{min} = 5.0$ V $f_0 = 1.38$ kHz
                $V_{max} = 10$ V $V_{out} = 15$ V$_{PP}$

Step 9 $V_{out} = 15$ V ($R_L = 100 \ \Omega$)
                $V_{out} = 15$ V ($R_L = 10 \ \Omega$)

QUESTIONS

1. The value of 4.9 kΩ is just slightly less than 1/3 of the total resistance in the voltage divider created by R_1 and R_2. Thus, it develops slightly less than 1/3 V_{CC}. If R_2 increases beyond this value, a valid trigger voltage cannot be produced. The

change in V_{CC} has no effect because the ratio of R_2 to $(R_1 + R_2)$ does not change as V_{CC} changes. The 555 timer still needs a trigger voltage that is less than 1/3 V_{CC}.

2. When V_{CC} increased, V_{min} and V_{max} increased because these values are determined from 1/3 V_{CC} and 2/3 V_{CC} respectively. V_{out} also increased since the output of the 555 timer is always equal to (or very close to) V_{CC}. The frequency of the output did not change because it is determined by the external passive component values and is not affected by changes in supply voltage.

3. The fact that the output did not change, even with a low value load, suggests that the output impedance of the 555 timer must be very low, or the output is well regulated.

Exercise 34

Silicon Controlled Rectifiers (SCRs)

Step 3 $I_{GT} = 220\ \mu\text{A}$ $V_{GT} = 850\ \text{mV}$

Step 4 No, the LED remains lit.

Step 5 $I_H \cong 5.5\ \text{mA}$

Figure 34.3 The output waveform should resemble the V_L waveform in Figure 20.15b of the text. The firing angle of the output waveform is approximately 75°.

Step 8 Firing angle = 15° (minimum)
Firing angle = 160° (maximum)

QUESTIONS & PROBLEMS

1. $I_{GT} = 200\ \mu\text{A}$ (rated)
   a. $V_{GT} = 800\ \text{mV}$ (rated)
   b. $I_H = 5\ \text{mA}$ (rated)
   c. The measured and rated values were very close.

2. The LED remained lit because the SCR had latched. Once the SCR is conducting, the only way to stop conduction is to drop I_F below I_H. Simply by decreasing I_{GT} or even making I_{GT} zero, the SCR will remain latched. It will remain in this state until I_F drops below I_H.

3. By varying the potentiometer (R_2), we control the amplitude of source voltage that is applied to the gate, and thus the gate current. Once there is enough gate current to trigger the SCR into conduction, it continues to pass the input signal until I_F drops below I_H. It then stops conducting until the input voltage is sufficient to generate enough I_{GT} to latch the SCR again.

4. C_1 is used to filter out any noise and prevent false triggering.

Exercise 35

Optoisolators

Step 2 $V_C = 5.8$ V $V_{RI} = 9.84$ V

   $I_C = 28$ mA $I_F = 12$ mA (IRD forward current)

Step 3   CRT $= I_C : I_F = 2.33$

Step 5   The input and output waveforms in Figure 35.2 are 180° out of phase.

Step 6 $f_{C1} = 4$ kHz $f_{C2} = 80$ kHz   BW $= 76$ kHz

QUESTIONS & PROBLEMS

1. The optoisolator configuration is similar to the CE amplifier (one of the most commonly used BJT amplifier configurations) that has a voltage phase shift of 180° between its input (base) and output (collector) terminals.

2. The greatest advantage of using an optoisolator is that the IRD and detector are electrically isolated from each other, yet signals can be readily coupled between the two. This makes it possible for low voltage and current source devices to control high voltage and current loads with complete isolation between the source and load circuits.

Exercise 36

IC Voltage Regulators

Step 2 $V_{OUT} = 1.25$ V to 29.2 V

Step 3 $V_{OUT} = 11.976$ V @ $V_{IN} = 15$ V

$V_{OUT} = 11.988$ V @ $V_{IN} = 25$ V

Step 4   Line regulation $= \dfrac{12\,\text{mV}}{10\text{V}} = 1.2\,\text{mV/V}$

Table 36.1 Load regulation.

R_L	V_L (Measured)	I_L (Calculated)
100 Ω (full-load)	3.97 V	39.7 mA
100 kΩ (no-load)	4.02 V	40.2 μA

Step 9   Load Regulation $= \dfrac{V_{NL} - V_{FL}}{\Delta I_L} = 1.26$ mV/mA.

Step 10 $R_{min} = 0.6\,\Omega$ $R_{max} = 4.89\,\text{k}\Omega$

QUESTIONS & PROBLEMS

1. $V_{out} \cong 1.25\left(\dfrac{R_2}{R_1} + 1\right) = 1.25$ V (minimum)

$V_{out} \cong 1.25\left(\dfrac{R_2}{R_1} + 1\right) = 62.37$ V (maximum)

The measured and calculated values of output voltage (minimum) should be close. It should be noted however that the actual values of output voltage (maximum) may vary significantly and will be limited by the amount of input voltage (in this case the input was set to $V_{IN} = 35$ V).

2. Yes, the measured values of load and line regulation were within expected values.

Exercise 37

A Practical Power Supply

Step 2 $V_{r(in)} = 645$ mV $V_{r(out)} = 945$ µV

Step 3 $V_{r(in)} = 645$ mV $V_{r(out)} = 1.1$ mV

Step 4 $V_{r(in)} = 20$ V $V_{r(out)} = 750$ mV

Step 7 $V_{r(in)} = 500$ mV $V_{r(out)} = 0.3$ mV

Step 8 $V_{r(in)} = 500$ mV $V_{r(out)} = 0.36$ mV

Step 9 $V_{r(in)} = 20.9$ V $V_{r(out)} = 14.27$ mV

QUESTIONS AND PROBLEMS

1. Rejection ratio = -56.7 dB (Both filters in place)
   Rejection ratio = -55.4 dB (C_2 removed)
   Rejection ratio = -28.5 dB (C_1 removed)

2. Rejection ratio = -64.44 dB (All filters in place)
   Rejection ratio = -62.85 dB (C_2 removed)
   Rejection ratio = -63.31 dB (C_1 removed)

3. The LM317 had the best ripple rejection ratio.

4. The zener-regulated circuit was affected by the removal of the filter capacitors to a greater degree than the LM317 circuit. This was particularly evident when the larger input capacitor (C_1) was removed. The zener regulated ripple increased by more than 28 dB while the LM317 regulated ripple only increased by 1.1 dB. This is because the LM317, by design, has a better ripple rejection ratio.

5. The 470 µF filter capacitor had the most significant effect on the ripple voltage of both the zener-regulated and the IC-regulated circuits. This is because it is by far the larger capacitor and will have the greatest filtering effect.

Test Item File

Contents

Chapter 1	Fundamental Solid-State Principles	190
Chapter 2	Diodes	197
Chapter 3	Common Diode Applications: Basic Power Supply Circuits	203
Chapter 4	Common Diode Applications: Clippers, Clampers, Voltage Multipliers, and Displays	210
Chapter 5	Special Application Diodes	218
Chapter 6	Bipolar Junction Transistors	224
Chapter 7	DC Biasing Circuits	231
Chapter 8	Introduction to Amplifiers	239
Chapter 9	Common-Emitter Amplifiers	246
Chapter 10	Other BJT Amplifiers	255
Chapter 11	Power Amplifiers	262
Chapter 12	Field-Effect Transistors	269
Chapter 13	MOSFETs	276
Chapter 14	Amplifier Frequency Response	282
Chapter 15	Operational Amplifiers	288
Chapter 16	Additional Op-Amp Applications	294
Chapter 17	Tuned Amplifiers	301
Chapter 18	Oscillators	307
Chapter 19	Solid-State Switching Circuits	313
Chapter 20	Thyristors and Optoelectronics Devices	320
Chapter 21	Discrete and Integrated Voltage Regulators	325

Chapter 1   Fundamental Solid-State Principles

1) The nucleus of an atom contains

    A) protons and electrons.

    B) neutrons and electrons.

    C) neutrons and protons.

    D) neutrons, protons, and electrons.

2) Gold has one valence electron, tin has four valence electrons, and argon has eight valence electrons. Which of these elements has the highest conductivity?

    A) Gold   B) Tin   C) Argon

3) As a result of covalent bonding, intrinsic silicon effectively acts as a/an

    A) insulator.   B) semiconductor.   C) conductor.

4) The difference between the energy levels of two orbital shells is called the

    A) conduction gap.

    B) energy band.

    C) valence band.

    D) energy gap.

5) Which of the following statements is true?

    A) Electrons cannot continually orbit the nucleus of an atom in the space that exists between orbital shells.

    B) There is no specific energy level that is associated with a given orbital shell.

    C) If an electron jumps from an orbital shell to one that has a higher energy level, it remains in the higher-energy shell permanently.

6) Which of the following is not a commonly used semiconductor in electronic applications?

    A) Carbon   B) Lead   C) Silicon   D) Germanium

7) Which of the following is a result of covalent bonding in intrinsic silicon?

    A) Atoms are held together.

    B) The atoms are electrically stable.

    C) The material acts as an insulator.

    D) All of the above are results of the bonding.

8) Which semiconductor element is most often used in the production of solid state devices?

    A) Carbon   B) Lead   C) Silicon   D) Germanium

9) Conduction through a material with a positive temperature coefficient tends to _____ as temperature increases.

    A) increase

    B) decrease

    C) remain relatively unchanged

10) Pentavalent elements have _____ valence electron(s).

    A) one   B) three   C) five   D) eight

11) Trivalent elements have _____ valence electron(s).

    A) one   B) three   C) five   D) eight

12) Doping is used to

    A) decrease the conductivity of an intrinsic semiconductor.

    B) increase the conductivity of an intrinsic semiconductor.

    C) limit the conductivity of an intrinsic semiconductor.

13) When pentavalent elements are used in doping, the resulting material is called _____ material and has an excess of _____.

    A) n–type; valence–band holes   B) n–type; conduction–band electrons

    C) p–type; valence–band holes   D) p–type; conduction–band electrons

14) When trivalent elements are used in doping, the resulting material is called _____ material and has an excess of _____.

    A) n–type; valence–band holes   B) n–type; conduction–band electrons

    C) p–type; valence–band holes   D) p–type; conduction–band electrons

15) The time between the forming of an electron–hole pair and recombination is called

    A) charge time.   B) recombination time.

    C) lifetime.   D) conduction time.

16) In an n–type material, the majority carriers are

    A) conduction–band electrons.

    B) conduction–band holes.

    C) valence–band electrons.

    D) valence–band holes.

    E) neutral atoms.

17) In a p-type material, the minority carriers are

    A) conduction-band electrons.

    B) conduction-band holes.

    C) valence-band electrons.

    D) valence-band holes.

    E) charged atoms.

18) N-type materials are electrically _____ in their natural state.

    A) negative   B) positive   C) neutral

19) A depletion layer acts as a/an

    A) insulator.   B) semiconductor.   C) conductor.

20) P-type materials are electrically _____ in their natural state.

    A) negative   B) positive   C) neutral

21) Pentavalent atoms are often referred to as

    A) donor atoms.   B) minority carriers.

    C) acceptor atoms.   D) majority carriers.

22) Trivalent atoms are often referred to as

    A) donor atoms.   B) minority carriers.

    C) acceptor atoms.   D) majority carriers.

23) The small amount of current that is present at the forming of a pn junction is called

    A) knee current.   B) diffusion current.

    C) barrier current.   D) depletion current.

24) A p-type material is joined with an n-type material. When forward biased, the voltage across the junction is approximately 700 mV (0.7 V). The two materials are most likely made of

    A) silicon.   B) germanium.   C) carbon.   D) lead.

25) When a pn junction is reverse biased, its resistance is

    A) high.

    B) low.

    C) determined by the components that are external to the device.

26) A pn junction is forward biased when

    A) the applied potential causes the n-type material to be more positive than the p-type material.

    B) the applied potential causes the n-type material to be more negative than the p-type material.

    C) both materials are at the same potential.

    D) Both A and C above.

27) Why is silicon more commonly used than germanium in the production of solid-state components?

    A) It is cheaper.   B) It is easier to produce.

    C) It is more tolerant of heat.   D) All of the above.

28) When a pn junction is forward biased, the depletion layer is at its _____ width and the device acts as a near-perfect _____.

    A) minimum; conductor   B) minimum; insulator

    C) maximum; conductor   D) maximum; insulator

29) When a pn junction is reverse biased, the depletion layer is at its _____ width and the device acts as a near-perfect _____.

    A) minimum; conductor   B) minimum; insulator

    C) maximum; conductor   D) maximum; insulator

30) When a pn junction is forward biased, the combined resistance of the p-type and n-type materials is called

    A) net resistance.   B) total resistance.

    C) bulk resistance.   D) forward resistance.

31) Which of the following is an advantage of transistors over vacuum tubes?

    A) Transistors are smaller.   B) Transistors use more power.

    C) Transistors are fragile.   D) All of the above

32) The simplest model of the atom is called the

    A) covalent bond model.   B) conduction bond model.

    C) Bohr model.   D) energy gap model.

33) Which of the following is not a trivalent doping element?

    A) Aluminum   B) Arsenic   C) Boron   D) Gallium

34) The voltage across a forward–biased germanium pn junction is approximately

A) 0.1 V.   B) 0.3 V.   C) 0.7 V.   D) 0.8 V.

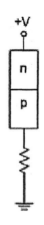

Figure 1–1

35) Referring to Figure 1–1. What type of junction bias is shown?

A) Forward bias   B) Reverse bias   C) Zero bias

Chapter 1 Fundamental Solid–State Principles
Answer Key

1) C
2) A
3) A
4) D
5) A
6) B
7) D
8) C
9) A
10) C
11) B
12) B
13) B
14) C
15) C
16) A
17) A
18) C
19) A
20) C
21) A
22) C
23) B
24) A
25) A
26) B
27) D
28) A
29) D
30) C
31) A
32) C
33) B
34) B
35) B

Chapter 2   Diodes

1) The n-type material of a diode is called the

   A) anode.   B) cathode.

2) The p-type material of a diode is called the

   A) anode.   B) cathode.

3) A pn-junction diode conducts when the arrow in the schematic symbol

   A) points to the more negative diode potential.

   B) points to the more positive diode potential.

4) Electron flow through a forward-biased pn junction is

   A) from cathode to anode.   B) from anode to cathode.

5) Conventional current through a forward-biased pn junction is

   A) from cathode to anode.   B) from anode to cathode.

6) The ideal model of a pn-junction diode represents the device as a

   A) switch.

   B) switch in series with a battery.

   C) switch in series with a battery and a resistor.

7) The _____ diode model is typically used in the initial stages of troubleshooting.

   A) ideal   B) practical   C) complete

8) The _____ diode model is typically used in circuit development applications.

   A) ideal   B) practical   C) complete

9) The _____ diode model is typically used in circuit calculations.

   A) ideal   B) practical   C) complete

10) A calculated value is generally considered to be accurate enough when it is within

   A) 20% of the measured value.   B) 15% of the measured value.

   C) 10% of the actual value.   D) 5% of the actual value.

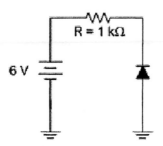

Figure 2-1

11) The voltage across the diode in Figure 2-1 is

    A) 6 V.   B) 5.3 V.   C) 0.7 V.   D) 0 V.

12) The voltage across the resistor in Figure 2-1 is

    A) 6 V.   B) 5.3 V.   C) 0.7 V.   D) 0 V.

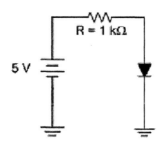

Figure 2-2

13) The voltage across the diode in Figure 2-2 is

    A) 5 V.   B) 4.3 V.   C) 0.7 V.   D) 0 V.

14) The voltage across the resistor in Figure 2-2 is

    A) 5 V.   B) 4.3 V.   C) 0.7 V.   D) 0 V.

15) The voltage across a resistor is calculated as being 4 V. The measured value of the voltage is 4.3 V. What is the percent of error between the two values?

    A) 6.98%   B) 7.5%   C) 0.698%   D) 0.075%

16) A maximum rating on a spec sheet is a

    A) quality.   B) limit.

    C) average value.   D) ac characteristic.

17) When substituting one diode for another, you must consider the

    A) average forward current and bulk resistance ratings.

    B) peak reverse voltage and diode capacitance ratings.

    C) average forward current and peak reverse voltage ratings.

    D) bulk resistance and diode capacitance ratings.

18) A silicon diode has a bulk resistance of 12 Ω and a forward current of 7 mA. The forward voltage drop across the diode is approximately

    A) 700 mV.   B) 784 mV.   C) 84 mV.   D) 884 mV.

19) A zener diode is designed to operate in the _____ region of its characteristic curve.

    A) forward operating   B) reverse breakdown   C) zero bias

20) A zener diode has the following ratings: $V_Z = 9.1$ V and $I_{ZT} = 20$ mA. The measured value of V_Z changes by 30 mV when $I_{zt} = 2$ mA. What is the value of Z_Z for the device?

    A) 1.5 Ω B) 15 Ω C) 30 Ω D) 3.0 Ω

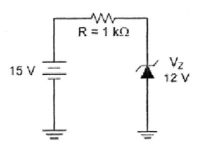

Figure 2-3

21) What is the value of I_T for the circuit in Figure 2-3?

    A) 3 mA   B) 1 mA   C) 5 mA   D) 12 mA

22) Which of the following is most likely to destroy a zener diode?

    A) Exceeding V_{BR} B) Exceeding I_{ZM}

23) An LED is typically wired in series with a current-limiting resistor.

24) The color of an LED is typically determined by the magnitude of the diode current.

25) The anode and cathode leads on an LED are usually identified by

   A) their color.

   B) their lengths.

   C) a marking on the LED case.

   D) their lengths and/or a marking on the LED case.

26) When tested with an ohmmeter, a diode should have _____ forward resistance and _____ reverse resistance.

   A) low; high   B) high; low   C) high; high   D) low; low

27) Which of the following steps should be taken when testing a diode with an ohmmeter?

   A) The ohmmeter should be calibrated using the zero adjust (when applicable).

   B) The relative polarity of the meter leads should be checked.

   C) The meter output current level for each resistance scale should be verified as being safe for the diode under test.

   D) All of the above.

28) Which diode type can be best utilized as a panel indicator?

   A) A pn-junction diode   B) A zener diode

   C) A light-emitting diode (LED)   D) None of the above.

29) The stripe on the body of a pn-junction diode is used to identify the _____.

   A) cathode   B) anode

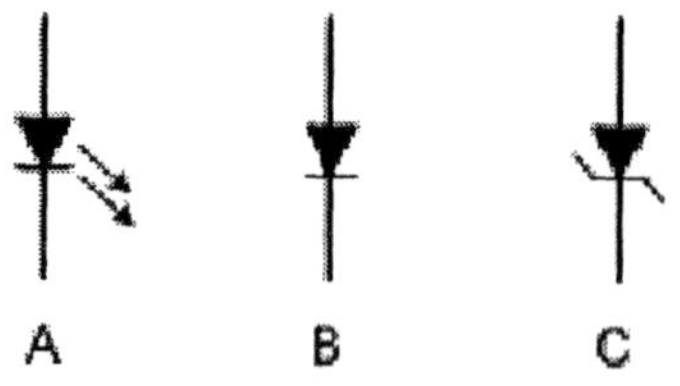

Figure 2–4

30) Refer to Figure 2-4. Symbols A, B, and C represent the _____, respectively.

   A) LED, zener diode, and pn-junction diode

   B) zener diode, pn-junction diode, and LED

   C) photo diode, zener diode, and LED

   D) LED, pn-junction diode, and zener diode

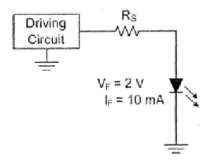

Figure 2-5

31) Referring to Figure 2–5. The driving circuit has a peak output of 6 V. What value of R$_S$ will protect the LED from excessive forward current?

   A) 470 Ω

   B) 560 Ω

   C) 680 Ω

   D) Any of the resistors listed will protect the LED.

32) A given LED has a maximum forward current rating of 30 mA. You should use I$_F$ = _____ to calculate the value of the current–limiting resistor.

   A) 30 mA   B) 24 mA   C) 36 mA   D) 20 mA

Chapter 2 Diodes
Answer Key

1) B
2) A
3) A
4) A
5) B
6) A
7) A
8) C
9) B
10) C
11) A
12) D
13) C
14) B
15) A
16) B
17) C
18) B
19) B
20) B
21) A
22) B
23) TRUE
24) FALSE
25) D
26) A
27) D
28) C
29) A
30) D
31) D
32) B

Chapter 3 Common Diode Applications: Basic Power Supply Circuits

1) A rectifier is used to

    A) convert ac to pulsating dc.

    B) reduce the variations in a pulsating dc signal.

    C) maintain a constant power supply dc output voltage.

    D) convert one dc level to another.

2) The basic power supply is made up of

    A) a regulator, a follower, and a rectifier.

    B) a filter, a follower, and a regulator.

    C) a rectifier, a filter, and a regulator.

3) A voltage regulator

    A) maintains a constant power supply dc output voltage.

    B) steps up or steps down the line voltage.

    C) reduces the variations in ac line voltage.

    D) Both A and C above.

4) The most commonly used type of rectifier is the

    A) half-wave rectifier.   B) full-wave rectifier.   C) bridge rectifier.

5) In the schematic for a half-wave rectifier , the diode points toward the ungrounded side of the load. The output from the rectifier is

    A) positive.

    B) negative.

    C) either positive or negative, depending on the polarity of the transformer secondary voltage.

6) A negative half-wave rectifier eliminates the _____ alternations of the transformer output.

    A) positive   B) negative

7) Why is the bridge rectifier used more commonly than the full-wave rectifier?

    A) It does not require the use of a center-tapped transformer.

    B) With equal input voltages, the bridge rectifier provides a higher dc output voltage.

    C) The bridge rectifier can be directly coupled to an ac line input.

    D) All of the above.

8) A 22 μF filter capacitor is connected to a half-wave rectifier. If the value of the capacitor is increased to 100 μF, the ripple in the circuit output will

    A) increase.   B) decrease.   C) remain the same.

9) Which of the following will reduce the ripple in the output from a filtered rectifier?

    A) Increasing the value of the filter capacitor.

    B) Increasing the load resistance.

    C) Adding a zener voltage regulator.

    D) All of the above.

10) The term *full load* means

    A) load resistance has increased to its maximum value.

    B) load resistance has decreased to its minimum value.

    C) the load is disconnected from the circuit.

    D) load current has decreased to its minimum value.

11) A bridge rectifier has values of $V_1 = 120$ Vac, turns ratio $= 5:1$, and $R_L = 500$ Ω. What is the dc output voltage?

    A) 14.4 Vdc   B) 7.19 Vdc   C) 20.8 Vdc   D) 22.6 Vdc

12) A half-wave rectifier is connected to a transformer with a secondary voltage of 20 V_{pk}. The average output voltage is

    A) 19.3 Vdc.   B) 13.7 Vdc.   C) 6.14 Vdc.   D) 12.3 Vdc.

13) A positive full-wave rectifier has a secondary voltage of 20 V_{pk}. The peak load voltage for the circuit is

    A) 20 V_{pk}.   B) 9.3 V_{pk}.   C) 19.3 V_{pk}.   D) 10 V_{pk}.

14) A full-wave rectifier has a 9.3 V_{pk} output and a 4.7 kΩ load resistance. What is the dc load current for the circuit?

    A) 1.26 mA   B) 2.61 mA   C) 629.8 μA   D) 1.4 mA

15) A filtered half-wave rectifier has a peak secondary voltage of 20 V_{pk}. The PIV rating for any diode in the circuit must be at least

    A) 20 V.   B) 30 V.   C) 10 V.   D) 40 V.

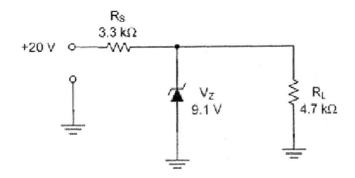

Figure 3-1

16) What is the total current that is being drawn through R_S in Figure 3-1?

   A) 6.06 mA   B) 3.3 mA   C) 2.76 mA   D) 2.15 mA

17) When testing a basic power supply, you see that the primary fuse is blown. This typically indicates that

   A) a short exists somewhere in the power supply.

   B) an open exists somewhere in the power supply.

   C) the fuse itself is the most likely cause of the circuit failure.

   D) Any of the above conditions could exist.

18) The term leaky is used to describe a capacitor that is

   A) partially open.   B) partially shorted.

   C) too high in value.   D) too low in value.

19) When troubleshooting a rectifier, it is important to check every diode in the rectifier.

1:10

Figure 3-2

20) Refer to Figure 3-2. For the transformer shown, which current and voltage have the greatest values?

   A) I_P and V_P B) I_S and V_S C) I_P and V_S D) I_S and V_P

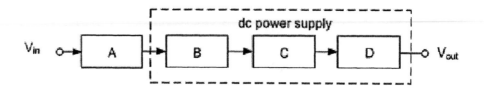

Figure 3-3

21) Identify the power supply circuits represented in Figure 3-3.

    A) A= transformer, B= rectifier, C= regulator, D= filter

    B) A= transformer, B= regulator, C= filter, D= rectifier

    C) A= filter, B= transformer, C= rectifier, D= regulator

    D) A= transformer, B= rectifier, C = filter, D= regulator

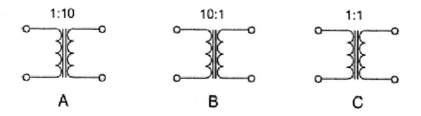

Figure 3-4

22) Refer to Figure 3-4. Which transformer could be used for the sole purpose of providing electrical isolation between a power supply and its ac line input?

    A) A   B) B

    C) C   D) none of the above

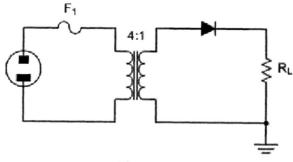

Figure 3-5

23) The normal load current in Figure 3-5 is 375mA. What is the minimum acceptable rating for F_1 ?

    A) 1.0 A   B) 2.0 A   C) 1/8 A (0.125 A)   D) 1/2 A (0.5 A)

24) A transformer with a 10:1 turns ratio has a 120 Vac line input. The transformer secondary is connected to a half–wave rectifier circuit using a capacitor filter. Ignoring any ripple, what is the dc output voltage from the circuit?

A) 16.3 V   B) 10.4 V   C) 5.7 V   D) 3.6 V

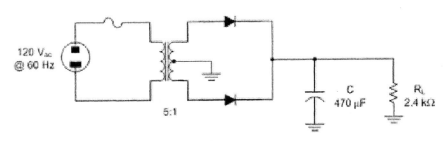

Figure 3–6

25) Refer to Figure 3–6. What is the value of the circuit's secondary voltage?

A) 24 V_{ac} B) 33.9 V_p

C) 67.8 V_{pp} D) All of the above.

26) Refer to Figure 3–6. What is the value of the load current?

A) 14.1 mA   B) 7.1 mA   C) 6.8 mA   D) 4.3 mA

27) Refer for Figure 3–6. What is the ripple voltage across the load?

A) 0.25 V   B) 0.126 V   C) 121 mV   D) 76 mV

28) Refer to Figure 3–6. What is the dc load voltage?

A) 33.2 V   B) 16.3 V

C) 11.3 V   D) None of the above.

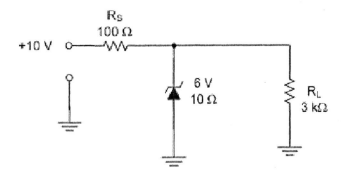

Figure 3–7

29) Refer to Figure 3–7. What is the value of I_Z for the circuit?

A) 40 mA   B) 38 mA   C) 20 mA   D) 2 mA

30) Refer to Figure 3-7. What is the value of the load voltage for the circuit?

A) 6.4 V

B) 6 V

C) 5.6 V

D) None of the above.

31) Refer to Figure 3-7. If you replace the 100 Ω resistor with a 400 Ω resistor, the output voltage for the circuit will be

A) 6.4 V.

B) 6.08 V.

C) 6 V.

D) 5.6 V.

Chapter 3 Common Diode Applications: Basic Power Supply Circuits
Answer Key

1) A
2) C
3) A
4) C
5) A
6) A
7) D
8) B
9) D
10) B
11) C
12) C
13) B
14) A
15) D
16) B
17) A
18) B
19) TRUE
20) C
21) D
22) C
23) C
24) A
25) D
26) C
27) C
28) B
29) B
30) B
31) C

Chapter 4 Common Diode Applications: Clippers, Clampers, Voltage Multipliers, and Displays

1) Which of the following circuits is used to change the dc reference of a signal without changing its shape?

    A) A clipper   B) A clamper   C) A voltage multiplier

2) Which of the following circuits is used to eliminate some portion of a signal?

    A) A clipper   B) A clamper   C) A voltage multiplier

3) A clipper is also known as a/an

    A) dc restorer. B) eliminator. C) limiter. D) regenerator.

4) A clamper is also known as a/an

    A) dc restorer. B) eliminator. C) limiter. D) regenerator.

5) A positive clipper performs the same basic function as a negative clamper.

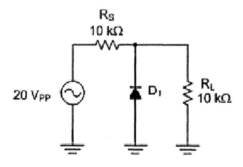

Figure 4–1

6) The circuit in Figure 4–1 is a

    A) positive clipper.   B) negative clipper.

    C) positive clamper.   D) negative clamper.

7) The output from the circuit in Figure 4–1 is approximately

    A) 10.7 V_{pp}. B) 5.7 V_{pp}. C) 20 V_{pp}. D) 9.3 V_{pp}.

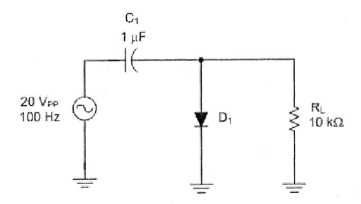

Figure 4 -2

8) The circuit in Figure 4–2 is a

    A) positive clipper.   B) negative clipper.

    C) positive clamper.   D) negative clamper.

9) The output from the circuit in Figure 4–2 is approximately

    A) 10.7 V_{pp}.   B) 5.7 V_{pp}.   C) 20 V_{pp}.   D) 9.3 V_{pp}.

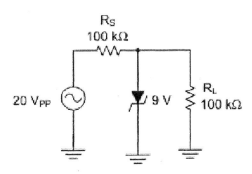

Figure 4-3

10) The positive peak output voltage for the circuit in Figure 4–3 is approximately

    A) 9 V.   B) 9.7 V.   C) 8.3 V.   D) 0.7 V.

11) The negative peak output voltage for the circuit in Figure 4–3 is approximately

    A) –5 V.   B) –9.7 V.   C) –8.3 V.   D) –0.7 V.

12) The circuit in Figure 4–3 is a

    A) series clipper.   B) shunt clipper.

    C) series clamper.   D) shunt clamper.

13) Which of the following circuits is commonly used to provide transient protection?

   A) A clamper   B) A multiplier

   C) A rectifier   D) A clipper

14) The clamper works on the basis of

   A) charging alternate capacitors to increase output voltage.

   B) shorting out a portion of the input signal to prevent it from reaching the load.

   C) switching time constants.

   D) alternating dc reference voltages.

15) Which of the following determines whether a given clamper is a positive clamper or a negative clamper?

   A) The type of diode used

   B) The physical orientation of the diode

   C) The placement of the diode (i.e., in series or shunt with the load)

   D) All of the above.

16) The output from a biased clamper has a dc reference voltage that is

   A) approximately equal to the dc voltage that is applied to the diode.

   B) approximately equal to 0 V.

   C) dependent on the peak-to-peak value of the ac input.

   D) equal to the dc average of the circuit's output signal.

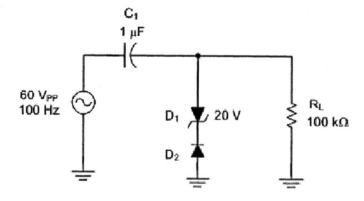

Figure 4-4

17) Assuming that D_2 in Figure 4-4 is an ideal component, the circuit reference voltage is

A) +20 V.   B) +0.7 V.   C) -0.7 V.   D) -20 V.

212

18) The dc average of the output from the circuit in Figure 4-4 is approximately equal to

A) +20 V.   B) +10 V.   C) –10 V.   D) –20 V.

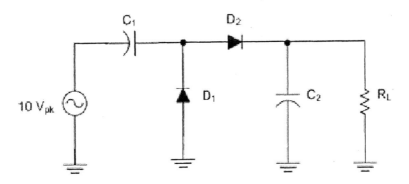

Figure 4-5

19) The circuit in Figure 4-5 is a

A) half-wave voltage doubler.   B) full-wave voltage doubler.

C) voltage tripler.   D) voltage quadrupler.

20) The output from the circuit in Figure 4-5 is approximately

A) 20 Vdc.   B) 30 Vdc.   C) 40 Vdc.   D) 60 Vdc.

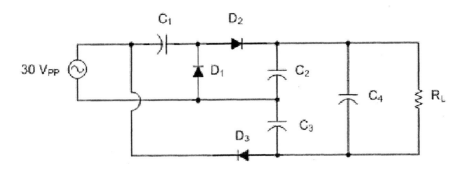

Figure 4-6

21) The circuit in Figure 4-6 is a

A) half-wave voltage doubler.   B) full-wave voltage doubler.

C) voltage tripler.   D) voltage quadrupler.

22) C_3 in Figure 4-6 is included to reduce the ripple in the dc output voltage.

23) The output voltage from the circuit in Figure 4-6 is approximately

A) 15 Vdc.   B) 30 Vdc.   C) 45 Vdc.   D) 60 Vdc.

213

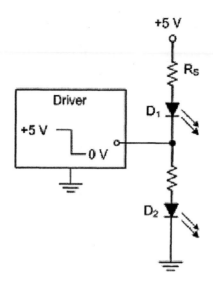

Figure 4–7

24) D₁ in Figure 4–7 will be *on* when the output from the driving circuit is

   A) 0 V.   B) +5 V.

25) D₂ in Figure 4–7 will be *off* when the output from the driving circuit is

   A) 0 V.   B) +5 V.

26) A _____ display has a single ground pin that is common to all of its LED segments.

   A) common–anode   B) common–cathode

   C) common–diode   D) common–segment

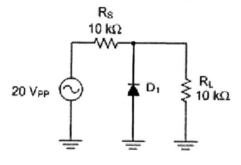

Figure 4–8

27) Refer to Figure 4–8. The circuit shown has a constant 0–V output. Which of the following is the most likely cause of the problem?

   A) R$_L$ open   B) D₁ open   C) R$_S$ open   D) R$_S$ shorted

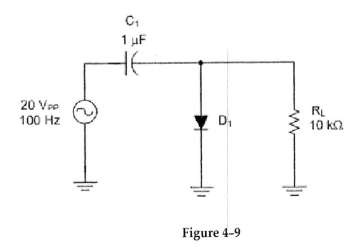

Figure 4–9

28) Refer to Figure 4–9. The output from the circuit is identical to the input signal. Which of the following is most likely true?

    A) The circuit is functioning normally.   B) C1 is open.

    C) The load resistor is shorted.   D) The diode is open.

29) Which of the following is best suited for use in a hand held solar powered (low power) calculator?

    A) An LED display

    B) An LCD display

    C) Seven–segment LED display

30) Which of the following is best suited for use as a computer surge protector?

    A) A voltage doubler

    B) A clamper

    C) A clipper

    D) All the above could be used for this purpose.

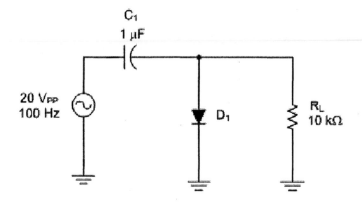

Figure 4–10

31) Refer to Figure 4–10. Assuming the forward resistance of the diode is 15 Ω, what is the charge time for the capacitor?

    A) 10 S   B) 10 mS   C) 75 μS   D) 50 mS

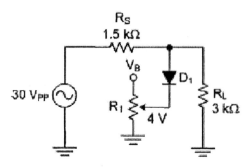

Figure 4–11

32) Refer to Figure 4–11. The potentiometer (R_1) is used to

    A) prevent accidental overload of D_1.   B) provide an adjustable clipped output.

    C) provide an adjustable clamped output.   D) remove negative voltage spikes.

33) Refer to Figure 4–11. The positive peak voltage across the 3 kΩ resistor is

    A) 0 V.   B) 0.7 V.   C) 10 V.   D) 4.7 V.

Chapter 4 Common Diode Applications: Clippers, Clampers, Voltage Multipliers, and Displays
Answer Key

1) B
2) A
3) C
4) A
5) FALSE
6) B
7) B
8) D
9) C
10) D
11) A
12) B
13) D
14) C
15) B
16) A
17) D
18) B
19) A
20) A
21) C
22) FALSE
23) C
24) A
25) A
26) B
27) C
28) D
29) B
30) C
31) C
32) B
33) D

Chapter 5   Special Applications Diodes

1) The varactor can be used as a

    A) current-controlled capacitance when forward biased.

    B) voltage-controlled capacitance when forward biased.

    C) current-controlled capacitance when reverse biased.

    D) voltage-controlled capacitance when reverse biased.

2) The capacitance of a varactor varies

    A) inversely with the width of its depletion layer.

    B) directly with the width of its depletion layer.

3) A varactor with a high capacitance ratio (C_R) rating would be well suited for use in

    A) a fine-tuning circuit.   B) a course-tuning circuit.

    C) a crystal-controlled oscillator.   D) any of the circuits listed here.

4) A tuned amplifier contains a 2.2 mH inductor in its tank circuit, along with a varactor with the following ratings: $C_t = 80$ pF when $V_r = 3$ Vdc and $C_R = 3$ for $V = 3$ Vdc to 6 Vdc. What is the resonant frequency of the circuit when $V_R = 3$ Vdc?

    A) 904.3 GHz   B) 758.7 kHz   C) 379.4 kHz   D) 189.9 MHz

5) A tuned amplifier has a 2.2 mH inductor and a varactor in its tank. The varactor has the ratings $C_t = 72$ pf when $V_r = 3$ Vdc and a $C_r = 2.7$ for $V = 3$ Vdc to 6 Vdc. What is the resonant frequency of the circuit described when $V_R = 6$ Vdc?

    A) 599.8 kHz   B) 479.9 kHz   C) 657 kHz   D) 1.20 MHz

6) Which of the following are characteristics of an effective surge protection circuit?

    A) High power dissipation capability and rapid turn-on time

    B) High power dissipation capability and slow turn-on time

    C) High voltage capability and rapid turn-on time

    D) High voltage capability and slow turn-on time

7) The maximum reverse standoff voltage (V_{RWM}) rating of a transient suppressor indicates

    A) the voltage across the device while in its zener operating region.

    B) the maximum reverse voltage that will not drive the component into its zener operating region.

8) The clamping voltage (V_C) rating of a transient suppressor indicates

    A) the maximum voltage across the device at a given value of reverse surge current.

    B) the maximum reverse voltage that will not drive the component into its zener operating region.

9) Back-to-back suppressors contain two components that are connected

    A) anode-to-cathode.

    B) anode-to-anode.

    C) cathode-to-cathode.

    D) either anode-to-anode or cathode-to-cathode.

10) Constant-current diodes are also known as

    A) current-restricting diodes.   B) current suppressors.

    C) current regulator diodes.   D) All of the above.

11) Constant-current diodes have

    A) extremely low internal impedance values.

    B) extremely high breakdown current ratings.

    C) extremely high internal impedance values.

    D) extremely low breakdown voltage ratings.

12) A series current regulator is used to

    A) provide a constant input current to a load over a wide range of input voltages.

    B) provide a load with an input current that equals the difference between the source current and the regulator current.

13) The tunnel diode is a

    A) lightly doped diode that is used in high-frequency communications applications.

    B) lightly doped diode that is used in low-frequency communications applications.

    C) heavily doped diode that is used in high-frequency communications applications.

    D) heavily doped diode that is used in low-frequency communications applications.

14) Forward voltage and current are directly proportional for a tunnel diode that is operated between its peak voltage (V_P) and its valley voltage (V_V).

15) The tunnel diode region of operation between V_P and V_V is called the

    A) constant resistance region.   B) constant current region.

    C) negative resistance region.   D) negative current region.

16) The tunnel diode can be used as the active device in a

    A) constant resistance amplifier.
        B) negative resistance oscillator.

    C) negative current rectifier.
        D) negative resistance linear amplifier.

17) Schottky diodes have extremely low

    A) V_F, V_{RRM}, and junction capacitance ratings.

    B) I_F, V_{RRM}, and junction capacitance ratings.

    C) V_F, V_K, and junction capacitance ratings.

    D) f_{max}, V_{RRM}, and V_F ratings.

18) The PIN diode actually contains _____ pn junction(s).

    A) zero
        B) one
        C) two
        D) three

19) When forward biased, the PIN diode acts as a

    A) current–controlled resistance.
        B) current–controlled capacitance.

    C) voltage–controlled resistance.
        D) voltage–controlled capacitance.

20) When reverse biased, the capacitance of a PIN diode can be varied like that of the varactor.

21) The step–recovery diode is a/an

    A) high–current diode.
        B) high–voltage diode.

    C) high–power diode.
        D) ultra–fast diode.

22) The doping level of a step–recovery diode

    A) is extremely high.

    B) is extremely low.

    C) decreases as the distance from the junction increases.

    D) increases as the distance from the junction increases.

23) A tunnel diode has the following values:
        $I_P = 10$ mA at $V_P = 250$ mV and
        $I_V = 200$ μA at $V_V = 480$ mV
    Calculate the dynamic resistance of the component.

    A) –2.4 kΩ to –25 Ω
        B) –23.5 Ω

    C) +23.5 Ω
        D) 25 Ω to 2.4 kΩ

Figure 5-1

24) Figure 5-1 shows the schematic symbol for a

    A) back to back suppressor.   B) constant current diode.

    C) tunnel diode.   D) Schottky diode.

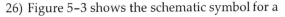

Figure 5-2

25) Figure 5-2 shows the schematic symbol for a

    A) back to back suppressor.   B) constant current diode.

    C) tunnel diode.   D) Schottky diode.

Figure 5-3

26) Figure 5-3 shows the schematic symbol for a

    A) back to back suppressor.   B) constant current diode.

    C) tunnel diode.   D) Schottky diode.

Figure 5-4

27) Referring to Figure 5-4. This is the schematic symbol of a _____.

    A) back to back suppressor   B) constant current diode

    C) tunnel diode   D) Schottky diode

28) The _____ is sometimes referred to as a barrier diode, hot-carrier diode, or surface-barrier diode.

    A) Tunnel diode   B) PIN diode

    C) Step recovery diode   D) Schottky diode

29) _____ diodes are used in the manufacture of integrated circuit chips to decrease the propagation delay time of the internal circuits.

A) Constant current

B) Step recovery

C) Schottky

D) Tunnel

30) An engineer is designing a television tuner circuit. Which diode would you expect to see in the design?

A) A constant-current diode.

B) A tunnel diode.

C) A varactor diode.

D) A PIN diode.

Chapter 5 Special Applications Diodes
Answer Key

1) D
2) A
3) B
4) C
5) C
6) A
7) B
8) A
9) C
10) C
11) C
12) A
13) C
14) FALSE
15) C
16) B
17) A
18) A
19) A
20) TRUE
21) D
22) D
23) B
24) B
25) D
26) A
27) C
28) D
29) C
30) C

Chapter 6   Bipolar Junction Transistors

1) Bipolar junction transistors (BJTs) are commonly used in

   A) linear amplifiers.

   B) high–speed electronic switches.

   C) rectifiers.

   D) all of the above.

   E) both A and B above.

2) The arrow on the BJT schematic symbol identifies

   A) the emitter terminal and the type of BJT.

   B) the collector terminal and the type of BJT.

   C) the base terminal and the type of BJT.

   D) none of the above.

3) The BJT is a

   A) voltage–controlled device.   B) current–controlled device.

   C) frequency–controlled device.   D) power–controlled device.

4) Under normal circumstances, which BJT terminal currents are approximately equal in value?

   A) I_C and I_B

   B) I_C and I_E

   C) I_E and I_B

   D) No two currents are ever approximately equal in value

5) V_{CE} is measured

   A) from the collector terminal to ground.

   B) from the collector terminal to the emitter terminal.

   C) from the emitter terminal to ground.

   D) from the collector–emitter junction to ground.

6) Which of the following biasing combinations is not normally associated with any of the three transistor operating regions?

   A) A forward biased E–B junction and a reverse biased C–B junction

   B) A reverse biased E–B junction and a reverse biased C–B junction.

   C) A reverse biased E–B junction and a forward biased C–B junction.

   D) A forward biased E–B junction and a forward biased C–B junction.

7) The condition where increases in I_B will not cause further increases in I_C is called

    A) cutoff.   B) saturation.

    C) active operation.   D) limit operation.

8) When both BJT junctions are reverse biased, the component is said to be in

    A) cutoff.   B) saturation.

    C) active operation.   D) limit operation.

9) Beta (β) is the ratio of

    A) collector current to emitter current.   B) base current to collector current.

    C) collector current to base current.   D) emitter current to collector current.

10) Ideally, the total collector current through a saturated transistor is determined by

    A) The voltage source and the total resistance in the collector and emitter circuits.

    B) V_{CE} and V_{CC}.

    C) V_{CC}, V_{CE}, and the total base circuit resistance.

    D) the transistor.

11) When a transistor is in saturation, V_{CE} is approximately equal to

    A) V_{CC}.   B) $I_C R_C$.   C) 0 V.   D) V_E.

12) When a BJT is in cutoff, V_{CE} is approximately equal to

    A) V_{CC}.   B) $I_C R_C$.   C) 0 V.   D) V_E.

13) A BJT has values of $I_E = 12$ mA and $I_B = 600$ μA. What is the exact value of beta?

    A) 20   B) 21

    C) 19   D) None of these are correct.

14) A BJT has values of $I_E = 15$ mA and $I_C = 14.95$ mA. What is the exact value of beta?

    A) 300   B) 299   C) 1.003   D) 250

15) A BJT has a beta rating of 400. What is the value of alpha for the device?

    A) 1.0025   B) 0.0025

    C) 0.9975   D) None of these are correct.

16) A BJT has values of $\alpha = 0.9985$ and $I_C = 15$ mA. What is the value of I_B for the component?

    A) 22.5 μA   B) 15.15 mA

    C) 14.85 mA   D) None of these are correct.

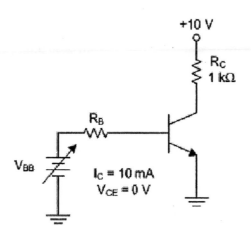

Figure 6–1

17) The transistor in Figure 6–1 is operating in

    A) cutoff.   B) saturation.

    C) the active region.   D) the limited region.

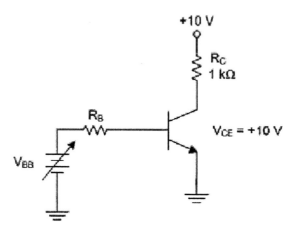

Figure 6–2

18) The transistor in Figure 6–2 is operating in

    A) cutoff.   B) saturation.

    C) the active region.   D) the limited region.

19) The value of I_C in a transistor amplifier is determined by

    A) the values of V_{CC}, R_C, and V_{CE}.

    B) the value of I_B (for any operating region other than saturation).

    C) the value of V_{CE} only.

    D) the value of V_B.

20) I$_C$ and V$_{CE}$ are directly proportional.

21) The higher the value of beta for a transistor, the greater the difference between the values of I$_C$ and I$_E$.

22) A transistor has ratings of I$_{C(max)}$ = 200 mA and β = 150 to 200. What is the maximum allowable value of I$_B$ for the device?

   A) 1 mA   B) 4 mA

   C) 1.33 mA   D) None of these are correct.

23) As temperature increases, beta

   A) increases.   B) decreases.   C) remains unchanged.

24) Which of the following labels is generally used to represent dc beta on specification sheets?

   A) β   B) β$_{dc}$ C) h$_{FE}$ D) h$_{DC}$

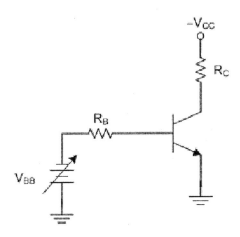

Figure 6–3

25) The circuit in Figure 6–3 won't work. Why not?

   A) R$_B$ is open.

   B) The transistor is in saturation.

   C) R$_C$ is open.

   D) The polarities of V$_{CC}$ and V$_{BB}$ are incorrect.

26) An integrated transistor is:

   A) a single transistor that is packaged in its own casing.

   B) one of a group of transistors contained in an IC package.

   C) an IC containing transistors that have extremely high power dissipation ratings.

   D) a special device that uses both solid state and steady–state electronics.

27) An engineer is designing a television CRT control circuit. What type of transistor do you expect to see in the design?

   A) High–voltage   B) High–current

   C) High–power   D) General purpose

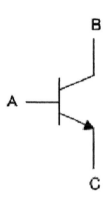

Figure 6–4

28) Refer to Figure 6–4. Which of the following correctly identifies the transistor terminals?

   A) A = collector, B = Base, C = Emitter   B) A = Base, B = Emitter, C = collector

   C) A = Base, B = collector, C = Emitter   D) A = collector, B = Emitter, C = Base

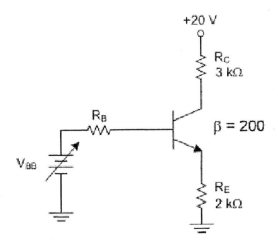

Figure 6-5

29) Refer to Figure 6-5. What is the value of $I_{C(sat)}$ for the circuit?

    A) 3.3 mA

    B) 4 mA

    C) 10 mA

    D) Can't be determined without knowing the value of $I_{B(sat)}$?

30) Refer to Figure 6-5. Assuming that $I_B = 10\ \mu A$, what is the value of I_C?

    A) 2 mA

    B) 2.01 mA

    C) 0.4 mA

    D) Can't be determined without knowing the value of R_B

31) Refer to Figure 6-5. Assuming that $I_B = 25\ \mu A$, what is the exact value of I_C?

    A) 4 mA

    B) 4.975mA

    C) 5 mA

    D) Can't be determined without knowing the value of R_B

32) Refer to Figure 6-5. Assuming that $I_B = 5\ \mu A$, what is the exact value of V_C?

    A) 3 V   B) 3.015 V   C) 16.985 V   D) 17 V

Chapter 6 Bipolar Junction Transistors
Answer Key

1) E
2) A
3) B
4) B
5) B
6) C
7) B
8) A
9) C
10) A
11) C
12) A
13) C
14) B
15) C
16) A
17) B
18) A
19) B
20) FALSE
21) FALSE
22) A
23) A
24) C
25) D
26) B
27) A
28) C
29) B
30) A
31) A
32) D

Chapter 7 DC Biasing Circuits

1) The simplest transistor biasing circuit is called
    A) voltage–divider bias.   B) emitter–feedback bias.
    C) base bias.   D) collector–feedback bias.

2) The most commonly used type of transistor biasing is
    A) voltage–divider bias.   B) emitter–feedback bias.
    C) collector–feedback bias.   D) emitter bias.

3) Which of the following is the likely to experience significant changes in the values of I_{CQ} and V_{CEQ} as a result of changes in temperature?
    A) Voltage–divider bias.   B) Emitter–feedback bias.
    C) Base bias.   D) Collector–feedback bias.

4) The change in I_{CQ} and V_{CEQ} that can occur when temperature changes is known as
    A) midpoint bias.   B) midpoint shift.
    C) output shift.   D) Q–point shift.

5) Base bias is used primarily in switching applications.

6) The term *quiescent* means
    A) midpoint biased.   B) at rest.
    C) active.   D) Both A and B above.

7) Why is midpoint bias desirable for most linear amplifiers?
    A) It extends the operating life of the transistor.
    B) It allows optimum ac operation of the circuit.
    C) It allows optimum dc operation of the circuit.
    D) It keeps V_{CEQ} at approximately half the value of V_{CC}.

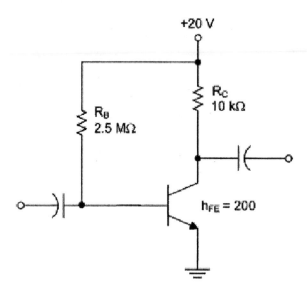

+20 V

R_B
2.5 MΩ

R_C
10 kΩ

$h_{FE} = 200$

Figure 7-1

8) Is the amplifier in Figure 7-1 midpoint biased?

   A) Yes   B) No

9) The value of $V_{CE(off)}$ for the circuit in Figure 7-1 is

   A) 20 V.

   B) 10 V.

   C) 5 V.

   D) Cannot be determined with the information given.

10) The value of $I_{C(sat)}$ for the circuit in Figure 7-1 is

   A) 1 mA.   B) 0 mA.   C) 2 mA.   D) 4 mA.

11) What is the primary drawback to using emitter bias?

   A) Emitter bias is beta dependent.

   B) Emitter bias cannot provide midpoint bias.

   C) Emitter bias requires the use of a dual-polarity power supply.

   D) Emitter bias has no quiescent state.

12) Which of the following is a characteristic of emitter bias ?

   A) The emitter potential is very low, typically less than -1 V.

   B) The base potential is very close to 0 V.

   C) The collector potential is approximately equal to V_{CC}.

   D) All of the above are characteristic of emitter bias.

   E) Both A and B are characteristic of emitter bias.

13) An emitter bias circuit has values of $V_{CC} = +8$ V and $V_{EE} = -8$ V. The value of $V_{CE(off)}$ for the circuit is

    A) 4 V.   B) 8 V.   C) 16 V.   D) 0.7 V.

14) A transistor has a rating of $h_{FE} = 50$ to 450. What value of h_{FE} should be used for circuit analysis purposes?

    A) 50   B) 250   C) 450   D) 150

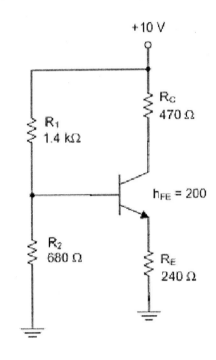

Figure 7-2

15) Is the circuit in Figure 7-2 midpoint biased?

    A) Yes   B) No

16) The value of $I_{C(sat)}$ for the circuit in Figure 7-2 is

    A) 21.3 mA.   B) 14.1 mA.   C) 7.04 mA.   D) 0 mA.

17) The value of $V_{CE(off)}$ for the circuit in Figure 7-2 is

    A) 10 V.   B) 20 V.   C) 5 V.   D) 0 V.

18) The spec sheet for a given transistor contains the following table:

$h_{FE} = 5$ to 200 when $I_C = 1$ mA

$h_{FE} = 70$ to 350 when $I_C = 10$ mA

$h_{FE} = 100$ to 400 when $I_C = 20$ mA

$h_{FE} = 150$ to 450 when $I_C = 100$ mA

The transistor is being used in a circuit with the following values: $V_{CC} = 20$ V, $R_C = 820\ \Omega$, and $R_E = 180\ \Omega$. What value of h_{FE} should be used in the analysis of the circuit?

A) 100

B) 157

C) 200

D) None of these are correct.

19) As temperature increases, the value of h_{FE}

A) increases.

B) decreases.

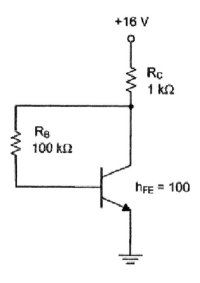

+16 V

R_C
1 kΩ

R_B
100 kΩ

$h_{FE} = 100$

Figure 7–3

20) Is the circuit in Figure 7–3 midpoint biased?

A) Yes

B) No

21) The circuit in Figure 7–3 found to be in saturation. Which of the following could cause this condition?

A) A open base resistor (R_B)

B) An open collector resistor (R_C)

C) An open transistor (Q_1) base-to-emitter

D) A shorted base resistor (R_B)

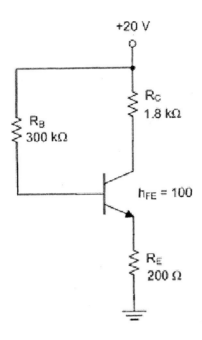

+20 V

R$_C$
1.8 kΩ

R$_B$
300 kΩ

h$_{FE}$ = 100

R$_E$
200 Ω

Figure 7-4

22) Is the circuit in Figure 7-4 midpoint biased?

    A) Yes   B) No

23) Refer to Figure 7-4. The circuit is a(n) _____.

    A) base bias

    B) emitter bias

    C) voltage-divider bias

    D) collector feedback

    E) emitter-feedback

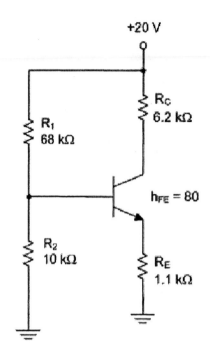

Figure 7–5

24) What type of bias is shown in Figure 7–5?

    A) Base bias

    B) Emitter bias

    C) Voltage–divider bias

    D) Emitter–feedback bias

    E) Collector–feedback bias

25) Refer to Figure 7–5. The circuit has measured values of $V_B = 0$ V, $V_E = 0$ V, and $V_C = 20$ V. Which of the following could account for these readings?

    A) The 68 kΩ resistor is open.

    B) The 10 kΩ resistor is open.

    C) The 6.2 kΩ resistor is open.

    D) The 1.1 kΩ resistor is open.

    E) There is no fault. The circuit is functioning as it should.

26) Refer to Figure 7–5. The circuit has measured values of $V_B = 1$ V, $V_E = 0.3$ V and $V_C = 0.4$ V. Which of the following could account for these readings?

    A) The 68 kΩ resistor is open.

    B) The 10 kΩ resistor is open.

    C) The 6.2 kΩ resistor is open.

    D) The 1.1 kΩ resistor is open.

    E) There is no fault. The circuit is functioning as it should.

27) Refer to Figure 7–5. The circuit has measured values of $V_B = 2.2$ V, $V_E = 1.5$ V and $V_C = 11.5$ V. Which of the following could account for these readings?

    A) The 68 kΩ resistor is open.

    B) The 10 kΩ resistor is open.

    C) The 6.2 kΩ resistor is open.

    D) The 1.1 kΩ resistor is open.

    E) There is no fault. The circuit is functioning as it should.

28) Refer to Figure 7–5. The value of R_{base} for the circuit is

    A) 1.1 k Ω.   B) 88 k Ω.   C) 8.97 k Ω.

29) What type of bias is used primarily in switching circuits?

    A) Base bias   B) Emitter bias

    C) Voltage–divider bias   D) Collector–feedback bias

30) What type of bias requires the use of a dual–polarity power supply?

    A) Base bias   B) Emitter bias

    C) Voltage–divider bias   D) Collector–feedback bias

Chapter 7 DC Biasing Circuits
Answer Key

1) C
2) A
3) C
4) D
5) TRUE
6) B
7) B
8) B
9) A
10) C
11) C
12) E
13) C
14) D
15) B
16) B
17) A
18) B
19) A
20) A
21) D
22) A
23) E
24) C
25) A
26) C
27) E
28) B
29) A
30) B

Chapter 8 Introduction to Amplifiers

1) An amplifier has signal values of $v_{in} = 30$ mV and $v_{out} = 1.8$ V. What is the voltage gain of the amplifier?

   A) 30   B) 0.06   C) 60   D) 54

2) An amplifier has values of $A_V = 300$ and $v_{out} = 2.63$ V. What is the magnitude of the amplifier input voltage?

   A) 786 mV   B) 8.77 mV   C) 8.77 μV   D) 114 mV

Figure 8-1

3) Refer to Figure 8-1. Assuming the source voltage is constant, v_{in} _____ if Z_{in} decreases.

   A) increases   B) decreases   C) remains unchanged

4) Refer to Figure 8-1. Assuming the source voltage is constant, v_L _____ if Z_{in} decreases.

   A) increases   B) decreases   C) remains unchanged

5) Refer to Figure 8-1. Assuming the circuit voltage gain is constant, what happens to v_L when Z_{out} decreases?

   A) It increases   B) It decreases   C) It remains unchanged

6) An amplifier is driven by a 200 mV source with an internal resistance (R_S) of 50 Ω. If Z_{in} is 150 Ω, what is the value of v_{in}?

   A) 600 mV   B) 66.7 mV   C) 50 mV   D) 150 mV

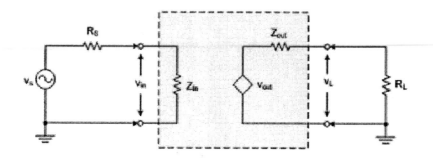

Figure 8–1

7) The amplifier in Figure 8–1 has the following values: $Z_{out} = 1.2$ kΩ, $R_L = 3.3$ kΩ, $v_{out} = 18.6$ V. What is the value of the load voltage?

A) 13.6 V   B) 6.78 V   C) 51.3 V   D) 4.07 V

8) Effective voltage gain is always _____ A_v.

A) greater than or equal to

B) less than or equal to

C) equal to

9) An *ideal* amplifier has _____ Z_{in}.

A) infinite   B) low   C) zero   D) high

10) An *ideal* amplifier has _____ Z_{out}.

A) infinite   B) low   C) zero   D) high

11) Which BJT amplifier configuration typically provides the highest power gain?

A) The common emitter amplifier

B) The common base amplifier

C) The common collector amplifier

12) Which BJT amplifier configuration typically provides the lowest input impedance?

A) The common emitter amplifier

B) The common base amplifier

C) The common collector amplifier

13) An amplifier draws 1.8 W from its dc power supply and delivers 250 mW to its load. What is the efficiency of the amplifier?

A) 45%   B) 13.9%   C) 87.8%   D) 12.2%

14) An amplifier with an efficiency rating of 18% draws 3.25 W from its dc power supply. What is the maximum power it can deliver to its load?

    A) 585 mW   B) 55 mW   C) 18 W   D) 58.5 mW

15) Which class of amplifier has the highest efficiency?

    A) Class A   B) Class B   C) Class C

16) Which class of amplifier conducts throughout 360° of its input signal?

    A) Class A   B) Class B   C) Class C

17) A _____ amplifier is normally a tuned amplifier.

    A) Class A   B) Class B   C) Class C

18) An amplifier with a 100 mW input provides a 3.25 W output. What is the power gain of the amplifier?

    A) 30.2 dB   B) –4.9 dB   C) 4.9 dB   D) 15.1 dB

19) An amplifier with a value of $A_V = 20$ dB. What input voltage is required for the amplifier to provide an 8.5 V output?

    A) 850 mV   B) 85 mV   C) 425 mV   D) 186 mV

20) What is the dB power gain of an amplifier if $A_V = 20$dB and R_{in} and R_{out} are equal?

    A) 20dB   B) 10dB   C) –3dB   D) 40dB

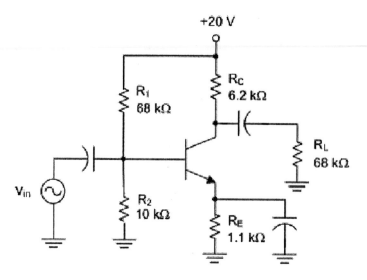

Figure 8–2

21) Refer to Figure 8–2. This circuit is a

    A) Class A amplifier   B) Class B amplifier

    C) Class C amplifier   D) Common base amplifier

22) An amplifier has two transistors, one npn and one pnp. The transistor emitters are connected to each other and to the load. The amplifier is most likely a

    A) Common Emitter amplifier.   B) Class A amplifier.

    C) Class B amplifier.   D) Class C amplifier.

23) An amplifier contains a single transistor with an LC tank in its collector circuit. The amplifier is most likely a/an

    A) Tuned amplifier.   B) Voltage–divider amplifier.

    C) Emitter follower.   D) Reactance amplifier.

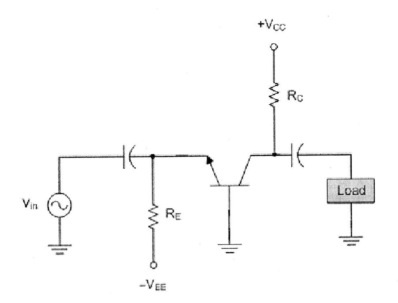

Figure 8-3

24) The circuit in Figure 8-3 is a _____ amplifier.

    A) Common emitter   B) Common collector

    C) Common base   D) Class C

25) Refer to Figure 8-3. This circuit would have relatively _____ Z_{in} and _____ Z_{out}.

    A) low; low   B) low; high   C) high; low   D) high; high

26) Refer to Figure 8-3. Which of the following circuit values is greater than the other two?

    A) Voltage gain (A_V)   B) Current gain(A_i)   C) Power gain (A_p)

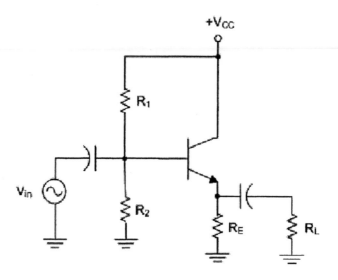

Figure 8-4

27) The circuit in Figure 8-4 is a _____ amplifier.

    A) Common emitter   B) Common collector

    C) Common base   D) Class C

28) Refer to Figure 8-4. This circuit would have relatively _____ Z_{in} and _____ Z_{out}.

    A) low; low

    B) midrange; midrange

    C) high; high

    D) low; high

    E) high; low

29) Refer to Figure 8-4. Which of the following circuit values is greater than the other two?

    A) Voltage gain (A_v)   B) Current gain(A_i)   C) Power gain (A_p)

30) A class B amplifier is subject to:

    A) non-linear distortion.   B) crossover distortion.

    C) class C interference.   D) Answer A and B

Chapter 8 Introduction to Amplifiers
Answer Key

1) C
2) B
3) B
4) B
5) A
6) D
7) A
8) B
9) A
10) C
11) A
12) B
13) B
14) A
15) C
16) A
17) C
18) D
19) A
20) A
21) A
22) C
23) A
24) C
25) B
26) A
27) B
28) E
29) B
30) B

1) The common–emitter amplifier provides

    A) voltage gain, current gain, and power gain.

    B) voltage gain and power gain, but no current gain.

    C) current gain and power gain, but no voltage gain.

    D) current gain and voltage gain, but no power gain.

2) The input and output signal *currents* for a common–emitter amplifier are

    A) always 180° out of phase.

    B) 180° out of phase in all but one amplifier configuration.

    C) in phase in all but one amplifier configuration.

    D) always in phase.

3) The input and output signal *voltages* for a common–emitter amplifier are

    A) always 180° out of phase.

    B) 180° out of phase in all but one amplifier configuration.

    C) in phase in all but one amplifier configuration.

    D) always in phase.

4) A CE amplifier has values of $V_B = 5$ V and $R_E = 2$ kΩ. What is the value of r'_e for the transistor?

    A) 10 Ω

    B) 5 Ω

    C) 11.7 Ω

    D) Cannot be determined with the information given.

5) A BJT has values of $h_{FE} = 200$ and $h_{fe} = 120$. The ac current gain for the device is

    A) 200.   B) 120.   C) 24,000.   D) 320.

6) A BJT has measured values of $I_B = 1$ mA and $I_C = 80$mA. When I_B is varied by ±100 μA, I_C changes by ±10 mA. What is the value of dc beta for the device?

    A) 80   B) 10   C) 100   D) 800

7) A BJT has measured values of $I_B = 1$ mA and $I_C = 80$mA. When I_B is varied by ±100 μA, I_C changes by ±10 mA. What is the value of ac beta for the device?

    A) 80   B) 10   C) 100   D) 800

8) By design, the reactance of a coupling capacitor is extremely _____ at the amplifier's lowest operating frequency.

    A) low   B) high

9) By design, the reactance of a bypass capacitor is extremely _____ at the amplifier's lowest operating frequency.

    A) low   B) high

10) If a bypass capacitor opens, the value of r'_e

    A) increases.   B) decreases.   C) does not change.

11) Why is dc isolation between amplifier stages important?

    A) It allows an ac signal to be coupled from a source stage to a load stage.

    B) It prevents the dc biasing of the source stage from affecting the dc biasing of the load stage.

    C) It allows a dc signal to be coupled from a source stage to a load stage.

12) Which of the following conditions would indicate that an emitter bypass capacitor is open?

    A) The presence of a dc voltage at the emitter terminal of the BJT

    B) The presence of an ac voltage at the emitter terminal of the BJT

    C) The loss of the ac signal at the base terminal of the BJT

    D) None of the above.

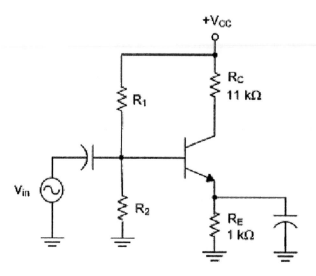

Figure 9–1

13) Refer to Figure 9–1. The amplifier has a value of $V_E = 1.1$ V. What is the approximate value of A_V for the circuit?

   A) 11

   B) 110

   C) 485

   D) Cannot be determined with the information given

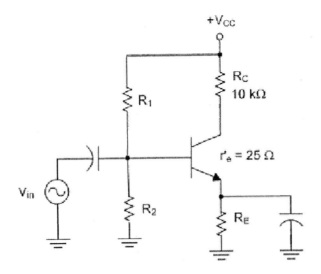

Figure 9-2

14) The amplifier in Figure 9-2 has values of R_C = 10 kΩ, r'e = 25 Ω, and A_i = 15. What is the value of A_p for the circuit?

A) 375

B) 6,000

C) 400

D) Cannot be determined with the information given.

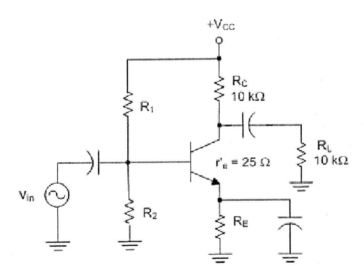

Figure 9-3

15) Refer to Figure 9-3. What is the value of A_V for the amplifier?

A) 400   B) 150   C) 200   D) 33.33

16) Which of the following would indicate that the load in Figure 9-3 has opened?

  A) An increase in the value of V_E

  B) An increase in the value of V_C

  C) An increase in the value of A_v

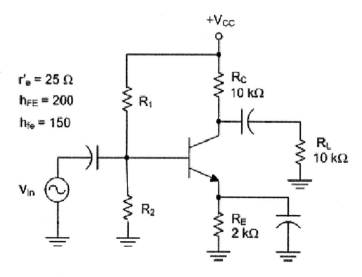

Figure 9–4

17) What is the value of Z_{base} for the circuit in Figure 9–4?

  A) 3.75 kΩ B) 300 kΩ C) 5 kΩ D) 400 kΩ

18) A common–emitter amplifier may be swamped to

  A) decrease the input impedance of an amplifier.

  B) reduce variations in voltage gain.

  C) increase the value of A_v for an amplifier.

  D) cause all of the above to occur.

19) The disadvantage of swamping a CE amplifier is that it

  A) increases voltage gain.   B) decreases voltage gain.

  C) increases input impedance.   D) decreases input impedance.

20) When using an oscilloscope to verify the operation of a CE amplifier, you must remember to

  A) adjust the TIME/DIV setting on the oscilloscope when going from the amplifier input to the amplifier output.

  B) adjust the VOLTS/DIV setting on the oscilloscope when going from the amplifier input to the amplifier output.

  C) connect the external trigger of the oscilloscope to the circuit under test.

  D) take all of the steps listed above.

21) The base input impedance of a BJT is listed on its spec sheet as

    A) h_{fe}.   B) h_{re}.   C) h_{ie}.   D) h_{oe}.

22) A transistor has the following values: $h_{fe} = 120$, $h_{FE} = 200$, $h_{ie} = 5\ k\Omega$, $h_{re} = 4 \times 10^{-4}$, and h_{oe} = 2500 μS. What is the value of r'_e for the device?

    A) $4 \times 10^{-4}\ \Omega$ B) $41.7\ \Omega$ C) $400\ \Omega$ D) $25\ \Omega$

23) For circuit analysis purposes, the most commonly used h–parameters are

    A) h_{ie} and h_{oe}.   B) h_{re} and h_{fe}.   C) h_{ie} and h_{re}.   D) h_{fe} and h_{ie}.

24) A CE amplifier is constructed using $R_C = 3.3\ k\Omega$ and $R_L = 12\ k\Omega$. The transistor has the following specifications: $h_{fe} = 120$, $h_{ie} = 5\ k\Omega$, $h_{re} = 4 \times 10\tilde{=}4$, and $h_{oe} = 2500$ μS. What is the value for A_V for this amplifier?

    A) Approximately 62.2   B) Approximately 79.1

    C) Approximately 287.8   D) None of the above.

25) A swamped amplifier has values of
$h_{ie} = 3\ k\Omega$, $h_{fe} = 150$, $h_{FE} = 200$, $r_E = 300\ \Omega$, and $R_E = 1.2\ k\Omega$.
What is the value of Z_{base} for the circuit?

    A) $3\ k\Omega$ B) $183\ k\Omega$

    C) $48\ k\Omega$ D) None of these are correct.

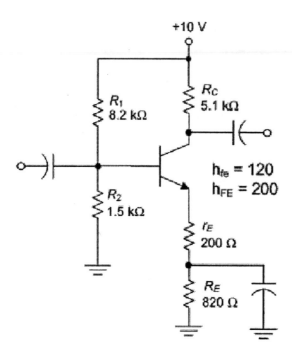

Figure 9-5

26) Referring to Figure 9-5. What is the value of r`e?

    A) 25 Ω   B) 26 Ω   C) 28 Ω   D) 30 Ω

27) Referring to Figure 9-5. What is the approximate value of Z_{base}?

    A) 2.77 kΩ   B) 4.62 kΩ   C) 27.6 kΩ   D) 45.8 kΩ

28) Referring to Figure 9-5. What is the approximate value of Z_{in}?

    A) 867   B) 992 Ω

    C) 1.21 kΩ   D) None of the above.

29) Referring to Figure 9-5. What is the approximate value of A_v?

    A) 22.2   B) 170

    C) 5   D) None of the above are correct.

30) Referring to Figure 9-5. If the 8.2 kΩ and 1.5 kΩ biasing resistors are changed to 16 kΩ and 3 kΩ respectively, the circuit voltage gain

    A) Increases.

    B) Decreases.

    C) Does not change significantly.

31) Referring to Figure 9-5. If a 10 kΩ load resistance is connected to the circuit, the voltage gain

   A) Increases.

   B) Decreases.

   C) Does not change significantly.

Chapter 9 Common–Emitter Amplifiers
Answer Key

1) A
2) D
3) A
4) C
5) B
6) A
7) C
8) A
9) A
10) C
11) B
12) B
13) C
14) B
15) C
16) C
17) A
18) B
19) B
20) B
21) C
22) B
23) D
24) A
25) C
26) D
27) C
28) C
29) A
30) C
31) B

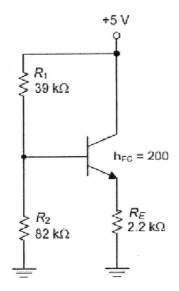

Figure 10–1

1) Is the circuit in Figure 10–1 midpoint biased?

    A) Yes   B) No

2) What is the value of $I_{C(sat)}$ for the circuit in Figure 10–1?

    A) 1.14 mA

    B) 3.41 mA

    C) 2.27 mA

    D) Cannot be determined with the information given.

3) Refer to Figure 10–1. The circuit values of $I_{C(sat)}$ and $V_{CE(off)}$ are _____.

    A) 2.273 and 5 V

    B) 2.273 mA and 5 V

    C) 2.73 mA and 2.5 V

    D) cannot be determined since R_C is a short.

4) Which of the following statements is true for a midpoint–biased emitter follower?

    A) The values of V_E and V_{CC} are approximately equal.

    B) The values of V_{CE} and V_E are approximately equal.

    C) The value of V_{CE} is approximately twice the value of V_E.

    D) None of the above statements are true.

5) An emitter follower has the following values: $h_{ic} = 3$ kΩ, $h_{fc} = 150$, and $R_E = 1.5$ kΩ. What is the approximate value of A_V for the circuit?

   A) 0.5

   B) 0.993

   C) 0.987

   D) Cannot be determined with the information given

6) Which of the following statements about emitter followers is true?

   A) The value of A_V is greater than the value of A_i.

   B) The value of A_i is greater than the value of A_p.

   C) The value of A_V is greater than the value of A_p.

   D) The values for A_V and A_p are approximately equal under normal circumstances.

7) Emitter followers can be used to match a _____ resistance source to a _____ resistance load.

   A) high; high   B) low; high   C) high; low   D) low; low

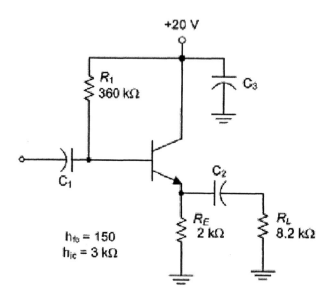

Figure 10–2

8) The value of A_V for the circuit in Figure 10–2 is

   A) 0.988.   B) 0.990.

   C) 0.998.   D) None of these are correct.

9) What is the approximate value of A_i for the circuit in Figure 10–2?

   A) 150   B) 20   C) 17.9   D) 22.5

10) C3 in Figure 10-2 is used to

    A) increase the voltage gain of the circuit.   B) increase the current gain of the circuit.

    C) couple V_{CC} to ground.   D) prevent unwanted variations in V_{CC}.

11) Refer to Figure 10-2. The circuit values of $I_{C(sat)}$ and $V_{CE(off)}$ are _____.

    A) 2.5 mA and 20 V   B) 2.5 mA and 10 V

    C) 5 mA and 20 V   D) 10 mA and 20 V

12) A common-base amplifier has values of $r'_e = 15\,\Omega$ and $R_E = 3\,k\Omega$. What is the approximate input impedance of the circuit?

    A) 3 kΩ B) 3015 Ω C) 15 Ω D) 200 Ω

13) A common-base amplifier does not provide _____ gain.

    A) voltage   B) current

    C) power   D) current and power

14) A common-base amplifier can be used to match a _____ resistance source to a _____ resistance load.

    A) high; high   B) low; high   C) high; low   D) low; low

15) Which of the following statements about the common-base amplifier is true?

    A) The value of A_v is greater than the value of A_i.

    B) The value of A_i is greater than the value of A_p.

    C) The value of A_p is greater than the value of A_v.

    D) The values of A_i and A_p are approximately equal under normal circumstances.

16) Which biasing circuits are commonly used in common-base amplifiers?

    A) Voltage-divider bias and base bias

    B) Base bias and emitter bias

    C) Emitter bias and voltage-divider bias

    D) Collector feedback and emitter follower bias

17) A Darlington pair has values of $h_{fc1} = h_{fc2} = 150$. What is the overall value of A_i for the pair?

    A) 300   B) 150

    C) 22,500   D) None of these are correct.

18) Replacing a standard transistor with a Darlington pair in an emitter follower will cause the value of A_p for the circuit to

    A) increase.   B) decrease.   C) remain the same.

19) Which of the following statements is true?

    A) Darlington emitter-followers provide extremely high values of A_v.

    B) An emitter follower containing a single transistor has lower output impedance than an identical circuit containing a Darlington pair.

    C) The Darlington emitter follower has extremely low input impedance.

    D) Darlington emitter followers have high input impedance and low output impedance.

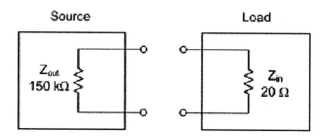

Figure 10–3

20) The source and load in Figure 10–3 exhibit:

    A) matched impedance.   B) saturated source impedance.

    C) mismatched impedance.   D) over loaded current gain.

21) Refer to Figure 10–3. Which of the following would be used to properly couple the source to the load?

    A) A common base amplifier with $Z_{in} = 150$ kΩ and $Z_{out} = 20$ Ω

    B) A common base amplifier with $Z_{in} = 20$ Ω and $Z_{out} = 150$ kΩ

    C) A common collector amplifier with $Z_{in} = 150$ kΩ and $Z_{out} = 20$ Ω

    D) A common collector amplifier with $Z_{in} = 20$ Ω and $Z_{out} = 150$ Ω

    E) A direct connection between the source and load

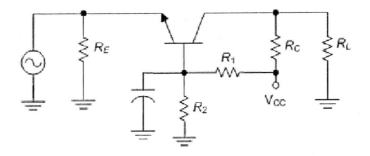

Figure 10–4

22) The circuit in Figure 10-4 is

A) voltage divider biased.

B) emitter biased.

C) common collector biased.

D) drawn incorrectly. The input should be applied to the base.

23) The circuit in Figure 10-4 is a _____ amplifier.

A) CE   B) CC   C) CB   D) V_{BB}

24) The circuit in Figure 10-4 has the following values:
$R_1 = 60$ kΩ, $R_2 = 20$ kΩ, $R_E = 1.5$ kΩ, $R_C = 3.3$ kΩ, and $R_L = 10$ kΩ, and $V_{CC} = 9$ V.
What is the circuit value of A_V?

A) About 1   B) 0.984   C) 102   D) 132

25) The circuit in Figure 10-4 has the following values:
$R_1 = 60$ kΩ, $R_2 = 20$ kΩ, $R_C = 3.3$ kΩ, $R_L = 10$ kΩ, $R_E = 1.5$ kΩ and $V_{CC} = 9$ V.
The values for $I_{C(sat)}$ and $V_{CE(off)}$ for the circuit are

A) 1.1 mA and 9 V.   B) 1.9 mA and 9 V.

C) 1.9 mA and 4.5 V.   D) 1.1 mA and 4.5 V.

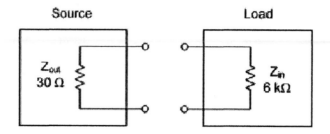

Figure 10-5

26) Refer to Figure 10-5. Which of the following would be used to properly couple the source to the load?

    A) A common base amplifier with $Z_{in} = 30\ \Omega$ and $Z_{out} = 6\ k\Omega$

    B) A common base amplifier with $Z_{in} = 6\ k\Omega$ and $Z_{out} = 30\ \Omega$

    C) A common collector amplifier with $Z_{in} = 30\ \Omega$ and $Z_{out} = 6\ k\Omega$

    D) A common collector amplifier with $Z_{in} = 6\ k\Omega$ and $Z_{out} = 30\ \Omega$

    E) A direct connection between the source and load

27) An engineer is designing a P.A. system. He intends to use a $300\ \Omega$ microphone and $8\ \Omega$ speakers. What values of Z_{in} and Z_{out} should this P.A. system amplifier have?

    A) $Z_{in} = 8\ \Omega$, $Z_{out} = 300\ \Omega$

    B) $Z_{in} = 300\ \Omega$, $Z_{out} = 8\ \Omega$

    C) Z_{in} much greater than $8\ \Omega$ and Z_{out} much lower that $300\ \Omega$

    D) Z_{in} much lower than $300\ \Omega$ and Z_{out} much greater than $8\ \Omega$

28) Which amplifier configurations produce no voltage phase shift from input to output?

    A) CC and CE   B) CB and CE

    C) CB, CC, and CE   D) CC and CB

29) Which best describes an emitter follower?

    A) The emitter follower is a voltage amplifier with a voltage gain that equals 1.

    B) The emitter follower is a current amplifier with a voltage gain that equals 1.

    C) The emitter follower is a power amplifier with a power gain that equals 1.

    D) The emitter follower is a current amplifier with a voltage gain that is less than 1.

Chapter 10 Other BJT Amplifiers
Answer Key

1) A
2) C
3) B
4) B
5) C
6) B
7) C
8) A
9) C
10) D
11) D
12) C
13) B
14) B
15) A
16) C
17) C
18) A
19) D
20) C
21) C
22) A
23) C
24) C
25) B
26) A
27) B
28) D
29) D

Chapter 11   Power Amplifiers

1) Which of the following is true?

    A) Efficiency is the ratio of dc input power to ac output power.

    B) The power that an amplifier delivers to its equals the difference between its dc input power and the power that the circuit dissipates.

    C) Power amplifiers are typically used to drive high impedance loads.

    D) None of the above statements are true.

2) Class B amplifiers usually contain

    A) two transistors.

    B) an LC tank circuit in the BJT collector circuit.

    C) a single BJT that conducts through 360° of the ac input cycle.

    D) a single BJT that conducts through 270° of the ac input cycle.

3) Class C amplifiers usually contain

    A) two transistors.

    B) an LC tank circuit in the BJT collector circuit.

    C) a single BJT that conducts through 360° of the ac input cycle.

    D) a single BJT that conducts through 270° of the ac input cycle.

4) The transformer–coupled class A amplifier has the lowest efficiency rating of all the class A amplifiers.

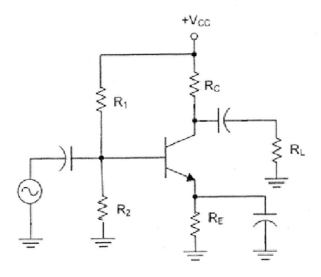

Figure 11–1

5) The circuit in Figure 11–1 has the following values:
   $V_{CC} = 12$ V, $R_1 = 48$ kΩ, $R_2 = 15$ kΩ, $R_C = 4.7$ kΩ,
   $R_E = 2.2$ kΩ, $R_L = 12$ kΩ, and $h_{fe} = h_{FE} = 200$
   What is the ac cut off voltage for this circuit?

   A) 6 V

   B) 8.5 V

   C) 12 V

   D) It cannot be determined with the information given.

6) The circuit in Figure 11–1 has the following values:
   $V_{CC} = 12$ V, $R_1 = 48$ kΩ, $R_2 = 15$ kΩ, $R_C = 4.7$ kΩ,
   $R_E = 2.2$ kΩ, $R_L = 12$ kΩ, and $h_{fe} = h_{FE} = 200$
   What is the ac saturation current for this circuit?

   A) 981 μA

   B) 1.74 mA

   C) 2.53 mA

   D) It cannot be determined with the information given.

7) The circuit in Figure 11–1 has the following values:
   $V_{CC} = 12$ V, $R_1 = 48$ kΩ, $R_2 = 15$ kΩ,
   $R_C = 4.7$ kΩ, $R_E = 2.2$ kΩ, $R_L = 12$ kΩ, and $h_{fe} = h_{FE} = 200$.
   What is the compliance of this circuit?

   A) 6.6 V

   B) 10.5 V

   C) 12 V

   D) It cannot be determined with the information given.

8) The circuit in Figure 11–1 has the following values:
   $V_{CC} = 12$ V, $R_1 = 48$ kΩ, $R_2 = 15$ kΩ, $R_C = 4.7$ kΩ,
   $R_E = 2.2$ kΩ, $R_L = 12$ kΩ, and $h_{fe} = h_{FE} = 200$
   How much power is the circuit drawing from the dc power source?

   A) 2.3 mW   B) 11.7 mW   C) 14.1 mW   D) 457 μW

9) The circuit in Figure 11–1 has the following values:
   $V_{CC} = 12$ V, $R_1 = 48$ kΩ, $R_2 = 15$ kΩ, $R_C = 4.7$ kΩ,
   $R_E = 2.2$ kΩ, $R_L = 12$ kΩ, and $h_{fe} = h_{FE} = 200$
   What is the approximate value of power dissipation for the transistor?

   A) 5.1 mW

   B) 7.4 mW

   C) 12 mW

   D) Cannot be determined without input signal

10) A circuit like the one in Figure 11–1 has values:
    $V_{CC} = 10$ V, $I_1 = 450$ μA, and $I_{CQ} = 10.55$ mA
    How much power is the circuit drawing from the dc power supply?

    A) 4.5 mW

    B) 1.21 mW

    C) 110 mW

    D) Cannot be determined from the information given.

11) A circuit like the one in Figure 11–1 has values:
    $I_1 = 1$ mA, $I_{CQ} = 50$mA, $V_{CC} = 15$ V, PP $= 9.3$ V, and $R_L = 680$ Ω
    What is the maximum efficiency of the amplifier?

    A) 16.62%   B) 15.9%   C) 20.8%   D) 25%

12) An amplifier has values of $2I_{CQ}r_C = 8.6$ V and $2V_{CEQ} = 12$ V. If the ac output voltage exceeds 8.6 Vpp, the amplifier will experience

    A) saturation clipping.   B) cutoff clipping.
    C) both saturation and cutoff clipping.   D) None of the above.

13) An amplifier has values of $2I_{CQ}r_C = 4.44$ V and $2V_{CEQ} = 7$ V. If the ac output voltage exceeds 7 V, the amplifier will experience

    A) saturation clipping.   B) cutoff clipping.
    C) both saturation and cutoff clipping.   D) none of the above.

14) A class A amplifier has an 8 V_{pp} output that is being applied to a 200 Ω load. What is the total ac load power?

    A) 320 mW   B) 640 mW   C) 40 mW   D) 80 mW

15) A class A amplifier has a compliance of 6 V_{pp} and a load resistance of 120 Ω. What is the maximum theoretical load power for the circuit?

A) 37.5 mW   B) 300 mW   C) 50 mW   D) 100 mW

16) The maximum theoretical efficiency of an RC–coupled class A amplifier is

A) 25%   B) 50%   C) 78.5%   D) 99%

17) The maximum value of V_{CE} in a transformer–coupled class A amplifier will be greater than V_{CC}. This is caused by

A) the input biasing network.

B) the efficiency characteristics of the amplifier.

C) the counter emf produced by the transformer primary.

D) the natural relationship between V_{CE} and V_{CC}.

18) A transformer–coupled class A amplifier has a transformer with a 3:1 turns ratio and values of $R_L = 100$ Ω, $V_{CEQ} = 6$ V, and $I_{CQ} = 8$ mA. What is the value of $v_{ce(off)}$ for the circuit?

A) 12 V

B) 6 V

C) 13.2 V

D) Cannot be determined from the information given.

19) A transformer–coupled class A amplifier has a transformer turns ratio of 4:1 and a load resistance of 25 Ω. The peak–to–peak value of V_{CE} is 12 V. What is the approximate load power for the circuit?

A) 45 mW   B) 160 mW   C) 90 mW   D) 60 mW

20) A transformer–coupled class A amplifier with a transformer turns ratio of 4:1 and a value of R_L = 25 Ω draws 220 mW from its dc power supply. What is the efficiency of the circuit?

A) 20.5%   B) 27.3%   C) 40.9%   D) 73%

21) A class B amplifier has a maximum theoretical efficiency of

A) 25%   B) 78.5%   C) 50%   D) 99%

22) Complementary–symmetry amplifiers are generally preferred over standard push–pull amplifiers because

A) they use complementary transistors.

B) they do not require the use of an output transformer.

C) they have high efficiency ratings.

D) they can drive lower impedance loads.

23) Crossover distortion in class B amplifiers is prevented by

    A) biasing the transistors deeply into cutoff.

    B) biasing the transistors slightly above cutoff.

    C) using complementary–symmetry transistors.

    D) increasing the load resistance.

24) A class AB amplifier has a value of $V_{CC} = 15$ Vdc. The value of $V_{CE(off)}$ for either transistor is approximately equal to

    A) 0.7 V.   B) 5 V.   C) 7.5 V.   D) 15 V.

25) A class AB amplifier has values of $V_{CC} = 12$ V and $R_L = 150$ Ω. What is the maximum theoretical ac load power for the circuit?

    A) 120 mW

    B) 240 mW

    C) 960 mW

    D) Cannot be determined from the information given.

26) When properly used, diode bias will prevent

    A) crossover distortion and thermal runaway.

    B) crossover distortion and saturation clipping.

    C) nonlinear distortion and thermal runaway.

    D) nonlinear distortion and saturation clipping.

27) When troubleshooting a class AB amplifier, you determine that one of the two transistors is faulty. At this point, you should

    A) test each of the transistors with an ohmmeter.

    B) simply replace both transistors.

    C) look for physical signs of damage to the two transistors.

    D) test each transistor with a transistor checker.

28) A given transistor has a power derating factor of 1.8mW/°C and a power dissipation rating of 400 mW at 25°C. How much power can the device dissipate at 120°C?

    A) 184 mW   B) 216 mW   C) 229 mW   D) 355 mW

29) Heat sink compound may be used to provide both a thermal connection and a mechanical connection.

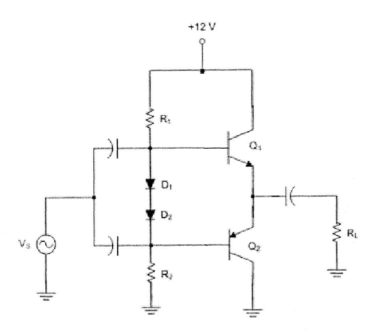

Figure 11-2

30) The circuit in Figure 11-2 is an example of a _____ amplifier.

   A) Class A   B) Class B   C) Class C   D) Class AB

31) The circuit in Figure 11-2 has the following values:
   $V_{CC} = 16$ V, $R_1 = R_2 = 470$ Ω, $R_L = 8$ Ω, and $h_{fe} = h_{FE} = 200$
   Determine the values of $I_{C(sat)}$ and $V_{CE(off)}$ for the transistors.

   A) 1 A, 8 V   B) 2 A, 8 V   C) 1 A, 16 V   D) 2 A, 16 V

Chapter 11 Power Amplifiers
Answer Key

1) B
2) A
3) B
4) FALSE
5) B
6) C
7) A
8) C
9) A
10) C
11) C
12) B
13) C
14) C
15) A
16) A
17) C
18) C
19) A
20) A
21) B
22) B
23) B
24) C
25) A
26) A
27) B
28) C
29) FALSE
30) D
31) B

Chapter 12   Field–Effect Transistors

1) The _____ terminal is the JFET counterpart of the BJT collector terminal.

   A) gate   B) drain   C) source

2) The _____ terminal is the JFET counterpart of the BJT base terminal.

   A) gate   B) drain   C) source

3) The _____ terminal is the JFET counterpart of the BJT emitter terminal.

   A) gate   B) drain   C) source

4) JFETs are

   A) current–controlled devices.   B) voltage–controlled devices.

   C) frequency–controlled devices.   D) impedance–controlled devices.

5) The _____ JFET uses a positive drain supply voltage (V_{DD}).

   A) n–channel   B) p–channel

6) As the channel width of a JFET decreases, the source–to–drain resistance of the device

   A) increases.   B) decreases.

7) Which of the following is usually used to control the channel width of a given JFET?

   A) V_S B) V_{GS}

   C) The operating frequency   D) I_D

8) The region of the JFET drain curve that lies between pinchoff and breakdown is called

   A) the constant–voltage region.   B) the ohmic region.

   C) the constant–current region.   D) Both B and C above.

9) The value of I_D is always _____ the value of I_{DSS} for a given JFET.

   A) less than   B) equal to

   C) less than or equal to   D) greater than

10) The value of V_{DS} that causes I_D to reach its maximum value at a constant value of V_{GS} is called

   A) $V_{D(max)}$.   B) pinchoff voltage.

   C) V_{DSS}.   D) None of these is correct.

11) A given JFET has values of $V_p = +10$ V and $I_{DSS} = 8$ mA. What is the value of $V_{GS(off)}$ for the device?

    A) +10 V

    B) –10 V

    C) –5 V

    D) Cannot be determined from the information given.

12) Which of the following statements is true?

    A) JFET drain current is controlled by its input (gate) current.

    B) JFET channel width is controlled by its gate–source voltage.

    C) There is only one way to vary JFET channel width.

    D) JFET drain current (at a given drain supply voltage) varies inversely with channel width.

13) A JFET has values of $I_{DSS} = 10$ mA and $V_{GS(off)} = –5$ V. What is the value of I_D at $V_{GS} = –3$ V?

    A) 1.6 mA   B) 3.6 mA   C) 25.6 mA   D) 4 mA

14) A JFET has the following ratings: $V_{GS(off)} = –2$ V to –5 V and $I_{DSS} = 4$ mA to 12 mA. The device is being used in a gate bias circuit with a gate supply voltage of $V_{GG} = –1$ V. What is the difference between the minimum and maximum values of I_D for the circuit?

    A) 7.68 mA   B) 9.6 mA   C) 6.68 mA   D) 8.6 mA

15) Which of the JFET biasing circuits listed below provides the best Q–point stability?

    A) Gate–bias   B) Self–bias

    C) Voltage–divider bias   D) Current–source bias

16) A JFET has values of $I_{DSS} = 12$ mA and $V_{GS(off)} = –4$ V. What is the value of I_D at $V_{GS} = –8$ V?

    A) 12 mA   B) 0 mA   C) 4 mA   D) 2 mA

17) A JFET has the following ratings: $V_{GS(off)} = –2$ V to –5 V and $I_{DSS} = 4$ mA to 12 mA. This device is being used in a self–bias circuit. When the bias line for the device is plotted, it is found that V_{GS} for the circuit will have a range of –1 V to –2.5 V. What are the corresponding $Q_{(min)}$ values?

    A) $V_{GSQ} = –1$ V, $I_{DQ} = 1$ mA

    B) $V_{GSQ} = –2.5$ V, $I_{DQ} = 250$ µA

    C) $V_{GSQ} = –1$ V, $I_{DQ} = 7.86$ mA

    D) Cannot be determined with the information given.

18) A JFET has the following ratings: $V_{GS(off)} = -2$ V to -5 V and $I_{DSS} = 4$ mA to 12 mA. The device is being used in a voltage divider circuit. When the load line is plotted, it is found that the V_{GS} for the circuit has a range of -1 V to -3.5 V. What are the corresponding $Q(max)$ values?

    A) $V_{GSQ} = -1$ V, $I_{DQ} = 7.68$ mA

    B) $V_{GSQ} = -3.5$ V, $I_{DQ} = 1.1$ mA

    C) $V_{GSQ} = -1$ V, $I_{DQ} = 1$ mA

    D) Cannot be determined with the information given.

19) The value of g_m is always _____ the value of g_{m0} for a given JFET.

    A) less than   B) equal to

    C) less than or equal to   D) greater than

20) A given JFET has values of $g_{m0} = 1200$ μS and $V_{GS(off)} = -4$ V. What is the value of g_m for the device at $V_{GS} = -2$ V?

    A) 600 μS

    B) 1200 μS

    C) 300 μS

    D) Cannot be determined with the information given.

21) A given JFET has values of $g_{m0} = 1200$ μs and $V_{GS(off)} = -4$ V. What is the approximate value of I_{DSS}?

    A) 4.8 mA

    B) 9.6 mA

    C) 2.4 mA

    D) Cannot be determined with the information given.

22) A given JFET has values of $g_{m0} = 1000$ μS and $V_{GS(off)} = -6$ V. The device is being used in a common–source amplifier with values of $R_D = 2.2$ kΩ, $R_L = 10$ kΩ, and $V_{GS} = -1$ V. What is the value of A_V for the circuit?

    A) 1.5

    B) 2.2

    C) 10

    D) Cannot be determined with the information given.

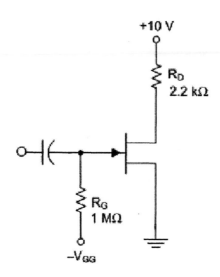

Figure 12-1

23) The JFET in Figure 12-1 has the following ratings:
VGS(off) = -2 V to -10 V, gm0 = 1000 μS to 1600 μS. What is the approximate input impedance of the circuit?

    A) 179 kΩ   B) 1 MΩ   C) 848 kΩ   D) 922 kΩ

24) Refer to Figure 12-1. Assume that the JFET has values of IDSS = 12 mA and VGS(off) = -6 V.
If VGG = -3 V, what is the value of ID for the circuit?

    A) 1 mA   B) 3 mA   C) 4.55 mA   D) 6 mA

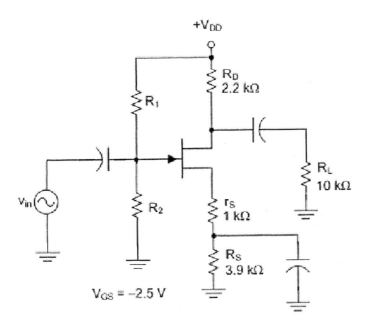

Figure 12-2

25) The JFET in Figure 12-2 has the following ratings: VGS(off) = –5 V and gm0 = 4000 μS. What is the value of Av for the circuit?

    A) 1.2   B) 1.47   C) 0.4   D) 0.9

26) The _____ amplifier has high input impedance, low output impedance, and low–voltage gain.

    A) common–gate   B) common–drain   C) common–source

27) The _____ amplifier has low input impedance, high output impedance, and high voltage gain.

    A) common–gate   B) common–drain   C) common–source

28) In a JFET amplifier, VGS = –2 V and ID = IDSS. Which of the following statements is true?

    A) The gate terminal of the JFET is probably open.

    B) The gate–source junction of the JFET is probably shorted.

    C) The drain terminal of the JFET is probably open.

    D) The readings do not indicate that any problem exists.

29) In a JFET amplifier, $V_{GS} = -5$ V, $I_G = 0$ mA, and $I_D = I_S = 5$mA. Which of the following statements is true?

    A) The gate terminal of the JFET is probably open.

    B) The gate–source junction of the JFET is probably shorted.

    C) The drain terminal of the JFET is probably open.

    D) The readings do not indicate that any problem exists.

30) The high input impedance of a JFET amplifier prevents it from being used as a buffer.

31) One advantage of using a JFET rf amplifier over a BJT amplifier is

    A) high input impedance.

    B) The JFET requires no signal input current.

    C) The JFET is less susceptible to noise.

    D) All of the above.

32) Gate–source breakdown voltage can be defined as

    A) the value gate–source voltage that will allow the channel to break down and conduct.

    B) the value of gate–source voltage that will damage the JFET.

    C) the maximum allowable value of V_{GS}.

    D) None of the above.

Chapter 12 Field-Effect Transistors
Answer Key

1) B
2) A
3) C
4) B
5) A
6) A
7) B
8) C
9) C
10) B
11) B
12) B
13) A
14) C
15) D
16) B
17) A
18) B
19) C
20) A
21) C
22) D
23) B
24) B
25) A
26) B
27) A
28) A
29) D
30) FALSE
31) D
32) B

Chapter 13   MOSFETs

1) MOSFETs typically have _____ input impedance than JFETs.

    A) higher   B) lower   C) similar

2) The main drawback to JFET operation is the fact that

    A) JFETs have low input impedance.

    B) JFETs are restricted to depletion–mode operation.

    C) JFETs are restricted to enhancement–mode operation.

    D) JFET amplifiers are poor buffers.

3) D–MOSFETs can operate in

    A) the depletion mode only.

    B) the enhancement mode only.

    C) the depletion mode and the enhancement mode.

4) The E–MOSFET can operate in

    A) the depletion mode only.

    B) the enhancement mode only.

    C) the depletion mode and the enhancement mode.

5) Which of the following is true for a D–MOSFET that is being operated in the depletion mode?

    A) $I_D > I_{DSS}$ B) $I_D < I_{DSS}$ C) $I_D = I_{DSS}$

6) A D–MOSFET has values of $I_{DSS} = 10$ mA and $V_{GS(off)} = -6$V. What is the value of I_D when $V_{GS} = 0$ V?

    A) 0 mA

    B) 5 mA

    C) 10 mA

    D) Cannot be determined from the information given.

7) _____ bias may be used with D–MOSFETs but not with JFETs.

    A) Source   B) Zero

    C) Drain–feedback   D) Current–source

8) An E-MOSFET has values of $V_{GS(th)} = 2$ V and $I_{D(on)} = 8$ mA @ $V_{GS} = 10$ V. What is the value of k for the device?

    A) 1×10^{-3}

    B) 1.25×10^{-4}

    C) 8×10^{-4}

    D) Cannot be determined with the information given.

9) An E-MOSFET has values of $V_{GS(th)} = 4$ V and $I_{D(on)} = 12$ mA @ $V_{GS} = 10$ V. The device is being used in a circuit that has a value of $V_{GS} = 6$ V. What is the value of I_D for the circuit?

    A) 13.33 mA   B) 1 mA   C) 1.33 mA   D) 0 mA

10) Which of the following biasing circuits can be used with E-MOSFETs?

    A) self bias   B) zero bias

    C) drain-feedback bias   D) current-source bias

11) The operation of standard MOSFETs is limited at high frequencies because of

    A) low maximum values of I_D.   B) high maximum values of I_D.

    C) high gate-to-channel capacitance.   D) low gate-to-channel capacitance.

12) What type of MOSFETs are designed to be used at high frequencies?

    A) VMOS   B) LDMOS

    C) E-MOSFETs   D) Dual-gate MOSFETs

13) Which of the following devices would normally have the highest current-handling capability?

    A) E-MOSFETs   B) D-MOSFETs

    C) LDMOS   D) Dual-gate MOSFETs

14) Groups of digital circuits with nearly identical characteristics are called

    A) logic groups.   B) logic families.

    C) logic subgroups.   D) logic subfamilies.

15) CMOS stands for

    A) complementary MOS.   B) current MOS.

    C) capacitive MOS.   D) conductive MOS.

16) A CMOS inverter has a +10 V supply and an input that varies between 0 V and +10 V. What is the circuit output when the input to the circuit is +10 V?

   A) –10 V.

   B) 0 V.

   C) +10 V.

   D) Cannot be determined with the information given.

17) One advantage that CMOS has over TTL is the fact that

   A) CMOS circuits have better power dissipation ratings.

   B) CMOS circuits have a lower packing density than TTL.

   C) CMOS circuits can be used with positive supply voltages.

   D) CMOS circuits are cheaper than TTL circuits.

18) The cascode amplifier is used primarily in

   A) high frequency applications.   B) digital switching circuits.

   C) audio amplifiers.   D) CMOS applications.

19) The dual–gate MOSFET makes a poor cascode amplifier device.

20) When used in an RF amplifier, dual-gate MOSFETs provide for the use of

   A) fading.   B) automatic gain control (AGC).

   C) CMOS logic family.   D) None of the above.

21) VMOS is a special–purpose type of

   A) D–MOSFET.   B) E–MOSFET.   C) JFET.   D) BJT.

22) To protect MOSFETs from static electricity, you should store them in conductive foam.

23) Many MOSFET devices now contain internal _____ that protect them from static electricity.

   A) BJTs   B) zener diodes

   C) pn junction diodes   D) capacitors

24) LDMOS is a special–purpose type of

   A) D–MOSFET.   B) E–MOSFET.   C) JFET.   D) BJT.

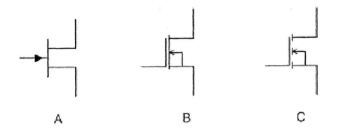

Figure 13–1

25) Refer to Figure 13–1. The symbol labeled A is a(n) _____.

    A) E–MOSFET   B) JFET

    C) D–MOSFET   D) None of the above.

26) Refer to Figure 13–1. The symbol labeled B is a(n) _____.

    A) E–MOSFET   B) JFET

    C) D–MOSFET   D) None of the above.

27) Refer to Figure 13–1. The symbol labeled C is a(n) _____.

    A) E–MOSFET   B) JFET

    C) D–MOSFET   D) None of the above.

28) The term packing density refers to:

    A) the number of IC chips that can be shipped in one package.

    B) the number of circuits or components that can be fabricated in a given amount of space.

    C) a particular design method that results in a complex circuit

    D) CMOS circuits but not BJT circuits.

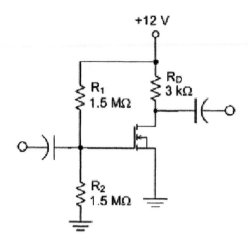

+12 V

R₁
1.5 MΩ

R_D
3 kΩ

R₂
1.5 MΩ

Figure 13-2

29) The circuit in Figure 13-2 is a(n) _____ amplifier.

   A) Voltage-divider biased common-emitter

   B) Voltage-divider biased common-drain

   C) Voltage-divider biased common-source

   D) Drain-feedback biased common-source

30) The MOSFET in Figure 13-2 has the following specifications:
   $I_{D(on)}$ = 10 mA @ $V_{GS(on)}$ = 10 V and $V_{GS(Th)}$ = 2 V. Determine the minimum value of k for this circuit.

   A) 1.56   B) 1.56 × 10⁻⁴   C) 0.001   D) 1.25 × 10-3

31) The MOSFET in Figure 13-2 has the following specifications:
   $I_{D(on)}$ = 10 mA @ $V_{GS(on)}$ = 10 V and $V_{GS(Th)}$ = 2 V. Determine the value of V_{GS} for this circuit.

   A) 2 V   B) 6 V   C) 10V   D) 12 V

32) The MOSFET in Figure 13-2 has the following specifications:
   $I_{D(on)}$ = 10 mA @ $V_{GS(on)}$ = 10 V and $V_{GS(Th)}$ = 2 V. Determine the value of I_D for this circuit.

   A) 2.5 mA   B) 3mA   C) 5 mA   D) 10 mA

33) The MOSFET in Figure 13-2 has the following specifications:
   $I_{D(on)}$ = 10 mA @ $V_{GS(on)}$ = 10 V and $V_{GS(Th)}$ = 2 V. Determine the value of V_{DS} for this circuit.

   A) 2 V   B) 4.5 V   C) 7.5 V   D) 12 V

Chapter 13 MOSFETs
Answer Key

1) A
2) B
3) C
4) B
5) B
6) C
7) B
8) B
9) C
10) C
11) C
12) D
13) C
14) B
15) A
16) B
17) A
18) A
19) FALSE
20) B
21) B
22) TRUE
23) B
24) B
25) B
26) C
27) A
28) B
29) C
30) B
31) B
32) A
33) B

Chapter 14   Amplifier Frequency Response

1) The <u>bandwidth</u> of an amplifier is

    A) the range of frequencies over which gain remains relatively constant.

    B) the range of frequencies between its lower and upper 3 dB frequencies.

    C) the difference between f_{c2} –and f_{c1}.

    D) All of the above.

2) An amplifier has values of $f_{c2} = 500$ kHz and $f_{c1} = 40$ kHz. The center frequency for the circuit is approximately _____.

    A) 141 kHz   B) 230 kHz   C) 270 kHz   D) 460 kHz

3) An amplifier has values of $f_{c1} = 100$ kHz and $f_0 = 200$ kHz. What is the value of f_{c2} for the circuit?

    A) 300 kHz   B) 141.4 kHz   C) 400 kHz   D) 460 kHz

4) An amplifier has values of $f_0 = 31.6$ kHz and $f_{c2} = 1$ MHz. What is the approximate value of f_{c1}?

    A) 31.6 Hz   B) 1 kHz   C) 178 kHz   D) 12 kHz

5) The low–frequency response of a BJT amplifier is affected by

    A) the BJT internal capacitances.

    B) the supply voltage (V_{CC}).

    C) the coupling and bypass capacitor values.

    D) All of the above.

6) The high–frequency response of a BJT amplifier is affected by

    A) the BJT internal capacitances.

    B) the supply voltage (V_{CC}).

    C) the coupling and bypass capacitor values.

    D) All of the above.

7) An amplifier has a midband power gain of 24,500. Which of the following expresses this gain in dB?

    A) 87.78 dB   B) 43.9 dB

    C) 4.39 dB   D) None of the above.

8) An amplifier has values of $P_{in} = 20$ mW and $P_{out} = 60$ W. What is the power gain of the circuit?

   A) 3000 dB

   C) 34.4 dB

   B) 69.5 dB

   D) None of the above.

9) An amplifier normally has a power gain of 12,000. If the power gain of the circuit drops by 3 dB, the value of A_p will be approximately

   A) 6,000.   B) 4,000.   C) 9,000.   D) zero.

10) Negative dB power values represent

   A) power gain.

   C) power values that do not change.

   B) power loss.

   D) None of the above.

11) Which of the following is an advantage of using dB representations of gain values?

   A) Positive and negative dB values represent gain and loss values that are reciprocals of each other.

   B) In multistage amplifiers, gain calculations are simplified by the use of dB values.

   C) Using dB values, we can represent large gain values with relatively small numbers.

   D) All of the above.

12) An amplifier has an output power of 500 W. What is the value of $A_{p(dB)}$ for the circuit?

   A) 26.99 dB

   B) 53.98 dB

   C) 56.99 dB

   D) Cannot be determined from the information given.

13) What frequency is two decades above 5 kHz?

   A) 25 kHz

   B) 105 kHz

   C) 500 kHz

   D) Cannot be determined from the information given.

14) What frequency lies four octaves above 1 kHz?

   A) 8 kHz

   C) 9 kHz

   B) 16 kHz

   D) None of these is correct.

15) A BJT amplifier has values of $f_{1B} = 5$ kHz, $f_{1E} = 78$ Hz, and $f_{1C} = 3.3$ kHz. What is the overall value of f_{C1} for the circuit?

   A) 3.3 kHz

   C) 5 kHz

   B) 78 Hz

   D) None of these is correct.

16) A BJT amplifier has values of f_{2B} = 120kHz and f_{2C} = 437 kHz. What is the overall value of f_{C2} for the circuit?

    A) 120 kHz

    B) 437 kHz

    C) 557 kHz

    D) None of these is correct.

17) A BJT amplifier has been analyzed and found to have lower cutoff frequencies of 3.3 kHz, 5 kHz, and 78 Hz. It was also found to have upper cutoff frequencies of 120 kHz, and 437 kHz. What is the overall bandwidth of the amplifier?

    A) 115 kHz

    B) 432 kHz

    C) 119.92 kHz

    D) None of these is correct.

18) The roll–off rate for an RC circuit is

    A) 20 dB per octave.

    B) 6 dB per decade.

    C) 6 dB per octave.

    D) None of these is correct.

19) A common–emitter amplifier has values of C_{bc} = 5pF and A_v = 15. What is the Miller input capacitance for the circuit?

    A) 80 pF

    B) 7 pF

    C) 163.1 pF

    D) None of these is correct.

20) Two identical amplifiers are cascaded. The overall bandwidth of the multistage amplifier is _____ the bandwidth of each individual stage.

    A) equal to

    B) more narrow than

    C) wider than

21) The value of f_{C1} for the input circuit of a JFET amplifier is normally _____ that of a comparable BJT amplifier.

    A) equal to

    B) lower than

    C) higher than

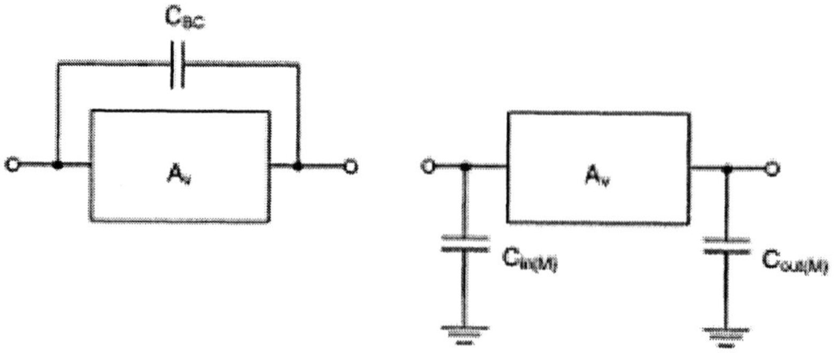

Figure 14–1

22) The component labeled $C_{out(M)}$ in Figure 14–1 represents the _____ ouput capacitance.

    A) medium.

    B) MOSFET.

    C) modulation.

    D) Miller.

23) The circuit in Figure 14-1 has values of $C_{bc} = 5$ pF and $A_v = 75$. What is the value of $C_{in(M)}$ for the circuit?

    A) 0.07 pF   B) 5 pF   C) 375 pF   D) 380 pF

24) The circuit in Figure 14-1 has values of $C_{bc} = 5$ pF and $A_v = 75$. What is the value of $C_{out(M)}$ for the circuit?

    A) 0.07 pF   B) 5 pF   C) 375 pF   D) 380 pF

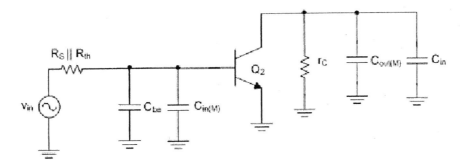

Figure 14-2

25) The equivalent circuit in Figure 14-2 is used to

    A) determine the values of f_{C1} and f_{C2}.

    B) determine the value of f_{C1}.

    C) determine the value of f_{C2}.

    D) determine none of the values listed here.

26) The transistor amplifier in Figure 14-2 has the following values: $h_{ie} = 2$ kΩ, $h_{fe} = 120$, $C_{bc} = 5$ pF, $C_{be} = 10$ pF, $R_S = 300$ Ω, $R_{th} = 1.2$ kΩ, $r_c = 4$ kΩ, and $C_{in} = 1200$ pF. What is the voltage gain of the circuit?

    A) 0.24   B) 2   C) 240   D) 480,000

27) The transistor amplifier in Figure 14-2 has the following values: $h_{ie} = 2$ kΩ, $h_{fe} = 120$, $C_{bc} = 5$ pF, $C_{be} = 10$ pF, $R_S = 300$ Ω, $R_{th} = 1.2$ kΩ, $r_c = 4$ kΩ, and $C_{in} = 1200$ pF. What is the value of $C_{in(M)}$ for the circuit?

    A) 6.2 pF   B) 15 pF   C) 1205 pF   D) 2410 pF

28) The transistor amplifier in Figure 14-2 has the following values: $h_{ie} = 2$ kΩ, $h_{fe} = 120$, $C_{bc} = 5$ pF, $C_{be} = 10$ pF, $R_S = 300$ Ω, $R_{th} = 1.2$ kΩ, $r_c = 4$ kΩ, and $C_{in} = 1200$ pF. What is the value of f_{2B} for the circuit?

    A) 307.5 kHz   B) 613.8 kHz   C) 6.631 MHz   D) 37.1 MHz

29) The transistor amplifier in Figure 14-2 has the following values: $h_{ie} = 2$ kΩ, $h_{fe} = 120$, $C_{bc} = 5$ pF, $C_{be} = 10$ pF, $R_S = 300$ Ω, $R_{th} = 1.2$ kΩ, $r_c = 4$ kΩ, and $C_{in} = 1200$ pF. What is the value of $C_{out(M)}$ for the circuit?

A) 4.979 μF   B) 5pF   C) 1200 pF   D) 1205 pF

30) The transistor amplifier in Figure 14-2 has the following values:
$h_{ie} = 2$ kΩ, $h_{fe} = 120$, $C_{bc} = 5$ pF, $C_{be} = 10$ pF, $R_S = 300$ Ω, $R_{th} = 1.2$ kΩ, $r_c = 4$ kΩ, and $C_{in} = 1200$ pF. What is the value if f_{2C} for the circuit?

A) 16.54 kHz   B) 33.02 kHz   C) 330 kHz   D) 7.958 MHz

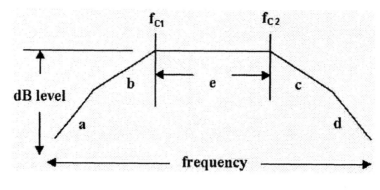

Figure 14-3

31) Refer to Figure 14-3. The graph of dB level vs frequency is called a _____.

A) Body graph   B) Body plot

C) Bode plot   D) All of the above.

32) Refer to Figure 14-3. The portion of the graph labeled "e" represents _____.

A) the 3dB cutoff band of frequencies   B) a 20dB/decade roll-off rate

C) a 6 dB/octave response curve   D) bandwidth

Chapter 14 Amplifier Frequency Response
Answer Key

1) D
2) A
3) C
4) B
5) C
6) A
7) B
8) C
9) A
10) B
11) D
12) D
13) C
14) B
15) C
16) A
17) A
18) C
19) A
20) B
21) B
22) D
23) D
24) B
25) C
26) C
27) C
28) B
29) B
30) B
31) C
32) D

Chapter 15   Operational Amplifiers

1) Solid–state devices that contain more than one active and/or passive component are called

    A) discrete devices.   B) integrated circuits.

    C) multiple–component circuits.   D) op–amps.

2) Which of the following statements is true?

    A) Op–amps are high–gain dc amplifiers.

    B) Op–amps have extremely high input impedance.

    C) Op–amps have extremely low output impedance.

    D) All of these statements are true.

3) An op–amp has the part number TL741CN. The prefix <u>TL</u> identifies

    A) the operating temperature range.   B) the type of op–amp.

    C) the device manufacturer.   D) the type of component casing used.

4) Op–amps are available in

    A) dual in–line packages (DIPs).   B) surface–mount packages (SMPs)

    C) type TO–5 metal cans.   D) all of these packages.

5) The voltage gain of an op–amp circuit is always less than or equal to the A_{OL} rating for the op–amp.

6) An op–amp circuit has ±15 V supply voltages and a voltage gain of 20. The noninverting voltage (V_2) is 0.3 V and the inverting voltage (V_1) is 0.35 V. What is the output voltage from the device?

    A) +1 V   B) +6 V   C) –1 V   D) –7 V

7) An op–amp has a 3 kΩ load and ±10 V supply voltages. What is the maximum possible peak–to peak output voltage for the circuit?

    A) Approximately 18 V   B) Approximately 16 V

    C) Approximately 20 V   D) None of the above.

8) The inverting and noninverting inputs to an op–amp are connected to a(n)

    A) inverting amplifier.   B) noninverting amplifier.

    C) differential amplifier.   D) open–loop amplifier.

9) An op-amp will not work if

   A) the supply voltages are less than ±5 V.

   B) the input offset voltage is less than 100 mV.

   C) either the inverting or noninverting input is not provided with an external current path.

   D) the input offset current is less than 1 mA.

10) When a given op-amp has 10 V common–mode inputs, the output of the device is 10 mV. When this same device has a 2 mV differential input, the output of the device is 10 V. What is the CMRR of the device?

   A) 5:1   B) 5000:1   C) 1000:1   D) 5,000,000:1

11) An op-amp has a slew rate of 0.2 V/μs. If the the circuit has a sine wave input and its peak output is 15 V, what is its maximum operating frequency?

   A) 2.12 kHz   B) 21.2 Hz   C) 471 Hz   D) 4.71 kHz

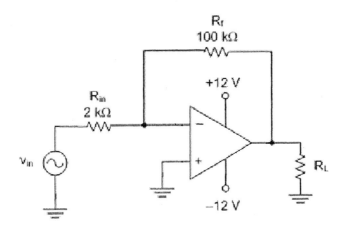

Figure 15–1

12) The value of A_{CL} for the circuit in Figure 15–1 is

   A) 50 k.   B) 200.   C) 50.   D) 51.

13) The common–mode gain of the op-amp in Figure 15–1 is 0.002. What is the CMRR of the amplifier?

   A) 25,000:1

   B) 0.002:1

   C) 100:1

   D) Cannot be determined from the information given.

14) The op-amp used in the circuit of Figure 15–1 has an input impedance of 2 MΩ. What is the input impedance of the circuit?

   A) 2 MΩ   B) 2 kΩ   C) 2.002 MΩ   D) 102 kΩ

15) The op-amp in Figure 15-1 has an output impedance of 100 Ω. The output impedance of the circuit is slightly less than

A) 100 Ω.   B) 100 kΩ.   C) 100.1 kΩ.   D) 50 Ω.

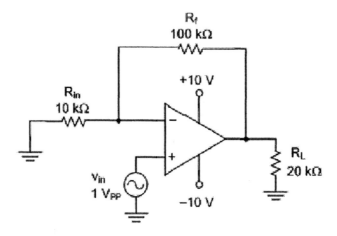

Figure 15-2

16) The circuit in Figure 15-2 has an output that is approximately

A) 10 V$_{pp}$.

B) 11 V$_{pp}$.

C) 1 V$_{pp}$.

D) Cannot be determined without knowing the value of A$_{OL}$.

17) The op-amp in Figure 15-2 has a slew rate of 12 V/µs. If the the circuit has a sine wave input and its peak output is 9 V, what is its maximum operating frequency?

A) approximately 212.2 kHz.   B) approximately 347.2 kHz.

C) approximately 382.0 kHz.   D) None of the above.

18) The op-amp in Figure 15-2 has an input impedance of 5 MΩ. What is the input impedance of the circuit?

A) 5 MΩ   B) 10 kΩ   C) 50 MΩ   D) 110 kΩ

19) The feedback resistor (R$_f$) in Figure 15-2 opens. What is the peak-to-peak output from the circuit?

A) 11 V$_{pp}$ (clipped)   B) 20 V$_{pp}$ (clipped)

C) 18 V$_{pp}$ (clipped)   D) 18 V$_{pp}$ (not clipped)

20) A voltage follower has values of $R_L = 12\,k\Omega$, $V_S = \pm 12\,V$, and $V_{in} = 10\,V_{pk}$. What is the peak-to-peak output from the circuit?

    A) 20 V_{pp}

    B) 21 V_{pp}

    C) 12 V_{pp}

    D) Cannot be determined from the information given.

21) Why is the CMRR of an inverting amplifier always lower than that of its op-amp?

    A) The common-mode gain of an op-amp increases when it is used in an inverting amplifier.

    B) The value of differential gain for an inverting amplifier is lower than that of its op-amp.

    C) Slew-rate limiting decreases the common-mode gain of the op-amp.

    D) Because of the lower input impedance of the inverting amplifier.

22) An inverting amplifier and a noninverting amplifier are built using the same values of R_f and R_{in}. Assuming that the op-amps being used in the two circuits have identical common-mode gain values, which circuit will have the higher CMRR?

    A) The inverting amplifier

    B) The noninverting amplifier

    C) Neither. The two CMRR values will be equal.

23) An inverting amplifier with $\pm 11\,V$ supply voltages normally has a $10V_{pp}$ sinusoidal output. Checking the circuit with an oscilloscope shows that the output is $0\,V$. Which of the following could account for this problem?

    A) R_i open   B) R_f open

    C) R_f shorted by a solder bridge   D) either R_1 is open or R_f is shorted

24) The voltage follower typically has a value of CMRR = 1.

25) Negative feedback

    A) decreases bandwidth.   B) increases circuit gain.

    C) increases amplifier noise.   D) decreases circuit gain.

26) The total phase shift around a negative feedback loop is

    A) 360° (or 0°).   B) 180°.   C) 90°.   D) 45°.

27) The total phase shift around a positive feedback loop is

    A) 360° (or 0°).   B) 180°.   C) 90°.   D) 45°.

28) Positive feedback is used to produce a special type of circuit called a/an

  A) inverting amplifier.   B) noninverting amplifier.

  C) oscillator.   D) feedback regulator.

29) A negative feedback amplifier has values of $V_{out} = 6$ V_{pp} and $V_f = 630$ mV_{pp}. What is the attenuation factor of the circuit?

  A) 4.28   B) 0.0641   C) 0.105   D) 9.52

30) A negative feedback amplifier has values of $\alpha_V = 0.114$ and $A_V = 244$. What is the value of A_{vf} for the circuit?

  A) 8.47   B) 2140   C) 35.1   D) 6.75

31) Negative feedback _____ the input impedance of a noninverting amplifier.

  A) increases   B) decreases   C) does not affect

32) Negative feedback _____ the output impedance of a noninverting amplifier.

  A) increases   B) decreases   C) does not affect

33) Negative feedback _____ the bandwidth of a noninverting amplifier.

  A) increases   B) decreases   C) does not affect

Chapter 15 Operational Amplifiers
Answer Key

1) B
2) D
3) C
4) D
5) TRUE
6) C
7) B
8) C
9) C
10) D
11) A
12) C
13) A
14) B
15) A
16) B
17) B
18) A
19) C
20) A
21) B
22) B
23) D
24) FALSE
25) D
26) B
27) A
28) C
29) C
30) A
31) A
32) B
33) A

Chapter 16   Additional Op-Amp Applications

1) The comparator may be used as a/an

    A) linear amplifier.

    B) oscillator.

    C) sine wave to rectangular wave converter.

    D) rectangular wave to triangular wave converter.

2) The gain of a typical comparator is approximately equal to

    A) unity (1).

    B) 3 dB.

    C) the open-loop voltage gain (A_{OL}) of its op-amp.

    D) 0 dB.

3) A comparator is a circuit that is used to provide a _____ output when the input voltage is more _____ than a fixed _____ reference voltage.

    A) positive; positive; positive   B) positive; negative; positive

    C) negative; positive; negative   D) All of these are correct.

4) A comparator has the following values: $R_L = 20$ kΩ, $V_S = +10$ V, and $V_{ref} = +2$ V (applied to the inverting input). If the noninverting input goes to +3 V, the output voltage

    A) will be approximately +9 V.

    B) will be approximately –9 V.

    C) will be approximately +3 V.

    D) cannot be determined without knowing the value of A_{CL} for the circuit.

5) The use of a variable comparator allows for

    A) changing the values of V_S.

    B) processing ultra-high frequency signals.

    C) changing the value of V_{ref}.

    D) changing the limits of V_{out}.

6) The ideal output from an RC integrator would be a triangular waveform when the input signal is a square wave. What is the actual output wave shape?

    A) Sinusoidal   B) Exponential   C) Triangular   D) Square

7) The ideal output from an op-amp integrator with a square wave input would be a triangular waveform. What is the actual output wave shape?

  A) Sinusoidal   B) Exponential   C) Triangular   D) Square

8) The key to obtaining a triangular output from an integrator with a square wave input is to provide

  A) a constant-current charging source for the capacitor.

  B) a constant-frequency charging source for the capacitor.

  C) a constant-voltage charging source for the capacitor.

  D) a short RC time constant.

9) The differentiator can be used to convert a

  A) square wave into a triangular wave.   B) square wave into a sine wave.

  C) triangular wave into a sine wave.   D) triangular wave into a square wave.

10) The output from a differentiator is proportional to

  A) the peak value of the input voltage.

  B) the rate of change of the input voltage.

  C) the rate of change of the input frequency.

  D) None of these are correct.

11) A summing amplifier provides an output that is always

  A) equal to the difference between its input voltages.

  B) equal to the sum of its input voltages.

  C) equal or proportional to the sum of its input voltages.

  D) None of these are correct.

12) A summing amplifier may be used as a/an

  A) linear amplifier.   B) oscillator.

  C) digital-to-analog converter.   D) analog-to-digital converter.

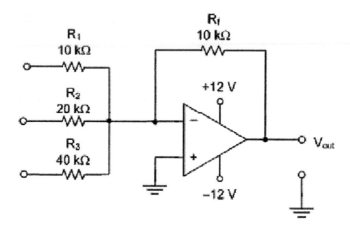

Figure 16–1

13) What is the general–class equation for the circuit in Figure 16–1?

    A) $V_{out} = V_1 + 2V_2 + 4V_3$ B) $-V_{out} = V_1 + 0.5V_2 + 0.25V_3$

    C) $-V_{out} = V_1 + 2V_2 + 0.25V_3$ D) None of these are correct.

14) The input voltages to the circuit in Figure 16–1 are as follows: $V_1 = 2$ V, $V_2 = 4$ V, and $V_3 = 8$ V. What is the output voltage from the circuit?

    A) +11 V   B) +6 V   C) –11 V   D) –6 V

15) A summing amplifier has the following values: $R_f = 10$ kΩ, and $R_1 = R_2 = R_3 = R_4 = 40$ kΩ. Which of the following statements is true about the circuits?

    A) The circuit will not work with the values given.

    B) The output will equal the average of the four input voltages.

    C) The output will equal the sum of the four input voltages.

    D) The output will equal the sum of the squares of the four input voltages.

16) Instrumentation amplifiers are used to amplify _____ signals.

    A) high frequency   B) out of phase

    C) high level   D) low level

17) Two common–mode inputs to an instrumentation amplifier have identical _____.

    A) amplitude   B) amplitude and phase

    C) frequency   D) amplitude and frequency

18) Which of the following can best be described as a high–gain, minimum distortion, high input impedance, low output impedance circuit operated between 20 Hz and 20 kHz?

    A) An op–amp audio amplifier   B) A high–z voltmeter

    C) An instrumentation amplifier   D) A subtractor

19) Which of the following can best be described as a high-gain, high CMRR circuit that is used to detect and amplify low-level signals?

A) An op-amp audio amplifier

B) A high-z voltmeter

C) An instrumentation amplifier

D) A subtractor

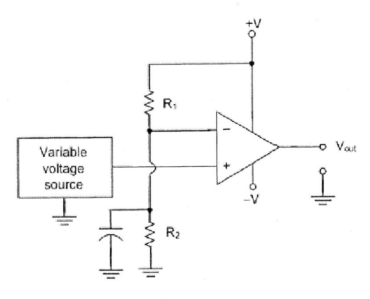

Figure 16-2

20) The circuit in Figure 16-2 has the following values: $R_1 = 7$ kΩ, $R_2 = 1$ kΩ, $C_B = 1$ μF, and supply voltages of ± 10 V. What is the value of V_{ref} for this circuit?

A) +1.25 V   B) –1.25 V   C) + 2.5 V   D) –7.5 V

21) The circuit in Figure 16-2 has the following values: $R_1 = 7$ kΩ, $R_2 = 1$ kΩ, $C_B = 1$ μF, and supply voltages of ± 10 V. The input is + 1 V. What is the approximate output voltage?

A) + 9 V   B) – 9 V   C) + 5 V   D) – 5 V

22) Refer to Figure 16-2. C_B is used to

A) filter out power supply current surges.

B) prevent variations in v_{in} from affecting the voltage divider.

C) filter out unwanted stray inductance.

D) filter out unwanted stray capacitance.

23) The circuit in Figure 16-2 is a(n) _____.

A) differentiator

B) comparator

C) instrumentation amplifier

D) ramp generator

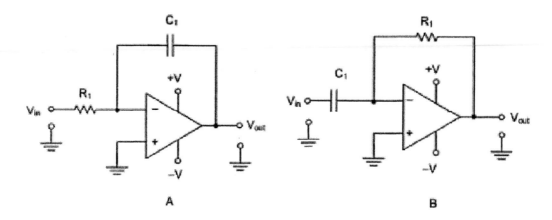

Figure 16-3

24) Refer to Figure 16-3. Circuit A is a(n) _____.

    A) linear amplifier   B) integrator

    C) differentiator   D) comparator

25) Refer to Figure 16-3. Circuit B is a(n) _____.

    A) linear amplifier   B) integrator

    C) differentiator   D) comparator

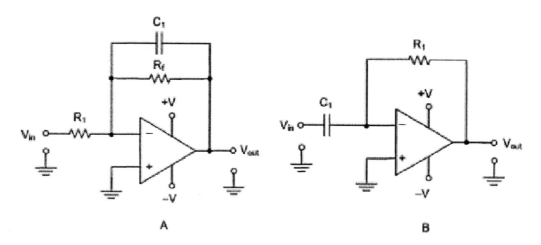

Figure 16-4

26) The circuit in Figure 16-4a has the following values: $R_1 = 10 \text{ k}\Omega$, $R_f = 180 \text{ k}\Omega$, and $C_1 = 0.1 \text{ } \mu\text{F}$. Which of the following statements is true?

    A) The maximum voltage gain of the circuit equals the ratio of R_f to R_1.

    B) The maximum voltage gain of the circuit is approximately equal to the A_{OL} rating of the op-amp.

    C) The circuit is an inverting amplifier with a bypassed feedback resistor.

    D) None of the above statements are true.

27) The circuit in Figure 16-4b has the following values: $R_1=10$ kΩ and $C_1 = 0.1$ μF. Which of the following statements is true?

    A) The maximum voltage gain of the circuit equals the ratio of R_f to R_1.

    B) The maximum voltage gain of the circuit is approximately equal to the A_{OL} rating of the op-amp.

    C) The circuit is an inverting amplifier with an input coupling capacitor.

    D) None of the above statements are true.

Chapter 16 Additional Op-Amp Applications
Answer Key

1) C
2) C
3) D
4) A
5) C
6) B
7) C
8) A
9) D
10) B
11) C
12) C
13) B
14) D
15) B
16) D
17) B
18) A
19) C
20) A
21) B
22) B
23) B
24) B
25) C
26) A
27) B

Chapter 17   Tuned Amplifiers

1) The voltage gain of an ideal tuned amplifier is reduced to _____ when operated at either cutoff frequency.

    A) 0 dB

    B) 3 dB

    C) $-\infty$ dB (zero)

    D) $A_V(mid) - 3$ dB

2) The voltage gain of a practical tuned amplifier is reduced to _____ when operated at either cutoff frequency.

    A) 0 dB

    B) 3 dB

    C) $-\infty$ dB (zero)

    D) $A_V (mid) - 3$ dB

3) The frequency range(s) outside of the bandwidth of a given tuned amplifier is referred to as the

    A) pass band.

    B) stop band.

    C) drop band.

    D) standard band.

4) In most applications, tuned amplifiers are designed to have

    A) the smallest possible bandwidth.

    B) the largest possible bandwidth.

    C) a specific bandwidth.

    D) an unspecified bandwidth.

5) A tuned amplifier has values of $f_0 = 455$ kHz and BW = 5 kHz. What is the value of Q for the circuit?

    A) 450   B) 2275   C) 5   D) 91

6) Two amplifiers are operated at the same center frequency (f_0). Which of the following statements is true?

    A) The amplifier with the higher roll-off rate has the wider bandwidth.

    B) The amplifier with the lower roll-off rate has the wider bandwidth.

    C) The bandwidth of each circuit is not related of its roll-off rate.

    D) The bandwidth of each circuit equals the product of its voltage gain and roll-off rate.

7) A tuned amplifier has values of $f_0 = 1.3$ MHz and Q = 54. What is the bandwidth of the circuit?

    A) 24 kHz

    B) 70.2 MHz

    C) 54 kHz

    D) None of these answers are correct.

8) A bandpass filter has values of $f_0 = 1.5$ MHz and BW = 100 kHz. What is the value of f_{C2} for the circuit?

    A) 1.6 MHz   B) 1.55 MHz   C) 1.45 MHz   D) 1.4 MHz

9) A low–pass Sallen–Key (two–pole) filter has an upper cutoff frequency of 2 kHz and a Butterworth response curve. The voltage gain of the circuit decreases by approximately _____ if its input frequency increases to 200 kHz.

A) 20 dB   B) 40 dB   C) 60 dB   D) 80 dB

10) Butterworth active filters are generally preferred over Chebyshev active filters because

A) Butterworth filters are easier to construct.

B) Butterworth filters have higher roll–off rates.

C) the midband gain of the Chebyshev filter is inconsistent.

D) Chebyshev filters have higher roll–off rates.

11) Which type of filter response provides the highest fidelity?

A) Butterworth   B) Chebyshev   C) Bessel

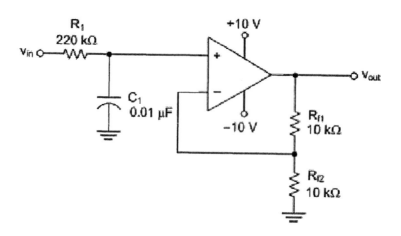

Figure 17–1

12) The circuit in Figure 17–1 is a

A) one–pole low–pass filter.   B) two–pole low–pass filter.

C) one–pole high–pass filter.   D) two–pole high–pass filter.

13) The cutoff frequency for the circuit in Figure 17–1 is approximately

A) 3 Hz.   B) 72 Hz.   C) 455 Hz.   D) 723 Hz.

14) The closed–loop gain of the circuit in Figure 17–1 is

A) 0 dB.   B) 6 dB.   C) 10 dB.   D) 26 dB.

302

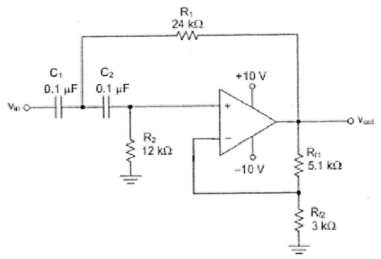

Figure 17-2

15) The circuit in Figure 17-2 is a

    A) multiple feedback bandpass filter.   B) multiple feedback notch filter.

    C) Sallen-Key low-pass filter.   D) Sallen-Key high-pass filter.

16) The cutoff frequency for the circuit in Figure 17-2 is approximately

    A) 66 Hz.   B) 94 Hz.   C) 133 Hz.   D) 188 Hz.

17) The closed loop gain of the circuit in Figure 17-2 is

    A) 12 dB.   B) 4 dB.   C) 1.3 dB.   D) 0 dB.

18) The filter in Figure 17-2 has a _____ response curve.

    A) Chebyshev   B) Butterworth   C) Bessel   D) band-stop

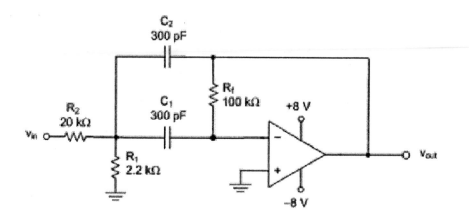

Figure 17-3

19) The circuit in Figure 17-3 is a

    A) Sallen–Key low–pass filter.   B) Sallen–Key high–pass filter.

    C) multiple-feedback bandpass filter.   D) multiple-feedback notch filter.

20) The center frequency of the circuit in Figure 17-3 is approximately

    A) 38 kHz.   B) 78 kHz.   C) 119 kHz.   D) 241 kHz.

21) The Q of the filter in Figure 17-3 is approximately

    A) 11.2.   B) 3.6.   C) 0.72.   D) 5.

22) The cutoff frequencies for the filter in Figure 17-3 are approximately

    A) 27.4 kHz and 48.6 kHz.   B) 85.9 kHz and 152.1 kHz.

    C) 32.7 kHz and 43.3 kHz.   D) 38 kHz and 119 kHz.

23) A tuned amplifier has the following values: f_0 = 800 kHz and Q = 1.5. What is the value of f_{C1} for the circuit?

    A) 310 kHz

    B) 534 kHz

    C) 577 kHz

    D) Cannot be determined from the information given.

24) A discrete tuned amplifier has the following values: L = 10 mH, R_W = 3 Ω, and C = 0.1 μF. What is the value of f_0 for the amplifier?

    A) 15.9 MHz   B) 1.59 kHz   C) 3.18 kHz   D) 5.03 kHz

25) A parallel LC circuit has the following values: f_r = 424 Hz, L = 5 mH, and R_W = 4 Ω. What is the Q of the circuit?

    A) 3.33   B) 3.33 × 10^{-3} C) 0.333   D) 33.3

26) A class C amplifier is biased

    A) at cutoff.   B) at saturation.

    C) deeply into cutoff.   D) deeply into saturation.

27) The operation of a class C amplifier is based on the

    A) LC effect.   B) flywheel effect.

    C) Miller effect.   D) class C effect.

28) A class C amplifier can be used to produce

    A) a dc output.   B) a triangular waveform.

    C) harmonics of the input frequency.   D) All of the above.

29) The transistor in a Class C amplifier will conduct for _____.

    A) less than 180°   B) more than 180° but less than 360°

    C) 360°   D) 0° since it is biased at cutoff

30) A class C amplifier is being designed to accept a +5 V_{pk} input. What biasing voltage should be applied to the base of the transistor?

    A) –5 V   B) –4 V   C) –3 V   D) +4 V

31) A tuned amplifier has the following values: $R_W = 50\ \Omega$, $X_L = 1\ k\Omega$, and $R_L = 10\ k\Omega$. What is the equivalent parallel resistance for R_W?

    A) 50Ω   B) 10 kΩ   C) Q = 20   D) 20 kΩ

32) A tuned amplifier has the following values: $R_W = 50\ \Omega$, $X_L = 1\ k\Omega$, and $R_L = 10\ k\Omega$. What is the quality (Q) of the circuit?

    A) 6.66   B) 20   C) 50   D) 100

33) A tuned amplifier has the following values: $R_W = 50\ \Omega$, $X_L = 1\ k\Omega$, and $f_0 = 1200$ Hz. Assuming the load resistance is infinite, what is the circuit bandwidth?

    A) 20 Hz   B) 40 Hz   C) 60 Hz   D) 200 Hz

34) A tuned amplifier has the following values: $R_W = 50\ \Omega$, $X_L = 1\ k\Omega$, $R_L = 10\ k\Omega$ and $f_0 = 1200$ Hz. What is the circuit bandwidth?

    A) 60 Hz   B) 180 Hz   C) 360 Hz   D) 500 Hz

Chapter 17 Tuned Amplifiers
Answer Key

1) C
2) D
3) B
4) C
5) D
6) B
7) A
8) B
9) D
10) C
11) C
12) A
13) B
14) B
15) D
16) B
17) B
18) B
19) C
20) A
21) B
22) C
23) C
24) D
25) A
26) C
27) B
28) C
29) A
30) B
31) D
32) A
33) C
34) B

Chapter 18   Oscillators

1) In a positive feedback system, the feedback signal and the amplifier input signal are

    A) in phase.   B) 45° out of phase.

    C) 90° out of phase.   D) 180° out of phase.

2) Positive feedback is also called

    A) degenerative feedback.   B) additive feedback.

    C) regenerative feedback.   D) regressive feedback.

3) An oscillator is a circuit that

    A) converts ac to dc.

    B) converts dc to ac.

    C) converts one ac frequency to another frequency.

    D) performs all of the above conversions.

4) An oscillator has the following values: $A_V = 188$ and $\alpha = 0.0048$. Which of the following statements is true?

    A) The circuit has a constant amplitude output.

    B) The output from the circuit fades out after several cycles.

    C) The output from the circuit clips after several cycles.

    D) None of the above statements are true.

5) The Barkhausen criterion states that the product of voltage gain and current gain in an oscillator must equal one (1).

6) Which of the following is not a requirement for oscillator operation?

    A) The circuit must fulfill the Barkhausen criterion.

    B) The circuit must initially be triggered into operation.

    C) The feedback network must contain an RC circuit.

    D) The circuit must provide positive feedback.

7) In a practical phase-shift oscillator, each RC circuit produces a 60° phase shift.

8) Phase–shift oscillators are rarely used because

    A) they are very difficult to produce.

    B) their output amplitudes are very hard to regulate.

    C) their output frequencies tend to be extremely unstable.

    D) they require the use of an op–amp.

9) A three–stage BJT amplifier is found to be producing unwanted oscillations. Which of the following will solve the problem?

    A) Reducing the overall voltage gain of the amplifier

    B) Using a regulated dc power supply

    C) Increasing the supply voltage for the amplifier

    D) Replacing the BJTs with JFETs

10) The negative feedback circuit in a Wien–bridge oscillator is used to

    A) determine the frequency of operation.   B) control the gain of the circuit.

    C) bias the positive feedback network.   D) prevent unwanted oscillations.

11) The Wien–bridge oscillator is limited to output frequencies that are around 1 MHz or less.

12) The positive feedback circuit in a Wien–bridge oscillator is used to

    A) determine the frequency of operation.   B) control the gain of the circuit.

    C) bias the negative feedback network.   D) prevent unwanted oscillations.

13) A Colpitts oscillator has _____ in its feedback network.

    A) a pair of tapped capacitors in parallel with an inductor

    B) a pair of tapped inductors in parallel with a capacitor

    C) a transformer with a capacitor in parallel with its primary winding

    D) a pair of tapped capacitors in parallel with an inductor and a third small–value capacitor

14) A Hartley oscillator has _____ in its feedback network.

    A) a pair of tapped capacitors in parallel with an inductor

    B) a pair of tapped inductors in parallel with a capacitor

    C) a transformer with a capacitor in parallel with its primary winding

    D) a pair of tapped capacitors in parallel with an inductor and a third small–value capacitor

15) A Clapp oscillator has _____ in its feedback network.

   A) a pair of tapped capacitors in parallel with an inductor

   B) a pair of tapped inductors in parallel with a capacitor

   C) a transformer with a capacitor in parallel with its primary winding

   D) a pair of tapped capacitors in parallel with an inductor and a third small–value capacitor

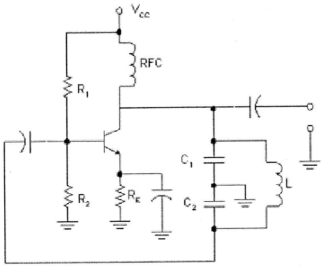

Figure 18–1

16) The circuit in Figure 18–1 has the following values: RFC = 100 µH, C_1 = 1 µF, and C_2 = 33 µF. What is the feedback factor (α_v) of the circuit?

   A) 0.03   B) 33   C) 0.01   D) 100

17) The circuit in Figure 18–1 has the following values: RFC = 100 µH, C_1 = 1 µF, and C_2 = 33 µF. What is the value of A_v for the circuit?

   A) 0.03   B) 33   C) 0.01   D) 100

18) The circuit in Figure 18–1 has the following values: RFC = 100 µH, L = 10 µH, C_1 = 1 µF, and C_2 = 33 µF. What is the output frequency of the circuit?

   A) 74.5 kHz   B) 25.6 kHz   C) 12.8 kHz   D) 51.1 kHz

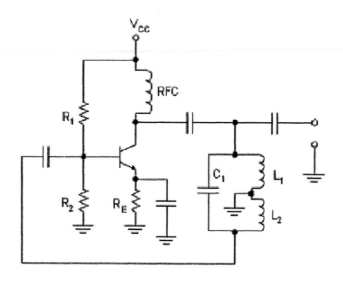

Figure 18–2

19) The circuit in Figure 18-2 has the following values: RFC = 1 mH, L_1 = 100 μH, L_2 = 22 μH, and C_1 = 0.001 μF. Assuming that the mutual inductance in the circuit is too low to be considered, what is the approximate output frequency of the oscillator?

    A) 456 kHz   B) 152 kHz   C) 503 kHz   D) 2.2 MhZ

20) The circuit in Figure 18-2 has the following values: RFC = 1mH, L_1 = 91 μH, L_2 = 20 μH. What is the feedback factor?

    A) 45.45   B) 4.55   C) 0.22   D) 111

21) A big advantage that LC oscillators have over RC oscillators is the fact that LC oscillators can generally be operated at much higher frequencies.

22) At f_s, a crystal has _____ impedance.

    A) high   B) low

23) At f_p, a crystal has _____ impedance.

    A) low   B) high

24) CCOs have

    A) very low operating frequencies.   B) very stable output frequencies.

    C) extremely simple biasing circuits.   D) All of the above.

25) Which of the following is not used as crystals in oscillator circuits?

    A) Lead crystal   B) Rochell salt   C) Quartz   D) Tourmaline

26) What type of crystal has the best frequency properties?

    A) Lead crystal   B) Rochell salt   C) Quartz   D) Tourmaline

27) Which of the following is considered the most durable when manufacturing CCOs?

    A) Lead crystal   B) Rochell salt   C) Quartz   D) Tourmaline

28) Which of the following is considered the least expensive when manufacturing crystal oscillators?

    A) Lead crystal   B) Rochell salt   C) Quartz   D) Tourmaline

29) When crystals are exposed to an electric field, they vibrate at a constant rate. This is called _____.

    A) the over tone mode   B) the CCO effect

    C) the piezoelectric effect   D) None of the above.

30) The inherent resonant frequency of a crystal is determined by _____.

    A) the L and C values in the circuit   B) the "cut of the crystal" frequency

    C) the physical dimensions of the crystal   D) All of the above.

31) A 20 MHz crystal is used to produce a 200 MHz oscillator output frequency. This is called _____ operation.

    A) resonant mode   B) overtone mode

    C) harmonic mode   D) Pierce

Chapter 18 Oscillators
Answer Key

1) A
2) C
3) B
4) B
5) FALSE
6) C
7) FALSE
8) C
9) B
10) B
11) TRUE
12) A
13) A
14) B
15) D
16) A
17) B
18) D
19) A
20) C
21) TRUE
22) B
23) B
24) B
25) A
26) B
27) D
28) C
29) C
30) C
31) B

Chapter 19   Solid–State Switching Circuits

1) A BJT in cutoff has the same characteristics as a/an

    A) open switch.   B) closed switch.

2) A BJT in saturation has the same characteristics as a/an

    A) open switch.   B) closed switch.

3) In most practical BJT inverters, the value of V_{in} that is used to saturate the transistor is approximately equal to

    A) V_{CC}.   B) $V_{EE} + 0.7$ V.   C) V_{EE}.   D) $V_{BE} + 0.7$ V.

4) In most practical BJT buffers, the value of V_{in} that is used to drive the transistor into cutoff is approximately equal to

    A) V_{CC}.   B) $V_{EE} + 0.7$ V.   C) V_{EE}.   D) $V_{BE} + 0.7$ V.

5) A JFET inverter is constructed using an n–channel JFET. This circuit produces a _____ output pulse when it receives a _____ input pulse.

    A) positive; positive   B) negative; positive

    C) positive; negative   D) negative; negative

6) An inverter

    A) produces a 180° voltage phase shift.   B) does not produce a voltage phase shift.

    C) is usually used to provide voltage gain.   D) requires at least two active devices.

7) A buffer

    A) produces a 180° input/output voltage phase shift.

    B) does not produce an input/output voltage phase shift.

    C) is usually used to provide voltage gain.

    D) requires at least two active devices.

8) The time required for I_C to reach 10% of its maximum value when a BJT is turned on is called

    A) delay time.   B) storage time.   C) rise time.   D) fall time.

9) The time required for I_C to increase from 10% of its maximum value to 90% of its maximum value is called

    A) delay time.   B) storage time.   C) rise time.   D) fall time.

10) The time required for I_C to drop to 90% of its maximum value when a BJT is turned off is called

   A) delay time.   B) storage time.   C) rise time.   D) fall time.

11) The time required for I_C to drop from 90% of its maximum value to 10% of its maximum value is called

   A) delay time.   B) storage time.   C) rise time.   D) fall time.

12) An inverter has output limits of 0 V and +10 V. When viewing the output of the circuit with an oscilloscope, you see that the output voltage drops from 9 V to 1 V in 50 μs. Which of the following conclusions can be drawn from this measurement?

   A) The circuit delay time is 50 μs.   B) The circuit rise time is 50 μs.

   C) The circuit storage time is 50 μs.   D) The circuit fall time is 50 μs.

13) A BJT has the following values: t_d = 20 nS, t_r = 20 nS, t_s = 150 nS, and t_f = 60 nS. What is the upper cutoff frequency for the device in any switching application?

   A) 6.7 MHz   B) 4 MHz   C) 17.5 MHz   D) 175 kHz

14) A BJT has the following values: t_d = 20 nS, t_r = 20 nS, t_s = 150 nS, and t_f = 60 nS. What is a practical limit on the operating frequency of the device in any switching application?

   A) 6.7 MHz   B) 4 MHz   C) 17.5 MHz   D) 175 kHz

15) A speed–up capacitor is used to reduce

   A) BJT storage time.   B) BJT delay time.

   C) BJT rise time and fall time.   D) BJT delay time and storage time.

16) The output from an inverter has a pulse width of 55 μs and a space width of 30 μs. What is the duty cycle of the circuit?

   A) 55%   B) 64.7%   C) 85%   D) 39.3%

17) The Schmitt trigger is a

   A) voltage level detector.   B) bistable multivibrator.

   C) current level detector.   D) astable multivibrator.

18) The difference between the UTP and LTP voltages for a Schmitt trigger is called

   A) the nontrigger voltage range.   B) hysteresis.

   C) the quiescent state.   D) the stable range.

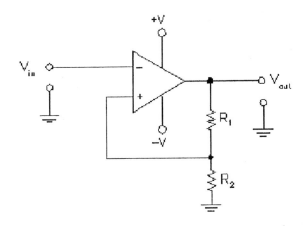

Figure 19-1

19) The circuit in Figure 19-1 has values of $R_1 = 10$ kΩ, $R_2 = 20$ kΩ, and ±10 V supply voltages. What is the UTP value for the circuit?

A) 6 V   B) –6 V   C) 5.4 V   D) –5.4 V

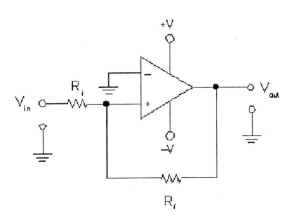

Figure 19-2

20) The circuit in Figure 19-2 has values of $R_f = 10$ kΩ, $R_i = 2$ kΩ, and ±10 V supply voltages. What is the LTP voltage for the circuit?

A) 1.8 V   B) 4.5 V   C) –1.8 V   D) –4.5 V

21) The astable multivibrator has _____ stable output states.

A) zero   B) two   C) one   D) three

22) A bistable multivibrator is also known as a

A) free-running multivibrator.   B) one-shot.

C) flip-flop.   D) Schmitt trigger.

23) A monostable multivibrator is also known as a

   A) free–running multivibrator.   B) one–shot.

   C) flip–flop.   D) Schmitt trigger.

24) You are holding a 555 timer so that there is an indentation on the left–hand side of the IC. Pin #1 is located on the

   A) lower left–hand side of the chip.   B) upper left–hand side of the chip.

   C) lower right–hand side of the chip.   D) upper right–hand side of the chip.

25) The 555 timer can be used as a linear amplifier.

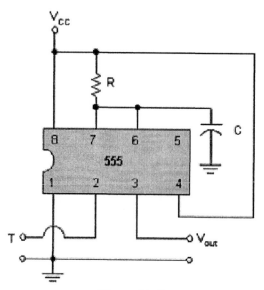

Figure 19–3

26) A 555 timer is connected as shown in Figure 19–3. If the cap on pin #6 is being held at 0 V by pin 7, pin #2 must go below _____ for the output from the timer to go high.

   A) +5 V   B) 0 V   C) +3 V   D) +15 V

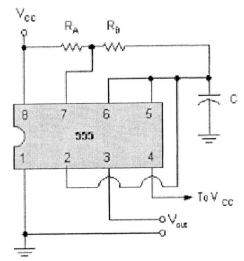

Figure 19-4

27) The circuit in Figure 19-4 has the following values: $R_A=R_B=10\ k\Omega$ and $C=0.01\ \mu F$. What is the operating frequency of the circuit?

    A) 7.2 kHz   B) 3.3 kHz   C) 4.8 kHz   D) 3.6 kHz

28) What is the duty cycle of the circuit in Figure 19-4?

    A) 66.7%   B) 33%   C) 50%   D) 20%

29) An engineer needs a circuit that oscillates at different frequencies based on the value of a dc input voltage. He should use _____.

    A) a one shot   B) a flip-flop   C) a VCO   D) a CCO

30) An engineer needs a circuit that pulses high for 30 ns when it receives an input trigger signal and then returns to its low output state. He should use _____.

    A) a one shot   B) a flip-flop   C) a VCO   D) a CCO

31) Which of the following switching circuits would have the lowest power dissipation?

    A) BJT   B) JFET   C) MOSFET   D) CMOS

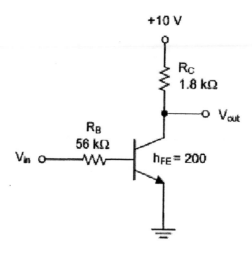

+10 V

R_C
1.8 kΩ

o V_{out}

R_B
56 kΩ

V_{in} o

h_{FE} = 200

Figure 19–5

32) What is the value of $I_{C(sat)}$ for the circuit in Figure 19–5?

    A) 5.17 mA   B) 5.56 mA   C) 7 mA   D) 10 mA

33) Refer to Figure 19–5. What value of I_B is required to drive the transistor into saturation?

    A) 25.8 μA   B) 27.8 μA   C) 35 μA   D) 100 μA

34) Refer to Figure 19–5. What is the minimum input voltage required to drive the transistor into saturation?

    A) 2.15 V   B) 2.26 V   C) 2.66 V   D) 6.3 V

Chapter 19 Solid–State Switching Circuits
Answer Key

1) A
2) B
3) A
4) C
5) C
6) A
7) B
8) A
9) C
10) B
11) D
12) B
13) C
14) D
15) D
16) B
17) A
18) B
19) A
20) C
21) A
22) C
23) B
24) A
25) FALSE
26) A
27) C
28) A
29) C
30) A
31) D
32) B
33) B
34) B

Chapter 20   Thyristors and Optoelectronics Devices

1) The silicon unilateral switch (SUS) is forced into forward conduction when V_{AK} exceeds the _____ rating of the device.

    A) forward conducting voltage   B) forward breakover voltage

    C) forward trigger voltage   D) forward breakdown voltage

2) Once an SUS is forced into forward conduction, it continues to conduct until I_F drops below the _____ rating of the device.

    A) minimum forward current   B) forward breakover current

    C) holding current   D) dropout current

3) What are the two methods that are commonly used to return an SUS to its nonconducting state?

    A) Anode current interruption and forced commutation

    B) Current holding and forced commutation

    C) Anode current interruption and current holding

    D) Forced commutation and current dropout

4) The forward operating curve of the SCR is identical to that for the SUS.

5) An SCR has a circuit fusing rating of 28 A^2s. Will the device be destroyed if it is subjected to a 25 A surge that lasts for 50 ms?

    A) Yes   B) No

6) An SCR has a circuit fusing rating of 36 A^2s. How long can the device withstand a 120 A surge?

    A) 360 ms   B) 90 ms   C) 129.6 ms   D) 2.5 ms

7) An SCR has a critical rise rating of 20 V/μs. The device is being used in a circuit where 10 ns (rise time) noise signals randomly occur. What noise amplitude is needed to cause false triggering?

    A) 200 nV   B) 200 μV   C) 200 mV   D) 20 V

8) False triggering can be prevented by a

    A) damping network.   B) snubber network.

    C) feedback network.   D) attenuating network.

9) The primary difference between the diac and the SUS is the fact that

   A) the diac has a higher maximum power dissipation rating.

   B) the SUS is capable of conducting in only one direction.

   C) the diac is no longer used in any practical applications.

   D) the SUS requires the use of a snubber.

10) Quadrant I triggering of a triac (similar to SCR triggering) is accomplished by applying a
    _____ gate potential when MT2 is more _____ than MT1.

   A) positive; positive   B) positive; negative

   C) negative; positive   D) negative; negative

11) The _____ is commonly used to control triac triggering.

   A) SUS   B) diac   C) SCR   D) JFET

12) The primary difference between the triac phase controller and the SCR phase controller is the
    fact that the triac circuit

   A) requires a higher turn-on voltage.

   B) allows conduction through the load during both alternations of the input cycle.

   C) requires an added UJT to operate properly.

   D) allows for higher load power ratings.

13) A UJT has the following values: $\eta = 0.72$ (maximum) and $V_{BB} = 12$ V. What is the maximum
    value of V_P required to trigger the device into conduction?

   A) 8.64 V   B) 17.4 V   C) 12 V   D) 9.34 V

14) UJTs are used almost exclusively as

   A) breakover devices.   B) amplifiers.

   C) thyristor triggering devices.   D) tuned oscillators.

15) A PUT has a value of $V_{GK} = +8$ V. What value of V_{AK} is needed to trigger the device into
    conduction?

   A) –8 V

   B) +16 V

   C) +8 V

   D) Cannot be determined from the information given.

16) What is the wavelength of a 200 THz signal?

   A) 50 pm   B) 6.7×10^{-5} nm   C) 1500 nm   D) 60 nm

17) The amount of light per unit area that is received by a photodetector is called

    A) light intensity.   B) spectral wavelength.

    C) light amplitude.   D) the light–area product.

18) An object that blocks light is referred to as being

    A) transparent.   B) translucent.   C) opaque.   D) solid.

19) A photodiode has a rating of $s = 1200$ nm. What is the optimum operating frequency for the device?

    A) 250 THz   B) 400 THz   C) 250×10^{21} Hz   D) 120 THz

20) A photo–detector has a sensitivity rating of 3 $\mu A/mW/cm^2$. This means that

    A) the forward current through the device will increase by 3 μA for every 1 mW/cm^2 increase in light intensity.

    B) the reverse current through the device will increase by 3 μA for every 1 mW/cm^2 increase in light intensity.

    C) the forward current through the device will increase by 3 μA for every 1 mW/cm^2 decrease in light intensity.

    D) the reverse current through the device will increase by 3 μA for every 1 mW/cm^2 decrease in light intensity.

21) An optocoupler has an isolation source voltage (V_{ISO}) rating of 5200 V_{ac}. This rating means that

    A) the device can handle a 5200 V_{ac} input.

    B) the device can provide an output voltage as high as 5200 V_{ac}.

    C) 5200 V_{ac} applied across the input/output terminals of the device will destroy the component.

    D) the device can be used to drive a 5200 V_{ac} load.

22) The solid–state relay contains an internal

    A) optocoupler.   B) optointerrupter.

    C) optoviewer.   D) optodivider.

23) An optoisolator is a device that uses light to couple a signal from its input to its output.

24) The speed of light (c) is _____.

    A) 300 m/s   B) 3×10^{-18} cm/s   C) 3×10^{-17} nm/s   D) 186 m/s

25) Photodiodes are normally _____ biased.

    A) forward   B) reverse   C) negatively   D) positively

26) Light current through a photodiode is generally less than dark current.

27) Irradiance is:

    A) The term used to describe anything that passes light.

    B) The forward current through a photo diode with an active light input.

    C) The forward current through a photo diode with no active light source.

    D) The amount of light per unit area received by a given photo detector.

28) Optoelectronic devices are divided into two types:

    A) light sensors and dark sensors   B) light emitters and dark emitters

    C) light emitters and light detectors   D) diodes and transistors

29) A phase controller is used to:

    A) vary the average value of its load voltage.

    B) prevent phase shift oscillations.

    C) protect a voltage–sensitive load for excessive voltage.

    D) eliminate false triggering.

30) A crowbar is used to:

    A) vary the voltage to a load.

    B) prevent phase shift oscillations.

    C) protect a voltage–sensitive load from excessive voltage.

    D) eliminate false triggering.

Chapter 20 Thyristors and Optoelectronics Devices
Answer Key

1) B
2) C
3) A
4) TRUE
5) A
6) D
7) C
8) B
9) B
10) A
11) B
12) B
13) D
14) C
15) C
16) C
17) A
18) C
19) A
20) B
21) C
22) A
23) TRUE
24) C
25) B
26) FALSE
27) D
28) C
29) A
30) C

Chapter 21   Discrete and Integrated Voltage Regulators

1) The ideal voltage regulator maintains a constant dc output voltage despite anticipated changes in

    A) its input voltage.

    B) its output voltage demand.

    C) its load current demand.

    D) its load current demand and/or its input voltage.

2) A voltage regulator has an output that changes by 2 μV when its input changes by 10 V. The line regulation rating of the device is

    A) 0.02 μV/V.   B) 50 μV/V.   C) 20 μV/V.   D) 9.998 V/V.

3) The ideal line regulation rating is

    A) extremely high.   B) in the range of 1 μV/V to 20 μV/V.

    C) in the range of 0.1 μV/V to 1 μV/V.   D) zero.

4) A voltage regulator is rated for an output range of $I_L = 0$ to 40 mA. Under no-load conditions, the output voltage from the circuit is 4 Vdc. Under full-load conditions, the output voltage from the circuit is 3.984 Vdc. What is the load regulation rating of the circuit?

    A) 400 μV/mA   B) 2.5 mV/mA

    C) 0.4 Ω D) Both 400 μV/mA and 0.4 Ω are correct.

5) The _____ the load regulation rating of a voltage regulator, the higher the quality of the circuit.

    A) lower   B) higher

6) A voltage regulator has the following ratings: $V_{in} = 10$ Vdc to 15 Vdc, $I_L = 20$ mA (maximum), and regulation = 0.01%. Which of the following statements is true?

    A) The load current demand on the regulator cannot exceed 20 mA.

    B) The rated output voltage must be some value that is less than 10 Vdc.

    C) The rated output voltage falls somewhere between 10 Vdc and 15 Vdc.

    D) As long as the input voltage remains within its rated range, V_{out} will equal 0.01% of V_{in}.

7) Regulator A has a line regulation rating of 4 %/V. Regulator B has a line regulation rating of 15 ppm/V. Assuming that both are rated for a 10 Vdc output voltage, which is the better regulator?

    A) Regulator A   B) Regulator B

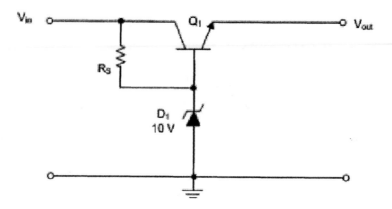

Figure 21–1

8) Q1 in Figure 21–1 is called a _____ transistor.

    A) pass   B) line   C) series   D) regulator

9) The regulated output voltage from the circuit in Figure 21–1 is

    A) 10.7 V.

    B) 10 V.

    C) 9.3 V.

    D) equal to the difference between V_{in} and the zener voltage rating.

10) Which of the following best describes the circuit in Figure 21–1?

    A) Series–pass regulator with voltage feedback

    B) Shunt regulator with voltage feedback

    C) Series–pass regulator without voltage feedback

    D) Shunt regulator without voltage feedback

11) Refer to Figure 21–1. What is the purpose of R_S?

    A) It provides shorted load protection

    B) It provides biasing current for Q_1

    C) It provides current for the zener diode

    D) It reduces the power dissipated by the transistor

12) Shunt voltage regulators require

    A) shorted–load protection.   B) overvoltage protection.

    C) high–frequency protection.   D) open–load protection.

13) Which of the following is not a type of IC voltage regulator?

A) Fixed negative

B) Adjustable

C) Variable polarity

D) Dual-tracking

14) What type of IC voltage regulator requires both positive and negative input voltages?

A) The fixed-negative regulator

B) The adjustable regulator

C) The variable polarity regulator

D) The dual-tracking regulator

15) The ability of an IC voltage regulator to attenuate any input ripple voltage is called its _____ rating.

A) ripple attenuation

B) ripple reduction

C) ripple rejection

D) ripple elimination

16) Switching voltage regulator supplies

A) are not very efficient.

B) usually get very warm.

C) are very cool running and efficient.

D) have a simple circuit design.

17) A disadvantages of switching regulator power supplies are their complex design and transmission of noise into the surrounding environment.

18) Switching regulators have _____ power handling capability than linear regulators.

A) higher

B) lower

C) the same

19) The diode in the filter and clipping section of the switching power supply provides _____ for the power switch.

A) rectification

B) current limiting

C) transient protection

20) Both linear and switching regulators can function as step-up regulators.

21) A switching power supply has the following values: $V_{in} = 18$ Vdc, $T_{on} = 4$ ms, and $T_{off} = 8$ ms. What is the value of V_{out} for the circuit?

A) 27 Vdc

B) 9 Vdc

C) 6 Vdc

D) 12 Vdc

22) Which type of voltage regulator would use a crowbar?

A) Series-pass regulator

B) Shunt regulator

C) Switching regulator

D) None of the above.

23) _____ is a rating that indicates the change in regulation output voltage that occurs per unit change in input voltage.

A) Regulation

B) Line regulation

C) Load regulation

D) Series regulation

24) A dual–polarity power supply would use a _____ regulator.

A) Fixed–positive regulator

B) Fixed–negative regulator

C) Dual–tracking regulator

D) Both A and B

25) Using a signal to vary the pulse width of a rectangular wave without affecting its cycle time is called _____.

A) variable off–time modulation

B) pulse width modulation

C) power switch conduction

D) None of the above.

Chapter 21 Discrete and Integrated Voltage Regulators
Answer Key

1) D
2) A
3) D
4) D
5) A
6) A
7) B
8) A
9) C
10) C
11) C
12) B
13) C
14) D
15) C
16) C
17) TRUE
18) A
19) C
20) FALSE
21) C
22) B
23) B
24) D
25) B